D1597501

From Mantegna to Picasso

From Mantegna to
Picasso

Drawings from the Thaw Collection at The Pierpont Morgan Library, New York

Catalogue by
Cara Dufour Denison,
Peter Dreyer,
William M. Griswold,
Evelyn J. Phimister,
Stephanie Wiles

With contributions from
Eugene Victor Thaw and
Charles E. Pierce, Jr.

Royal Academy of Arts, London

Royal Academy of Arts, London
9 November 1996–23 January 1997

The exhibition has been organized by The Pierpont Morgan
Library in association with the Royal Academy of Arts.
The catalogue has been published by The Pierpont Morgan
Library.

The Royal Academy is grateful to Her Majesty's government
for its help in agreeing to indemnify the exhibition under the
National Heritage Act 1980 and to the Museums and Galleries Commission for their help in arranging this indemnity.

Front cover:
Jean Honoré Fragonard, *Interior of a Park: The Gardens of
the Villa d'Este* (enlarged detail; No. 26)
Back cover:
Rembrandt, *Four Negroes with Wind Instruments* (No. 14)
Frontispiece:
Andrea Mantegna, *Three Standing Apostles* (No. 2)

Photography Credits
All Morgan Library and Thaw Collection materials by David
A. Loggie. No. 28, fig. 1, J. Paul Getty Museum, Los Angeles;
No. 50, fig. 1, Hamburger Kunsthalle; No. 58, fig. 1, Fogg Art
Museum, Harvard University Art Museums; No. 63, fig. 1,
The Art Museum, Princeton University; No. 69, fig. 1, Davis
Museum and Cultural Center, Wellesley College; No. 97, fig.
1, Fitzwilliam Museum, Cambridge.

Acknowledgments
The authors would like to acknowledge the assistance of the
following individuals: Douglas Druick, Alison Goodyear,
Phyllis Dearborn Massar, Asher Miller, Joseph Rishel,
Katherine Sachs, David Scrase, Jennifer Tonkavich, and
Jennifer Vanim. Patricia Tang and Lorna Kettaneh Saleh of
E. V. Thaw & Co. have also been very generous in providing
information as needed. Several entries, written by Felice
Stampfle, Curator Emerita (Nos. 7, 15, 16, 35, 38), and
William W. Robinson, Ian Woodner Curator of Drawings
at the Harvard University Art Museums (Nos. 6, 17), are
included from previous Thaw Collection catalogues.

Library of Congress Cataloging-in-Publication Data

Pierpont Morgan Library.
    From Mantegna to Picasso : drawings from the Thaw Col-
lection at the Pierpont Morgan Library, New York : catalogue
/ by Cara Denison … [et al.] ; with contributions from
Eugene Victor Thaw and Charles E. Pierce, Jr.
            p.   cm.
    Catalog of an exhibition organized by the Pierpont
Morgan Library, New York at the Royal Academy of Arts,
London, Nov. 9, 1996–Jan. 23, 1997.
    Includes bibliographical references and index.
    ISBN 0-87598-116-x (alk. paper)
    1. Drawing—Exhibitions. 2. Thaw, Gene—Art collec-
tions—Exhibitions. 3. Thaw, Clare—Art collections—Exhibi-
tions. 4. Drawing—Private collections—New York (State)—
New York—Exhibitions. 5. Drawing—New York (State)—
New York—Exhibitions. 6. Pierpont Morgan Library—Exhi-
bitions. I. Denison, Cara D. II. Royal Academy of Arts (Great
Britain) III. Title.
NC 17.G7L646 1996
741.9′074421′32—dc20   96-9895
                                            CIP

ISBN 0-87598-116-x
(The Pierpont Morgan Library)
ISBN 0-900946-51-2
(Royal Academy of Arts)

Interview with Eugene Victor Thaw copyright © 1994
Umberto Allemandi & Co. Publishing S.R.L. Published with
kind permission of *The Art Newspaper*.

Printed in Italy

Contents

President's Foreword   ix

Director's Preface   xi

An Interview with Eugene Victor Thaw   xiii

Catalogue   1

Sources Cited in Abbreviated Form   217

Index of Artists   237

President's Foreword

FOR THIRTY YEARS Eugene Victor Thaw has been patiently building his collection of drawings. While he continues to make important acquisitions in this field, several of which are included in the present exhibition, he has also begun to explore other areas of collecting.

Drawings are vulnerable in many ways: Paper is easily damaged, light can fade colour; conservation is a matter of great importance. But it is also important that drawings should be available to delight and instruct artists, scholars, and art enthusiasts of the present and future generations. In keeping with his great public spirit, Mr Thaw has decided to donate his entire drawings collection to The Pierpont Morgan Library for its safekeeping and for the education and pleasure of all those who live in or visit New York. For the British public he has now selected the hundred drawings that he considers best represent the collection in terms of range and quality to be shown at the Royal Academy.

Our warmest thanks go first to Eugene and Clare Thaw for the generosity and enthusiasm with which they have followed every process in the planning and preparation of this exhibition, from the selection of drawings to the manner of their display and the design of the catalogue. Next, we are deeply indebted to Mr Charles E. Pierce, Jr., director of The Pierpont Morgan Library, for his unfailing help. This is the second time in recent years that the Academy has shared an exhibition with the Morgan Library: In 1994–5 *The Painted Page,* an exhibition of superb Italian Renaissance manuscripts, was shown in both places; once again the Royal Academy's staff has benefited from a very happy collaboration with the staff of the Morgan Library. William M. Griswold, the Library's Charles W. Engelhard Curator of Drawings and Prints; Cara Dufour Denison, curator; and Stephanie Wiles, associate curator; together with a team of scholars, have written the handsome catalogue that was especially produced for this exhibition in London. We thank all those who were responsible for its writing and production.

It is difficult for an artist to hide behind a drawing; drawing reveals an artist's way of thinking and working. A collection of drawings is also a form of personal expression and reveals something of the collector's character. In the case of Eugene Thaw, we discover an unerring eye for quality and a love of coherent form. We are certain that these drawings will provide the British public with as much visual delight and instruction as they have to the Thaws and those who have seen the collection at the Morgan Library.

SIR PHILIP DOWSON, C.B.E.
President, Royal Academy of Arts

Director's Preface

IT IS A GREAT PLEASURE for The Pierpont Morgan Library to join Clare and Gene Thaw in presenting this exhibition of their drawings at the Royal Academy of Arts. A Fellow, Trustee, and friend of the Library, Gene has spent more than thirty years assembling one of the most significant collections of its kind in the United States. Many of these drawings have been displayed at the Morgan Library in one of the three exhibitions devoted to the Thaw Collection in 1975, 1985, and 1994. Quite a few will be familiar to visitors to other exhibitions since Gene and Clare have always been among the most generous of lenders.

The tremendous presence, or "wall power," of the majority of drawings in the collection makes it a striking ensemble. Gene has always preferred the painterly drawing to the sketch, and many works in the exhibition were rendered with a good deal of color and substance. Most of the French drawings are nineteenth century; however, a number of seventeenth- and eighteenth-century French artists are also represented. Earlier masters, such as Mantegna, Altdorfer, and Cranach, are included, as are those of our own century, such as Picasso, Matisse, and Pollock. The collection is not simply a selection of brilliant pieces but reflects Gene's highly individual taste and his innate preference for certain periods and artists. For Italian draughtsmanship, he is partial to the sixteenth and eighteenth centuries; for German drawings, the sixteenth and nineteenth centuries; his preference for eighteenth- and nineteenth-century English drawings culminates in the fine series of Turner watercolors. Favorite artists, including Rembrandt, Claude, Watteau, Tiepolo, Goya, Turner, Géricault, Delacroix, Daumier, Degas, Cézanne, and Redon, are identified by the number of their works seen here. Degas, Cézanne, and Pollock are further represented by sketchbooks. Also notable is the great care Gene has taken in the mounting and framing of each drawing.

Gene's collecting interests encompass small oil paintings and sketches as well as finely wrought art objects, which range from the late Middle Ages to the twentieth century. The 1985 exhibition included a number of these along with a selection of drawings of interiors. In recent years Gene has been largely occupied with the collecting of Native American artifacts, now displayed in a new wing of the New York State Historical Association in Cooperstown, New York, but he has continued to collect drawings. Recent acquisitions included in this exhibition are the eight drawings by Gerbrand van den Eeckhout, Stefano della Bella, Panini, Boullée, J. R. Cozens, Runge, Fantin-Latour, and Redon. More than half of the present selection was in the 1994 exhibition at the Library, while most of the remaining drawings appeared in the two previous exhibitions.

I should like to take this opportunity to express, on behalf of the Library, my gratitude to Clare and Gene for making this exhibition possible as well as for their promise to give the collection to the Morgan Library during the next few years as they see fit. This great benefaction will enrich the Library's preexisting collection of Old Master drawings with beautiful examples by artists already represented in the collection. Furthermore, with the acquisition of a number of drawings by important artists not previously represented, especially those of the nineteenth and twentieth centuries, areas that were only outlined will have acquired significant depth. The collection closely traces, and in many cases fully realizes, the development from neoclassicism and romanticism to realism, impressionism, symbolism, and cubism.

On a more personal note, I wish to thank Gene for the sound advice and wise counsel he has given me on a variety of matters. I commend his respect for quality. He has always sought to buy the finest available sheet of a great artist. And he has succeeded because he has both a fine mind and a fine eye. Much has been made of his celebrated eye, but equal credit should be given to his scholarly sensibility. He is a formidable connoisseur, but he is more than that as he seeks to place a work within larger contexts, aesthetic and historical. Finally, as anyone who has discussed drawings with Gene knows, these works of art appeal to him at the deepest level of his being. They are the principal means by which he seeks to remain in touch with the practitioners of great art. As he himself has written, "But it is a particular quality of drawings, their kinship to handwriting, which most attracts us to them as evidence of the authentic touch of the artist's own hand. In this age of computers, multiples, and other devices for graphic programming and duplication, the artist's hand seems to be getting less and less important. All the more reason to cherish such survivals from other times when the hand of genius was a sign of civilization."

CHARLES E. PIERCE, JR.
Director, The Pierpont Morgan Library

An Interview with Eugene Victor Thaw

In the summer of 1994, Jason Edward Kaufman, for The Art Newspaper, *interviewed Eugene Thaw, taping his answers to questions about his career as a dealer and collector. The interview was published in October 1994, during the third exhibition of drawings from the Thaw Collection at The Pierpont Morgan Library in New York. At the opening of that exhibition, consisting of seventy new acquisitions and thirty of the best sheets from the previous two selections (of 1975 and 1985), Eugene Thaw announced that the exhibited drawings would remain forever at the Morgan Library.*

Eugene Thaw feels that the interview contains much of his thinking about collecting and about his and Clare Thaw's feelings about their connections with the Library. Therefore, rather than repeat those ideas in another format, we have reprinted, with permission, relevant parts of that interview.

There have been a number of books of late trying to define what makes collectors tick. As one of the great dealers of the second half of the century, and a formidable collector as well, you are uniquely positioned to offer insight on the subject. Just what is collecting all about?

To me, the most important element of collecting is the hands-on experience of the work of art. With possession—either as a dealer who owns a piece temporarily, or as a collector who keeps it long-term—you can get to know an object in an entirely different way than you can from photographs, slides, or books. This experience flies in the face of everything that is happening in the current age, in which people are looking forward to museums with nothing in them except television monitors where you can dial the Louvre, or dial the Metropolitan, and get some kind of holograph. We seem to be satisfied with images of things, with multiples and reproductions. Even artists "make" things without using their hands. I still believe in the hand of the artist, and the only way to experience that is to experience an original.

The motivation comes from the need for aesthetic eye satisfaction and the need to order the resulting accumulations. People whose eye must be aesthetically satisfied begin to surround themselves with things that have that effect on them. That causes accumulation, and once you have several things that aesthetically please you, you have another problem of making some sort of order out of them. That becomes an intellectual process. All true collectors have this ordering drive, whether they're collecting butterflies or shells or Old Master drawings. They want to have a group that reflects their own taste and judgment of what's best.

There are psychologists who say that it's compensating for an unhappy childhood or it's bad toilet training, or one form or another of infantile deprivation. That kind of analysis doesn't bring any kind of helpful insight. If you're a collector, it's one of the joys of life to assemble and order something that ends up having true meaning. It's also one of the joys of life to share it and show it to others who have some glimmering of what you're doing. There is an overall motivation in any project. One wants it to have an end, a final resting place. Some collectors are satisfied with a good auction catalogue after they're dead. But one can ask for a higher meaning than that.

Your Old Master drawings are deservedly famous. What distinguishes your collecting from that of your contemporaries and predecessors?

One of the chief collecting traits that applies to me is that of aesthetic response. Other collectors of Old Master drawings collect for identification. What excites them is to find an anonymous drawing and identify it, even if it is not of any great aesthetic merit in itself. That's not the issue that appeals to me. I don't collect the drawing for the left foot of the saint in the fresco of "Saint Pancras by Giovanni de Fettucini." I collect for the aesthetic impact of the sheet itself. So I tend to have more finished sheets, though not always—I have summary Van Dycks and other pure working sketches. But it's the aesthetic impact that turns me on, not the discovery. Maybe I'm missing something, but that's what I like.

Have you intentionally avoided certain areas, such as Italian baroque?

I never was turned on by the Counter-Reformation, neither the paintings nor the drawings. The baroque artists were out of fashion when I was studying. I was in the Berensonian snobbery tradition of dismissing the Lanfrancos and Guido Renis, who were so famous in the early nineteenth century for their sentimental appeal. They became the curators' favorites when the greater things were no longer available. I've come to see that Guido Reni, for example, is a very great artist. But they didn't achieve a drawing style as distinctive and significant as other artists—like Giambattista Tiepolo, whose drawings are inimitable and dazzling. Or Rembrandt drawings, for that matter: with their sketchy shorthand they evoke emotional experiences tremendously insightful into the human condition. I need this from a Daumier, a Turner—some kind of emotional and aesthetic impact. And I get it also from Delacroix, Géricault, Redon—from many artists whom I've collected in depth. I have more than ten Delacroixs, over ten Cézannes, fifteen Degas, five or six Géricaults, maybe twenty Tiepolos father and son, and at least eight Fragonards. I'm not doing a survey, but collecting multiple examples by those artists who I feel have been essential to my own understanding of draughtsmanship and of Western art.

What about Dutch drawings other than Rembrandt?

That's a special field. For instance, the George and Maida Abrams Collections is *only* Dutch seventeenth-century drawings. There are a great number of what the French call *petits maîtres* who are wonderful artists, but not the peaks of draughtsmanship that I'm talking about. There certainly are others than Rembrandt—I would love to have a Cuyp landscape or an Avercamp "skaters" watercolor.

So you've collected favorite artists in depth and individual examples representative of certain important schools?

That's right. And the other area is work by artists who are wonderful, but outside the mainstream of Western traditional collecting. Fairly early in the game I was able to get a wonderful Caspar David Friedrich gouache, and now I have a total of five by Friedrich. I was able to buy a Wilhelm von Kobell from Munich of people on horseback meeting a peasant, one of the "encounter pictures," which are little known masterpieces of Biedermeier painting. And I have Danish artists—Købke and others—who are now talked of as participants in a golden age.

How did you develop such a close relationship with the Morgan Library?

As a drawings collector, very early on I was obviously attracted to the Library, and early on I offered them a Callot drawing as a gift. Fred Adams, who was director at the time, rejected it, saying, "We don't take gifts from dealers." So my first attempt to become friendly with the Library was summarily rejected, and I was rather crestfallen. Fred Adams is now a good friend and we joke about these things, but when Charles Ryskamp

became director (he is now director of the Frick Collection), I began a series of donations from my collection which led to the 1975 exhibition of 115 drawings, the first catalogue of the Thaw Collection. It was a great success and put me in the firmament of serious collectors. And at that time I made a promise in the catalogue to give the Morgan my entire collection of drawings, which by opportunity and instinct is very strongly weighted in favor of the nineteenth century, their greatest need. Since then, there has been another show in 1985, and the Library has used my drawings in a number of exhibitions. I've pursued the transfer little by little, as for tax reasons it seemed beneficial.

Not long ago the trustees needed to buy the building next door, the Morgan mansion, because it was the only possible way the Library could ever expand. I gave a substantial cash donation toward that purchase. Even though Charles Ryskamp had left by that time, and a new group was in charge of the board, they invited me to become a trustee. So the relationship has been a very happy one. Charles E. Pierce, Jr., the current director, has become a great friend, and we collaborate closely on many projects. Nothing that I've done in life has made me more proud or happier than supporting this great institution.

What is it about the Morgan that merits your undivided support?

Its collecting standards, its exhibiting standards, and its standards of scholarship are so far above the average. In a period of declining standards its staff has maintained the old ways of scholarship, and I believe in that.

We know the urgency to go in for blockbusters, with box office being the determining factor. The Library has vast collections in areas of basically scholarly interest, like illuminated manuscripts, illustrated books and literature—not the stuff of public blockbusters. But they make wonderful exhibitions out of these things, some of which turn out to be highly popular; yet it's always combined with a sense of quality and scholarship. The Morgan's catalogues are not flashy, but meticulous and informative.

How have other institutions compromised standards?

The politically correct has become so dominant in our universities and even in our journalism. The idea that nothing is true or false except the ethnic, gender or sexual preference bias we personally bring to it, and that these are the only things that matter in a work of art; not what the artist conceived, but his or her ethnic background, economic position, or parents' religion—all of this nonsense has taken over the world of scholarship as it emanates from our universities, where we look for leadership in scholarship. And that is why politically neutral ground, like the Morgan Library, becomes so valuable now, because there are so few enclaves where this kind of thing has not taken over.

But the Morgan Library suffers for it. Some of the great foundations which should be pouring money into an enterprise of this quality are uninterested because it's not dealing with ethnic or sexual or political background issues. If the Morgan Library were to devote itself to inner-city slum art it probably would get foundation funds, which, in our climate today, an exhibition on Shakespeare or the French Revolution or Holbein would not. It's very odd. The Library lives on the money it raises each year, and it's coming up against these problems *because* of the quality and purity of its scholarship and exhibitions.

Have you acquired drawings specially for the Morgan?

Yes, I'm always thinking of the end result of where the collection is going, and after a point the activity of collecting often had the Morgan and its needs specifically in mind.

Are you still dealing?

I still have a firm and I still own things in shares with other dealers. But I decided to stop selling pictures on my own because I really prefer not to dwell on how much a picture is worth or going to be worth. I used to talk too much when I sold pictures—as you can probably tell from listening to me now. Unlike dealers such as the late Alexandre Rosenberg, who never said a word—he just put the picture on the easel and you either bought it, or you didn't—I was full of information, and I loved to share it. But the business had lost its charm.

When I started, collecting opportunities were there for everyone with a little money and any eye at all. You could go around New York to the small auction houses, like Kende Gallery—where there were a lot of fakes—and the old Parke-Bernet before Sotheby's, to antique shops and booksellers, smaller dealers and drawings shops, like Walter Schatski on 57th Street. And if you had a good eye you could find things that were right and worth a lot more than you paid for them. There was still the air of discovery in the market.

We were impecunious and struggling, but it was a great deal of fun. Then at some point in the early 1980s— sometime around 1982 or 1983, if not a bit before—art turned completely into money, and then the fun went out of it.

In what other activities are you involved?

With another trustee, I run the Pollock-Krasner Foundation, which gives nearly two million dollars a year to worthy and needy artists under the will of Lee Krasner. That is an important part of my life right now. Also, my wife and I have the Eugene and Clare Thaw Charitable Trust in Sante Fe, which supports groups, not individuals, in the arts, ecology, and animal rights. It has strongly supported a group that restores and maintains the old adobe churches in New Mexico, which have been in sad disrepair.

I have friends in business with whom I still work, and I am a member of several boards, although not a very active one. Also I support the Glimmerglass Opera in Cooperstown, New York. I read a lot, and I'm a contributing editor of *The New Republic* magazine for which I write occasional art pieces and book reviews. I love the out-of-doors. We have a ranch with some horses, where I like to get out and walk with my wife and our dogs.

Catalogue

Anonymous, Rhenish school(?)

15th century

1

Drapery Study

Point of brush and gray bodycolor, heightened with white, on ochre-prepared ground, the surrounding ground covered with brush in varying layers of purple bodycolor. Verso: *Martyrdom of Saint Matthew*. Pen and black ink (on unprepared white paper). 8 1/16 × 5 5/8 inches (205 × 144 mm). Watermark: bow and arrow (close to Piccard 1980, no. X, 1776–97). Inscribed on verso, in pen and ink, *MS / 1495*.

The recto and verso of the sheet are by different hands and vary in quality. While the recto is an extremely fine drawing, the verso, which bears a spurious old attribution to Martin Schongauer and is dated 1495, is primarily of documentary interest. It is clearly a copy, probably made after a painting, which may have been the left wing of an altarpiece. The composition belongs to the same iconographic tradition as the representation on the right inner wing, now in the Städelsches Kunstinstitut, Frankfurt, of the Last Judgment Altar (*Weltgerichtsaltar*) by Stephan Lochner from Cologne (died 1451). The faces depicted on the present sheet—in profile, with round foreheads and pug noses—are also not far from types found in Lochner's work. Our drawing, however, would seem to depict an earlier painting by a master who may also have worked on the Lower Rhine in the first half of the fifteenth century.

The watermark—a bow and arrow, the arrow pointing upward—is visible in raking light at the left margin of the composition at the height of the soldier's head. Although the watermark has not been identified, it clearly belongs to a type found in papers of the fourteenth (and early fifteenth) century in Italy, Vienna, Middelburg (Zeeland), and Utrecht. This provides further evidence that the copyist was from the Lower Rhine, as does the graphic pattern used to form the higher parts of the drapery, namely through rows of short parallel strokes angled to the direction of the folds. This feature is found in many Netherlandish drawings of the fifteenth and sixteenth centuries, for example, in the circle of the Master of Flémalle (Boon 1978, no. 10), Jan de Beer (Boon 1978, no. 27), and Maerten van Heemskerck. The date of the copy remains open, but it most likely belongs to the fifteenth century.

Neither localization nor dating is helpful in identifying the drawing on the recto, and it is not even clear which side of the sheet was used first. The most convincing interpretation of the drapery study, suggested in Thaw I, is that the cloth is covering the knees of a seated person or that it is draped over two hands, possibly those of the priest receiving the child, or even those of the Virgin, in a Presentation of Christ in the Temple. The artist is primarily interested in the disposition of the light cast over the carefully arranged folds. Technically the execution of the sheet is closer to that of a painting than of a drawing. The draughtsman successfully depicts both the long folds, which fall freely from the proposed supporting hands or knees, as well as the minute forms, where the drapery puddles as though supported by an undefined ground.

The artist's use of organic, undulating folds instead of harsh, angular forms removes the master from the circle of Konrad Witz, which was proposed as one possibility by Julius Held, who, in his review of Felice Stampfle's Netherlandish catalogue, added "one more region and artist to consider for this fascinating study: Ferdinando Gallego, in whose *Madonna* in Salamanca the angular treatment of the folds offers considerable similarities" (see Białostocki 1972, pl. 22, repr. in color). Other suggestions have been that the drawing is Franco-Flemish, South German, Austrian, Netherlandish, or French, or that it may have been executed in the Lower Rhone Valley (see Felice Stampfle, especially in Thaw I). Forms similar to those in this sheet are to be found in the 1470s in the art of Martin Schongauer on the Upper Rhine (*Adoration of the Christ Child*, Berlin) and in the 1480s on the Lower Rhine in paintings by the Master of the Bartholomew Altarpiece (Thomas Altar, Cologne).

Provenance:
Bought from Helmut Wallach, New York.

Bibliography:
Morgan Library, *Fellows Reports*, XVI, pp. 87–88; Held 1981a, p. 174; Stampfle 1991, pp. 2–4, no. 2; Held 1993, p. 291.

Exhibitions:
Thaw I, no. 1, repr.; New York 1974, no. 33, repr.; New York 1981, no. 9, repr.; Thaw III, no. 1, repr. (recto and verso).

Thaw Collection, The Pierpont Morgan Library, acc. no. 1970.14

PD

3

Andrea Mantegna

Isola di Carturo 1431–
1506 Mantua

2

Three Standing Apostles

Pen and brown ink on paper slightly tinted with red chalk. 7 × 7½ inches (178 × 190 mm). Watermark: none visible through lining.

That the three saints depicted in this drawing are apostles can be confirmed by the presence of Saints Peter and Paul in a related drawing from the Koenigs Collection (see below). Yet only one saint displays an identifying attribute—a cross, which alludes to the martyrdom of Saint Philip rather than to that of Saint Andrew, since it is not of the X shape usually associated with the latter. The extremely low viewpoint suggests that the figures were intended to be situated above eye level. The drawing closest to this one, now in the British Museum (London and New York 1992, no. 24), is of a saint reading and originally may have been part of the left side of the present sheet. The scale of the British Museum figure, however, is somewhat larger (the sheet measures 6¾ × 2¼ inches [172 × 70 mm]), and the superior condition of the drawing makes such a connection less convincing. Four standing apostles who are reading are represented with other figures on the aforementioned sheet from the Koenigs Collection, formerly in The Boijmans Van Beuningen Museum, Rotterdam (Byam Shaw 1976, III, pl. 33; Moscow 1995–96, no. 89, repr.). Traditionally regarded as autograph, the study from the Koenigs Collection was recently published by David Ekserdjian as a copy after a Mantegna drawing (London and New York 1992, no. 23—Ekserdjian accepts as autograph only the two drawings of St. John the Baptist on the left, a position adopted by Marina Maiskaya in Moscow 1995–96; George R. Goldner does not accept two different hands but leaves the whole sheet with Mantegna). Among the saints are Peter and Paul and, again, a saint with a cross. Stylistically they are extremely close to the figures in the present drawing, although they are depicted from a higher vantage point and rendered somewhat more coarsely. Both sheets may have served the same commission. The connections between them and the study of an apostle in London suggest they were all made in preparation for a mural decoration or a polyptych with two registers of six or three of four apostles each, one row above the other. On the other hand, Ekserdjian argues that the drawings represent alternative ideas for the same apostles, intended to be grouped around a central figure or figures, possibly a Virgin and Child. He proposes a date in the early 1460s, while Goldner is inclined to argue for a date in the mid-1450s.

Provenance:
Edward Pearf or Edmund Prideaux(?) (Lugt 893 and suppl.); sale, London, Christie's, 7 July 1959, lot 70; Baron Hatvany; his sale, London, Christie's, 24 June 1980, lot 3; Thaw Collection, New York.

Bibliography:
Heinemann 1962, p. 84, no. 338 bis; Degenhart and Schmitt 1968, II, p. 363, no. 13; Robertson 1968, p. 25, no. 6; Byam Shaw 1976, III, p. 17, no. 34b; Lightbown 1986, pp. 481–82, no. 178; *Drawing* 1987, p. 135, repr.; Morgan Library 1993, pp. 276–77, no. 2, repr.; Goldner 1993, pp. 172–73; Moscow 1995–96, under no. 89.

Exhibitions:
Thaw II, no. 1, repr. in color; New York 1991a, no. 2; London and New York 1992, pp. 173–74, no. 23; Thaw III, no. 2, repr.

Thaw Collection, The Pierpont Morgan Library, acc. no. 1985.100

PD

Baccio della Porta,
called
Fra Bartolommeo

Florence 1472–
1517 Pian di Mugnone

3
Barren Trees
(recto and verso)

Pen and brown ink; traces of graphite to the right of the trunk of the tree on the verso. 11⁷⁄₁₆ × 8½ inches (285 × 215 mm). Watermark: none.

This double-sided sheet, like most of Fra Bartolommeo's other known studies of trees, comes from an album of drawings assembled during the first half of the eighteenth century by the Florentine painter, scholar, and collector Cavaliere Francesco Maria Niccolò Gabburri (1676–1742). Misleadingly entitled *Raccolta di Paesi e Vedute da Vero di Mano d'Andrea del Sarto*, the volume was made up of forty-one drawings of landscapes, rocks, and trees by Fra Bartolommeo as well as an unusual study of rocks by Baccio Bandinelli and a view of Tivoli that would appear to have been executed by a northern artist working in Italy. Despite its title, the album contained no drawings by Andrea del Sarto.

Gabburri's mistaken belief that the works in the album were by Fra Bartolommeo's great contemporary is somewhat surprising in light of the fact that he owned at least two other volumes of drawings by Fra Bartolommeo, and so might be expected to have recognized the work of that artist. Those albums are now in The Boijmans Van Beuningen Museum, Rotterdam. According to the title page of the first of the volumes in Rotterdam, which together contained 507 sheets of figure studies by the artist, Gabburri purchased the drawings directly from the Dominican convent of Santa Caterina in Florence, to which they had been presented by the painter Suor Plautilla Nelli (1523–88). Suor Plautilla had been a pupil and follower of Fra Paolino da Pistoia (ca. 1490–1547), who had in turn inherited the drawings from his teacher, Fra Bartolommeo. Although Gabburri seems to have been unaware of Fra Bartolommeo's authorship of the album of landscape and tree studies, it is by no means impossible that they share the same impeccable early provenance as the volumes in Rotterdam. After Gabburri's death, his collection appears to have found its way to England with "un Anglois nommé Kent"—perhaps, but not necessarily, the architect William Kent. The album from which the present drawing was removed turned up at Sotheby's in 1957, at which time it was disbound and its contents dispersed. (For the provenance of the Rotterdam drawings and of the album of landscape studies, see Gronau 1957 and Rotterdam and elsewhere 1990–92, pp. 12–18, 375.)

Chris Fischer has classified the contents of the album by subject, dividing the drawings into five main categories: townscapes, landscapes with convents, landscapes with farmhouses, studies of cliffs, and sketches of trees (Rotterdam and elsewhere 1990–92, p. 375). With the exception of several black-chalk studies of trees, all the drawings are in pen and ink and are relatively uniform in style. Comparably swift, delicate pen strokes and stippling appear in other sketches by Fra Bartolommeo that can be dated toward the end of the fifteenth and beginning of the sixteenth centuries. For this reason, Fischer has proposed that the landscape drawings were executed between about 1495 and 1508, when Fra Bartolommeo left Florence for a brief sojourn in Venice, after which he seems to have all but abandoned pen and ink in favor of chalk (Rotterdam and elsewhere 1990–92, p. 375).

The present drawing represents a pollarded mulberry and a small thorn tree on the recto and another leafless tree on the verso. As Peter Dreyer was the first to suggest, the rocky setting depicted on the recto appears to have been added by Fra Bartolommeo after he had drawn the trees, presumably to create a more satisfying composition (Thaw III, p. 25). Like the majority of Fra Bartolommeo's drawings of landscapes and trees, the present sheet appears to have been drawn outdoors, not in the studio, and it was most likely made for pleasure, rather than as a study for a painting. Indeed, even though motifs in two or three of Fra Bartolommeo's landscape drawings reappear in paintings by the artist and his followers, none of his studies of trees is directly related to a finished work. In this connection, Fischer has pointed out that, while the trees in Fra Bartolommeo's pen studies are invariably barren, leafless trees are otherwise extremely rare in his oeuvre (Paris 1994–95, p. 51, under no. 26).

Provenance:
Fra Paolino da Pistoia (?); Suor Plautilla Nelli (?); convent of Santa Caterina da Siena, Florence (?); Cavaliere Francesco Maria Niccolò Gabburri; William Kent (?); private collection, Ireland; sale, London, Sotheby's, 20 November 1957, no. 29; private collection, Switzerland.

Bibliography:
Gronau 1957, no. 39, repr.

Exhibitions:
Rotterdam and elsewhere 1990–92, not in catalogue; Thaw III, no. 4, repr. (recto and verso).

WMG

recto

verso

7

Lucas Cranach the Elder

Kronach 1472–1553 Weimar

4

Portrait of a Man in a Black Cap

Oil on paper, possibly over black chalk; some retouching in cap and bust. 9½ × 7¾ inches (250 × 195 mm). Watermark: most probably a high crown (Piccard 1961, VI, no. 7, which is documented between 1511 and 1516 in Thuringia, Saxony, and elsewhere). Upper corners are repaired; some wrinkles and tears. Inscribed on the verso in an old, possibly sixteenth-century hand, *H. HOLBEEN* and *2.*

This drawing and its companion piece (see below) were attributed to Hans Holbein until F. W. B. Watson connected them with Cranach and brought them to the attention of Jakob Rosenberg, who confirmed the new attribution. In this portrait, precisely rendered in a thin layer of oil paint on paper, the master is interested only in his subject's head and face, not in the bust. This type of portraiture seems to be an innovation of Cranach (Geissler 1979, I, no. A 15) and is found in his work as well as in the generally more colorful production of his highly gifted son Lucas Cranach the Younger. Both were excellent portrait painters. Some of the known oil studies from the Cranach atelier served as models for a tapestry of 1553/54 at the University of Greifswald (Hannes 1984, pp. 45–80), while others were used for portrait paintings (Schade 1974; *Cranach* 1980, p. 49, pl. 155, pp. 116, 167).

The present portrait is one of two that remained together until they were sold separately by Bob P. Haboldt & Co. in 1992. The companion piece, *Portrait of a Young Man with a Hat*, was acquired by the J. Paul Getty Museum in Malibu (*Cranach* 1994, no. 165). Haboldt had them cleaned, and they now look very different from their reproductions in earlier publications, where the busts are extended to the margins of the sheets and the hats of both sitters are painted out, giving them the appearance of portrait paintings rather than of oil studies of heads. The sitters have eluded identification. The beardless faces and hairstyles—cut short above the forehead, sometimes with a lock appearing beneath the cap in front, and extending at the sides to a point just above the earlobes—are found in portraits by Cranach datable between about 1529 and 1533 (Friedländer and Rosenberg 1978, p. 133, no. 128, dated 1529; p. 134, no. 332, dated 1526; p. 137, no. 343, dated 1533). A portrait study of Martin Luther of about 1532 in the collection of the duke of Buccleuch is particularly close in style to the Thaw drawing (Schade 1974, pl. 167).

The Thaw and Getty drawings have been connected with technically similar portrait studies in the Reims museum and have even been thought to have belonged originally to the same series (Rosenberg 1960, p. 29, under no. 77, and pp. 32, 33, nos. 90, 91; Paris 1992; and in the label at the exhibition of master drawings from the Getty Museum, The Metropolitan Museum of Art, New York, 1993). However, the Reims studies are not necessarily by Cranach the Elder; some are definitely by his son Lucas (Schade 1974, p. 99, attributes none to Lucas Cranach the Elder and illustrates two as Lucas the Younger [pls. 218 and 219]). These latter evoke the same Renaissance character as the Berlin drawings *Bearded Man* (Rosenberg 1960, no. 92; given convincingly to Cranach the Younger by Schade 1974, pl. 223) and *Duchess Elizabeth of Saxony* (1552–70), which is preparatory for a painting of 1564, some ten years after the elder Cranach's death (Schade 1974, pls. 245 and 246). An attribution of the present drawing to Cranach the Elder must therefore not be based on comparison with the Reims sheets. The perspective of the faces and especially the rendering of the eyes in both the Thaw and the Getty Museum drawings give them a nearly Gothic look when compared with the portraiture of the younger master. This visual information, combined with the early date, precludes the authorship of Lucas Cranach the Younger, who was born in 1515 and to whom some of the most beautiful and famous oil sketches, until recently attributed to his father, seem to belong (Rosenberg 1960, no. 92, and possibly 87; Schade 1974, pl. 223). The sheets combine the Gothic roots of the Cranach workshop with the highest quality of workmanship and can thus convincingly be attributed to Lucas Cranach the Elder.

Provenance:
Since ca. 1900 in the family of Michael Bluett Winch; Michael Bluett Winch; his sale, London, Sotheby's, *Old Master Paintings*, 11 December 1991, lot 45; Bob P. Haboldt & Co., New York and Paris.

Bibliography:
Rosenberg 1960, p. 33, no. 91, p. 32, under no. 90, repr.; Paris 1992, pp. 40–41, under no. 15, repr.

Exhibitions:
Manchester 1961, no. 8; Thaw III, no. 5, repr.

PD

Albrecht Altdorfer

Regensburg (?) ca. 1480–
1538 Regensburg (?)

5

Two Lovers by a Fountain in a Landscape

Pen and black and white ink, on brown prepared paper; framing lines in black ink. 6⅝ × 4⅝ inches (167 × 119 mm); the framing line 6⅝ × 4⅔ inches (167 × 113 mm). Watermark: none visible through lining. Inscribed on verso in black ink, monogrammed on lining, in red chalk, *AB 98,* and inscribed in graphite, *G.f.B.*

The attribution of this drawing has long been disputed, and its author at times identified as Albrecht Altdorfer, at times as the Master of the *Historia Friderici et Maximiliani.* The latter attribution refers to the illustrator of a manuscript on the lives of the Holy Roman Emperor Friedrich III and his son and successor, Emperor Maximilian I (Vienna, Haus-, Hof- und Staatsarchiv, HS Böhm no. 24). Commissioned by Maximilian for the instruction of his grandson, who became Emperor Charles V, the *Historia* was an important part of Maximilian's efforts to create a memorial to himself and his family. Indeed, the emperor's "monuments," for which the most celebrated German artists were employed, were produced mainly through works on paper and parchment. Albrecht Dürer, Lucas Cranach, and Altdorfer were among the illustrators of his prayer book. Dürer created the *Triumphwagen* (Triumphal Chariot) and was one of the inventors and draughtsmen of the gigantic woodcuts of Maximilian's *Ehrenpforte* (Triumphal Arch), an undertaking in which Altdorfer was also involved. Hans Burgkmair was the draughtsman of the woodcuts in the *Theuerdank,* a history of the life of the emperor, and was also involved with the *Triumphzug* (The Triumph of Maximilian). The commission for illustrating the *Historia Friderici et Maximiliani* was another of Maximilian's biographical-artistic enterprises and would not have been given to a marginal figure.

Scholars have long considered the Master of the *Historia* to be among the closest followers of Altdorfer, sometimes identifying him as Altdorfer himself, at others as an anonymous painter called the Master of Pulkau. While earlier scholars have suggested a date around 1515 for both the manuscript and the illustrations of the *Historia,* Hans Mielke has proposed the date 1508–10 and has shown that the style of draughtsmanship is consistent with Altdorfer's during those years, effectively removing further doubts about the attribution. There has been no published contradiction to Mielke's attribution of the *Historia* drawings to Altdorfer, but it was not unanimously accepted, and no less eminent a scholar than Fritz Koreny has verbally disagreed. It would seem that the difficulty in accepting Altdorfer and the *Historia* Master as one and the same artist stems from, on the one hand, the inner coherence of a series of drawings made in a very short span of time and, on the other, the scattered, fortuitously preserved remaining works drawn over a period of several decades. The *Historia* group displays a stylistic unity that cannot be expected nor indeed found throughout Altdorfer's remaining drawings. The stylistic connec-

tion pointed out by Mielke, however, is convincing to me.

The refinement of line has also been dealt with extensively by Mielke, and I agree that it, too, remains within Altdorfer's artistic breadth. Those who would prefer to attribute the present sheet to a different hand would have difficulty naming an artist working at this time with such high faculties as a draughtsman but no individual personality. While Mielke has suggested the years 1511–13 for the Thaw sheet, I would be inclined to date it somewhat earlier. A drawing in Berlin that exhibits the same technique, *St. Margaret Standing on the Demon,* dated 1509, appears particularly close. In addition, the subject matter seems to have interested Altdorfer at about that time. There are two other drawings by his hand, both dated 1508 (Winzinger 1952, nos. 11 and 12), and a woodcut, dated 1511 (Bartsch 63; Winzinger 1963, no. 17), that depict a soldier sitting with a married woman (as indicated by her *Haube,* or bonnet) against a landscape background.

Altdorfer produced such small, picturelike compositions as independent works of art, sometimes having them repeated in his workshop to provide more copies for sale (see Berlin and Regensburg 1988, pp. 18–19, 122–25, nos. 55–56). Although many of his drawings of this type are extant in workshop replicas and copies, no other version of this superb sheet has come to light.

Provenance:
Christian von Mechel; Peter Vischer, Basel (ca. 1800); Daniel Burckhardt-Wildt, Basel (ca. 1806); Daniel Burckhardt-Wert[h]emann, Basel; by inheritance to a private owner, Basel; Claude Kuhn, Basel; negotiated sale, London, Sotheby's.

Bibliography:
Hugelshofer 1927, p. 57, pl. 67; Becker 1938, no. 2 (as copy?), repr.; Winzinger 1952, no. 136, repr. (as *Historia* Master); Benesch and Auer 1957, p. 130, no. 13 (as Altdorfer); Oettinger 1959, p. 117, fig. 49 (as *Historia* Master); Winzinger 1960, p. 16, fig. 7 (as *Historia* Master).

Exhibitions:
Berlin and Regensburg 1988, pp. 108–9, no. 47, repr. in color (as Altdorfer); Thaw III, no. 6, repr. in color (as Altdorfer).

PD

11

Hans Sebald Beham

Nuremberg 1500–
1550 Frankfurt am Main

6

Portrait of a Man

Red chalk, heightened with white bodycolor. 10⅝ × 7⁷⁄₁₆ inches (270 × 190 mm). Watermark: bull's head surmounted by a cross and serpent (Briquet 15405). Monogram at left, in red chalk, *H[?]S B* (in ligature).

This vigorously executed portrait is an important addition to the extensive but insufficiently studied corpus of drawings by Hans Sebald Beham, a follower of Albrecht Dürer best known for his numerous small engravings.

Although Beham executed several expressive head studies and portrait drawings, few were done with chalk and none is closely related in style to the present example. Were it not for the presence of his monogram—which appears, slightly truncated, at the left side of the sheet—the work might never have been attributed to him. It certainly dates from after 1531, the year Beham altered the last letter of his monogram from *P* to *B*. The change in spelling was brought about by the artist's emigration in 1531 from southern Germany to Frankfurt am Main, where he settled in 1532. The watermark on the Thaw sheet is also found on paper circulated in Switzerland and the Rhineland, among other locations, between 1519 and about 1535.

Comparison of the swirling, impetuous strokes of this drawing with the fine, regular hatchings of a formal black chalk portrait in the Albertina, which dates from before 1531 (Schönbrunner and Meder, 1896–1908, IV [n.d.], no. 412), demonstrates the remarkable diversity in Beham's style and handling of the chalk. The spontaneity of the Thaw work is anticipated in another head study, dated 1523 and executed with similar freedom and graphic energy (Schilling 1973, I, no. 39, II, pl. 11). It is possible that Beham employed this vigorous style for expressive character heads, while reserving the restrained manner of the Albertina sheet for formal portraits from life. The use of red chalk was rare in German art during the first half of the sixteenth century, although Hans Baldung, Hans Schäufelein, and Wolf Huber also utilized it for portrait studies.

The interpretation of the Thaw drawing poses manifold problems. First, it is difficult to determine whether the study represents an actual person, as does the Albertina sheet, or depicts an ideal type or character head of the kind that appears elsewhere in Beham's work and in the drawings of his contemporaries, such as Baldung, Schäufelein, and Huber. Dr. George Szabo has noted in correspondence that the sitter's aquiline features and forked beard resemble those found in portraits of Emperor Sigismund of Luxembourg (1361–1437), especially the painting Dürer made for the Rathaus in Nuremberg between 1511 and 1513 and the preparatory drawing for it, in which Sigismund is portrayed in imperial regalia (see Wilde 1930, IV, pp. 213–22, and Strauss 1974, III, no. 1510/5). The decorated collar worn by the man in the Thaw work also sug-

gests the costume of an important personage. However, the resemblance to the portraits of Sigismund, who died a century earlier, is not absolutely compelling, nor is it clear why Beham should have depicted the emperor without any attributes except for the curious assortment of objects he delineated along the upper left side of the sheet.

That these objects add a satirical slant to the drawing is certain, but their precise meaning remains elusive. Hanging from a rod at the very top are the cap and bells worn by jesters. The rod and a pair of ass's ears, another attribute associated with folly, seem to grow out of a chamber pot that rests upon a dome-shaped object, probably a beehive. Beneath that is a pile of dung on a cushion. This last motif, as Walter Strauss pointed out in conversation, figures prominently in two woodcuts by Erhard Schoen that satirize those who dissipate time and money by eating and drinking excessively (Strauss 1984, nos. 196–97). It also appears, with drinking vessels, ass's ears, cap and bells, and other attributes of gluttony and folly, in the side borders of the first pages of Thomas Murner's *Narrenbeschwörung* (Strassburg, 1512), which John Rowlands related in conversation to Beham's drawing. The vertical arrangement of the objects in the woodcut borders of Murner's book recalls the disposition of the items in the margin of Beham's study. The significance of the beehive—if it is a beehive—in the context of these symbols of gluttony and folly is particularly obscure. In Pieter Bruegel's *The Ass in the Schoolhouse* of 1556, one of the ineducable pupils affirms his stupidity by thrusting his head in an active beehive, but whether it conveys a similar idea in Beham's drawing remains to be seen (Münz 1961, no. 129).

Finally, the connection between these objects and the individual or character type portrayed here also requires clarification. It is possible, though unlikely, that he is a jester. The cap and bells and ass's ears, along with the other attributes at the left, probably allude to the folly of mankind in general, as they do in the moralizing literature of the period.

Provenance:
W. J. Goldsmith, Ochiltree Castle near Linlithgow, Scotland; Baskett & Day, London.

Bibliography:
Thaw III, p. 272, repr.

Exhibition:
Thaw II, no. 3, repr.

WR

13

Jörg Breu the Younger

Augsburg after 1510– 1547 Augsburg

7

Horseman Attacking a Fallen Warrior

Pen and black ink, heightened with pen and white ink, some brushwork in both black and white ink, on paper brushed with a dark gray wash. 8¾ × 6¹¹⁄₁₆ inches (222 × 171 mm). Watermark: bear (see Briquet 12.278). Signed with monogram and dated *1543* at lower center in pen and white ink.

Little can be added to the observation of Campbell Dodgson, who first published this German Renaissance drawing in 1931, when it was in the possession of Mrs. Alfred Noyes, wife of England's poet laureate. The more than sixty years that have elapsed since its publication have not dimmed the pristine quality of its preservation, on which Dodgson remarked, nor has anyone come forth with any further suggestions for the identification of the curious subject of a horseman attacking a fallen warrior with the assistance of his mount, which fiercely bites the victim's head. Dodgson suggested the possibility that the drawing represents the death of the consul Caius Flaminius at the hands of the Insubrian horseman Ducarius at the Battle of Lake Trasimenus in 217 B.C. (Livy XXII, Ch. 6). However, there is no mention of the action of the horse in Livy's account.

That the subject was somewhat familiar to sixteenth-century audiences is suggested by its reappearance in a second version, executed in pen and brown ink (7⅘ × 5½ inches; 198 × 141 mm). Formerly in the collection of Mrs. A. K. M. Boerlage-Koenigs, it was sold at Sotheby's, London, on 26 June 1969, as lot 74 and has since also been acquired by the Morgan Library (acc. no. 1974.10). That drawing is likewise by a German artist, a draughtsman close in style to the Nuremberg artist Virgil Solis (1514–62), whose monogram has been added to the sheet along with the notation *V.72*. The two drawings, similar in the essentials of the composition but considerably different in details of setting, the dress of the figures, and the trappings of the horse, would appear to be based on a common prototype, which has yet to be traced. Dodgson tentatively suggested that the horse's action might have been Breu's invention, but the presence of the motif in the second drawing would seem to rule out such an idea.

The Morgan drawing is important as a monogrammed and dated work in this technique. There is another specimen in the Leipzig Museum der bildenden Künste (inv. no. N1 42), a design for the decoration of a dagger sheath on a gray ground, likewise signed with the monogram and dated 1545 (see Dresden 1963, no. 52, repr.; for another, see no. 50). A drawing in The Boijmans Van Beuningen Museum, Rotterdam, a representation of Marcus Curtius, on a bright red ground, has been attributed to the younger Breu by Byam Shaw on the basis of comparison with the present drawing. There is also a drawing of a horseman, on a dark red ground, attributed to the younger Breu in the 1956 catalogue of the Berne auctioneers Gutekunst and Klipstein (no. 36, repr.). Often, Breu seems to have

drawn with the pen without the preparation of a colored ground and elaboration of the ornamental white heightening. The high finish of the present drawing plus the fact that it is signed with the monogram and dated would make it suitable as a presentation piece. The monogram, it might be noted, is the mark of the Breu workshop, which the younger Breu took over from his father.

Like his better-known father, the short-lived younger Breu was active as a painter and more particularly as a draughtsman designing for woodcuts and glass. He was also employed as an illuminator. His woodcut work began in 1530, and by 1540 he was working as an illuminator of such manuscripts as Eton College's *Antiquitates*, written by his brother-in-law, the architect Hans Tirol. In 1543, the year he executed the present drawing, Breu is recorded as having three assistants and double that number two years later, an indication of the workshop's productivity and prosperity, which was cut short by his premature death.

Provenance:
Thomas Weld, Lulworth Castle, Dorset; Mrs. Alfred Noyes, London; Baskett & Day, London; Thaw Collection, New York.

Bibliography:
Dodgson 1931, p. 15, pl. 15; Dodgson 1934–35, no. 2, p. 203 n. 20; Thöne 1936, p. 81 n. 405; London 1969, under no. 74; Rotterdam 1974, under no. 20; Stuttgart 1979–80, I, p. 10; Morgan Library, *Fellows Reports*, XIX, p. 180; Thaw III, p. 272, repr.

Exhibitions:
London 1974a, no. 8, repr.; Thaw I, no. 10, repr.; Augsburg 1980, no. 612, repr.; New York 1981, no. 36, repr.; New York 1982; Princeton and elsewhere 1982–83, no. 3, repr.

Thaw Collection, The Pierpont Morgan Library, acc. no. 1978.38

FS

15

Jacopo Tintoretto

Venice 1518–1594 Venice

8

Samson Slaying the Philistines

Charcoal and, on the recto, additional white chalk on faded blue-green paper. 17½ × 11⅜ inches (443 × 285 mm). Watermark: none.

In 1584, Raffaello Borghini noted that Tintoretto produced drawings after sculpture throughout his career. According to Borghini, Tintoretto drew after "all the good things" that Venice had to offer, including statues by Jacopo Sansovino and casts of works by Michelangelo and Giovanni Bologna (Borghini 1584, p. 551). Among Tintoretto's extant drawings are heads after the antique as well as heads and entire figures after sculptures by Michelangelo.

In 1508 and again in 1528, the republican rulers of Florence commissioned Michelangelo to create a group representing Samson slaying the Philistines. The artist prepared a model but never executed the sculpture; the marble block was eventually used by Baccio Bandinelli for his *Hercules and Cacus*, which stands in the Piazza della Signoria. However, Michelangelo's intentions for the group are well documented through the description in Giorgio Vasari's biography of the artist; from a sketch, possibly by the master himself (Casa Buonarotti, Florence, 63Fr; Tolnay 1975, no. 61); a painting of 1557 by Daniele da Volterra; engravings (Hollstein [German], Lucas Kilian, nos. 528–30; Baljöhr 1990, nos. 15a–c); small bronzes (for the history of the undertaking and the bronzes, see Pope-Hennessy 1970, pp. 186–94, and most recently Hass 1993, pp. 383–86); a drawing by Naldini (Bean 1982, gift of Cornelius Vanderbilt, 80.3.301, no. 138); another by Cristofano Roncalli (Hass 1993, p. 385 n. 4); and a number of drawings by Tintoretto and his workshop (for lists, see Tietze and Tietze-Conrat 1944, p. 278ff., and Rossi 1975, under Bayonne, Musée Bonnat, no. 143, pp. 13–15; for later contributions, see London 1992, no. 10; Eitner 1993, pp. 16–19, no. 19; New York 1994a, no. 114). These latter drawings were probably made after a model in wax or clay, since some of them display the staff necessary to support the figure in such a model (among them, drawings in the Fogg Art Museum, Harvard University, the Princes Gate Collection in the Courtauld Institute, London [Rossi 1975, figs. 27–29], and the drawing in London 1992, no. 10).

The double-sided sheet in the Thaw Collection belongs to this group of drawings. It depicts Samson facing three-quarters left with his head in profile once on the verso and twice on the recto. In an autograph version in Bayonne (Rossi 1975, figs. 20, 21), the group is turned slightly farther toward the left, while other sheets, ascribed to Tintoretto's workshop, present at least five more different views (Rossi 1975, figs. 25–35). Lorenz Eitner has recently dealt with questions of the attribution of such drawings to Tintoretto himself or to his pupils, as well as to questions of originals and copies (Eitner 1993, pp. 16–19, no. 19). The Thaw drawing is executed in a very powerful hand, which speaks in favor of an attribution to the master himself.

It is extremely difficult to date Tintoretto's drawings. Borghini writes that after drawing Sansovino's *Mars* and *Neptune*, Tintoretto made Michelangelo his principal master (Borghini 1584, p. 551), which would date most of his Michelangelo copies after 1567, when Sansovino finished the statues. While earlier scholars have accepted this argument, in recent years the drawings after Michelangelo have been dated to Tintoretto's formative period, that is, the 1540s or 1550s (Rossi 1975, pp. 3–6; this earlier date is also accepted in Dobei 1991, p. 19).

Provenance:
Lord Wharton, Rushton Manor, Kettering and London; Adrian Ward-Jackson, London.

Exhibition:
Thaw III, no. 8, repr. (recto and verso).

PD

Jacques de Gheyn II

Antwerp 1565–1629 The Hague

9
Animal Studies

Black chalk, metalpoint, watercolor and gouache, pen and brown ink on prepared paper; framed with black ink lines. 4½ × 5½ inches (115 × 140 mm). Watermark: none. Numbered at upper left in graphite, *92*; inscribed on the verso in pencil, *De Gyn / 1880*. (According to Rotterdam and Washington 1985, this inscription is by the same hand as that on the verso of the Goltzius self-portrait in London; Reznicek 1961, II, no. 254, pl. 113, where the script is dated to the end of the seventeenth century.) On the verso, at lower left, *No 760*.

At the upper left is a fantastic bird with an oversize head, four wings, and four legs; it is prepared in black chalk, outlined in pale brown ink, and further defined with watercolor. The dragonfly shows preparation in metalpoint; its wings were then outlined with pen and pale brown ink, their texture indicated in gray watercolor applied with point of brush, and its body rendered with gouache and some watercolor. The frog at the lower left is executed in pen and brown ink over traces of metalpoint, while the head of the frog at the lower right is rendered in watercolor.

Jacques de Gheyn II followed the examples of Hans Verhagen, Hans Bol, and Joris Hoefnagel in his fascination with depicting the natural world. He drew many sheets with flowers and animals, which he also included in his paintings, particularly his still lifes. At times he focused exclusively on nature; however, he often imbued his drawings with a disturbing note by depicting dead and decaying animals or adding fantastic inventions, as in this sheet.

The handling of the frog's head at the lower right seems very close to that of the living frog among the *Four Studies of a Frog* in the Rijksmuseum, Amsterdam, which Van Regteren Altena has dated to the first years of the seventeenth century (Van Regteren Altena 1983, no. 888, pl. 334). More dragonflies are studied in a sheet in the Maida and George Abrams collection (Van Regteren Altena 1983, no. 900a, pl. 359a), dated by William W. Robinson to the period of the artist's residence in Leiden (ca. 1596–1601/2), where De Gheyn studied the university's collection of *naturalia* and began analyzing and drawing the natural world (Amsterdam and elsewhere 1991–92, p. 34). Another dragonfly is included in a vellum booklet, dating from 1600 to 1604 and acquired in 1604 by Emperor Rudolf II, containing watercolors of plants, insects, and small animals (Fondation Custodia, Paris, fol. 11, dated 1600; Van Regteren Altena 1983, no. 919, pl. 182).

Provenance:
Burgomaster De Vries (suggested by Van Regteren Altena); C. Ploos van Amstel (Lugt 2987); De Balliencourt, sold 1893, Paris (according to Mireur 1911, III, p. 300); private collection, New York.

Bibliography:
Van Regteren Altena 1983, II, p. 83, no. 508, III, pl. 332; William W. Robinson in Washington and New York 1986, pp. 140–41, under no. 48.

Exhibitions:
Rotterdam and Washington 1985, p. 79, no. 81; Thaw III, no. 9, repr. in color.

PD

Jan Brueghel

Brussels 1568–1625 Antwerp

10

A View of the Tiber in Rome with the Ponte Sisto and St. Peter's in the Distance

Pen and brown ink, brown and blue watercolor. 6⁵⁄₁₆ × 10¹⁄₁₆ inches (160 × 255 mm). Watermark: none. Inscribed at upper right corner, in pen and ink, *Paolo Veronese.*

Egbert Haverkamp-Begemann was the first to attribute this drawing to Jan Brueghel the Elder. Son of Pieter Bruegel the Elder, Jan Brueghel traveled to Italy in 1589, where he is documented as having been in Naples (1590), Rome (1592–95/96), and Milan (1593 and 1596). He returned to the Netherlands in 1596. Without proposing a definitive conclusion, Matthias Winner has discussed the suggestion that the drawing was done on the spot. While, in his view, certain technical points—the blurred pen lines resulting from the rapid application of wash—support this hypothesis, others, notably the carefully constructed *repoussoir* foreground, suggest a studio-composed view. Winner dates the sheet to the end of Brueghel's stay in Rome.

In addition to this vista, at least two more drawings by Brueghel using the same technique to depict the Tiber in Rome are known: one with the Ponte and Castel Sant'Angelo, and St. Peter's in the distance, now in Darmstadt (AE 397; Winner 1985, p. 89, fig. 11); and the other, a view of the Tiberine isle, formerly in Stuttgart and now destroyed (Winner 1985, p. 89, fig. 10). Other drawings from Brueghel's Italian sojourn are known, either from his own hand (Winner 1961, pp. 190–241, figs. 5, 5a, 5c; Berlin 1975, nos. 109 and 112, pls. 212 and 213) or through copies by Frederik van Valckenborch (Gerszi 1990, pp. 173–89, figs. 7, 10–15). The color combination of the drawing was employed by certain of Brueghel's compatriots as well—Pieter Stevens, for example—but here the character is typically Brueghel's. He employed the same palette in a view of Heidelberg made on the same trip (The Metropolitan Museum of Art, New York, Purchase, David T. Schiff Gift and Harris Brisbane Dick Fund, 1995.15).

Provenance:
Unidentified collector's mark upper right; anonymous sale, New York, Sotheby's, 3 June 1981, lot 124; private collection, New York; Bob P. Haboldt & Co., New York, 1990.

Bibliography:
Winner 1985, pp. 87–89, fig. 9; Haboldt 1990, p. 2, repr. in color.

Exhibitions:
Washington and New York 1986, pp. 89–90, no. 23, repr.; Thaw III, no. 11, repr.

PD

Paolo Veronese

21

Peter Paul Rubens

Siegen 1577–1640 Antwerp

11

The Descent from the Cross
Verso: *Saint Andrew*

Pen and brown ink, brown wash, occasional point of brush on light brown paper. Verso: slight indication of a head in black chalk. 13⁹⁄₁₆ × 9¹⁄₁₆ inches (345 × 233 mm). Watermark: none. Numbered at upper right, in brown ink, *3*, at lower left, in a more modern hand, in graphite, *6*; numbered on verso, at lower left, in graphite, *2*.

The recto, on which Rubens's ideas for a *Descent from the Cross* are vigorously inscribed, and the progression of his work on this sheet have been carefully described by Julius Held and subsequent writers, most recently by Anne-Marie Logan (Wellesley and Cleveland 1993). Rubens began with the head of the dead Christ, then inverted the sheet and laid out the image anew. He repeated the basic conception farther down to the right on a smaller scale, partly overlapping the first sketch and changing the position of the Magdalen, who embraces Christ's legs. This second version is repeated more clearly in a drawing in the Museum of Fine Arts, Boston (Wellesley and Cleveland 1993, no. 51), which seems to have been executed immediately after the Thaw drawing. The two figures at the right, lowering Christ's body into the arms of the Virgin, have been interchanged: The old man with the turban now leans over the arm of the cross, while the younger man, St. John, stands on the ladder before and below him. In both drawings Rubens has not yet decided whether to leave these two figures one above the other or to shift the upper figure farther to the left, as we learn from the faint indications outlining the head and shoulders in the present drawing or those outlining the head alone, to the left of the vertical beam of the cross, in the Boston sheet.

In March 1617, Rubens worked on a *Descent from the Cross,* now at the museum in Lille (Jaffé 1989, no. 434; New York 1992b, no. 1). An oil sketch for the painting is also in Lille (Jaffé 1989, no. 433; New York 1992b, no. 2). Another painting of the same subject, at the Hermitage in St. Petersburg, is generally dated 1617–18 (Jaffé 1989, no. 435). Both the Lille and Hermitage works were painted for the Order of the Capuchins. The Thaw drawing has affinities to each work. While the body of Christ corresponds closely, although in reverse, to the altarpiece in Lille, and the Magdalen occupies a similar place in the composition, other details, such as the positions of the two men on the ladder at the right, are closer to the Hermitage painting. Here, however, the figure of the Virgin is reversed and placed to the left and the Magdalen to the right. Rubens may have used this drawing in developing his ideas for both the Lille and St. Petersburg altarpieces.

The drawing on the verso is preparatory for the outer right wing of an altarpiece planned no later than September 1617 but painted between 5 February 1618 and 11 August 1619 at the behest of the Fishmongers' Guild for their altar in Notre-Dame-au-delà-de-la-Dyle in Mechelen (Jaffé 1989, no. 505E, repr. in reverse). In the painting, the saint holds a fish in his left hand. Two studies for the same figure, both in black chalk, are in Copenhagen and Munich (Held 1986, pls. 93 and 95). While in the Munich study Rubens depicts a standing man in much the same attitude as his St. Andrew, albeit in a short robe and without any indication of his identity, the X-shaped cross at the right in the Copenhagen sheet proves that the man—in this case clothed in a long, voluminous robe—is the saint. The Thaw drawing comes closest to the wing as executed, corresponding to it in many details, for example, the posture of the feet and the position of the right arm with the fingers resting on the beam of the cross.

Provenance:
Mrs. G. W. Wrangham, London; Edward Wrangham; Baskett & Day, London.

Bibliography:
Parker 1928, pp. 1–2, pl. 1; Dobroklonsky 1930–31, p. 32; Parker 1936, pp. 50–51, pl. 46; Evers 1943, p. 137, pl. 45; Antwerp 1956, under no. 65; Held 1959, no. 42, pl. 39, under no. 36, p. 22; Burchard and d'Hulst 1963, pp. 160–61, under no. 96; Białostocki 1964, p. 517, fig. 12; Held 1974, pp. 252–53, pl. 28; Varshavskaya 1975, pp. 104–13, under no. 14, repr.; Logan 1977, p. 409; Held 1986, no. 121, pl. 121, pp. 27, 55, under no. 95; Logan 1987, p. 73; Söding 1987, p. 566; New York 1992b, under no. 1, p. 61 n. 18.

Exhibitions:
London [1972], no. 8, recto and verso repr.; Thaw I, no. 11, repr.; Antwerp 1977, no. 146, repr.; Paris and elsewhere 1979–80, no. 14, repr.; New York 1981, no. 60, repr.; Wellesley and Cleveland 1993, no. 50, repr.; Thaw III, no. 13, repr. (recto and verso).

PD

recto

verso

Pieter Saenredam

Assendelft 1597–1665 Haarlem

12

Interior of the New Church of Haarlem

Pen, watercolor, and some red chalk. 14¹³⁄₁₆ × 20 inches (376 × 507 mm). Watermark: none visible through lining. Inscribed by the artist on the plinth of the column in the right foreground, *Den 14 Junij 1650 dit mette pen geteeckent in / de Nieuwe St. Anna kerck in haerlem*, and signed at the bottom of the pedestal of the same column, *Aldus van my Pieter Saenredam gemaeckt*; in the upper left corner, the motto *VIM VIRTVS*.

As a painter, Pieter Saenredam specialized in architectural subjects, which he rendered with great accuracy. Townscapes and individual architectural monuments—both secular buildings and churches—appear in his paintings. A great portion of his work is dedicated to church interiors, recording the Romanesque and Gothic architectural legacy of the northern Low Countries. This drawing depicts the only modern church within his oeuvre, the Nieuwe Kerck, or New Church, of Haarlem, erected between 1645 and 1649 after designs by Jacob van Campen (1595–1657). It is a central-plan building—the nave and transepts forming a Greek cross—attached to a slightly older tower. The view is taken from north to south and shows the pulpit between the south pillars of the crossing (see Schwartz and Bok 1989, pp. 215–38, and Rotterdam 1991, p. 121, no. 18).

Saenredam, who lived in Haarlem from 1609, was able to study the building process of the New Church. He drew a site plan of how the city appeared before construction began and, in 1651, copied Van Campen's design of the layout of the streets, indicating the position of the church. Shortly after the building was completed, he portrayed it in drawings and paintings, sometimes basing his representations on Van Campen's plans rather than on the actual building. Fourteen drawings, dating from 1650 to 1653, are known. Two show the exterior; the remainder depict the interior and the coats of arms on a stained glass window. The majority of these sheets are dated by the master to the day, as was Saenredam's habit. The Thaw interior, made on 14 June 1650, is the first of six drawings of the church dated to that year and covering the period between 14 June and 8 July. The four known paintings of the church date from 1652, 1653, 1655, and 1658.

Saenredam's work is rare. Our knowledge of it has not greatly increased since the catalogue of 1970, in which the number of his paintings was given as fifty-five and that of his drawings, which include depictions of flowers, trees, and portraits, as 140. To our knowledge, this is one of only three of his drawings in the United States; the two others are in the Woodner family collection, now on long-term loan to the National Gallery of Art, Washington, D.C., and the J. Paul Getty Museum, Malibu.

Provenance:
Six Collection, Amsterdam; Six sale, Fr. Muller's, Amsterdam, 16–18 October 1928, no. 449; Jonckvrouwe H.M.A.F. Six, 's Graveland; Noortman, London.

Bibliography:
Schwartz and Bok 1989, no. 79, pp. 217, 226, fig. 236.

Exhibitions:
Utrecht 1961, no. 79, repr.; Paris 1970, no. 20, repr.; Thaw III, no. 15, repr. in color.

PD

Anthony van Dyck

Antwerp 1599–1641 London

13

Portrait of Jacques Dubroeucq

Brush and different shades of brown ink, over black chalk; incised for transfer. 8¹¹⁄₁₆ × 6⁹⁄₁₆ inches (221 × 168 mm). Watermark: none visible through lining. Inscribed at lower right, with brush and brown ink, *VANDYK F:*.

This half-length figure of a man holding a compass in his right hand as his attribute was preparatory for Paulus Pontius's engraving in the collection of portraits known as Van Dyck's *Iconography*, first published by Martinus van den Enden between 1636 and 1641 and later republished with a title page that in the second version is dated 1645. The tonal modulation of the washes is typical of this type of finished drawing intended for engraving, which can be identified as *delineatio*, the Latin word indicating the work of the draughtsman in old prints. The second state of the engraving is inscribed with the name of the sitter, *JACOBVS DE BREVCK*. In the fourth state, his profession, architect, and his hometown, Mons (Bergen) in Hennegau, have been added in a line that reads *ARCHITECTUS MONTIBVS IN HANNONIA*. The names of the artist, engraver, and publisher—*Ant. van Dyck pinxit* (painted by Anthony van Dyck), *Paul. Pontius sculp.* (engraved by Paulus Pontius), and *Mart vanden Enden excudit . . .* (published by Martinus van den Enden)—are indicated in several of the states (see Maquoy-Hendrickx 1956, pp. 11, 207–8, no. 44; idem 1991, pp. 4, 33, no. 44).

While the raised compass, pointing upward, may stand for the allegory of *disegno* (Ripa) as well as for the theoretical aspects of architecture, the compass pointing down, as shown here, signifies practice—in this case the practicing architect. Such an image of an architect had been well known since 1562, when Giacomo Vignola published his *Regola delli cinque ordini d'architettura* with his portrait on the title page (Thoenes 1983, pp. 345–76; for the date of the first edition, see p. 348; for the iconography of the compass, pp. 372–74). Because the long beard as well as the attire in Van Dyck's drawing are typical of the sixteenth century, the identification of the sitter as the well-documented sculptor and architect from Mons, who lived from 1500/1510 to 1584, seems more probable than his identification as a younger artist of the same name, as suggested by Maquoy-Hendrickx (1956, pp. 11–12) and repeated by Christopher Brown (New York and Fort Worth 1991). That this latter artist even existed has been doubted by R. Hedicke (see Thieme-Becker, X, pp. 12–13).

In the published papers of the symposium organized by the Center of Advanced Study in the Visual Arts, Washington, D.C., in conjunction with the Van Dyck exhibition of 1990–91, Joaneath Spicer discussed, among other problems, the presence of the term *pinxit* (painted)—as opposed to *delineavit* (drew)—in the inscriptions on the engravings. She pointed out that the engravings indeed reproduced formal painted portraits, while small-scale monochrome oil sketches, and *delineationes* in black chalk, with or without additional wash, served as models for the engraver (see Spicer 1994).

Provenance:
Sale, London, Christie's, 1 December 1970, lot 54; William H. Schab Gallery, New York, 1972; private collection, Switzerland; William H. Schab Gallery, New York, 1986.

Bibliography:
Spicer 1985–86, p. 539, no. 17, pl. 23; Jaffé 1991, p. 341; Spicer 1994, no. 44, p. 359.

Exhibitions:
New York 1972a, no. 52, repr. and on cover in color; New York and Fort Worth 1991, no. 57, repr. in color; Thaw III, no. 17, repr.

PD

Rembrandt Harmensz. van Rijn

Leiden 1606–1669 Amsterdam

14
Four Negroes with Wind Instruments

Pen and brown ink, brown wash, some red chalk and yellow wash in the two figures at the left, probably some black chalk in the figure at the right. 7 1/16 × 5 1/4 inches (179 × 135 mm). Watermark: none. Numbered at lower left, in pen and ink, *11*.

In recent decades, there has been an extensive reevaluation of Rembrandt's paintings and drawings. While the corpus of his drawings compiled by Otto Benesch (first published 1954–57) has proven to be overly generous in its attributions, no new monograph has yet replaced it. Only in museum and exhibition catalogues are the parameters of Rembrandt's work as a draughtsman beginning to be redefined. In the important 1991 exhibition, *Rembrandt: The Master and His Workshop: Drawings & Etchings*, the present drawing was discussed and accepted in the entry on its companion piece, *Two Mummers on Horseback*, also in the collection of The Pierpont Morgan Library (acc. no. I, 201).

These sheets, which belong to Rembrandt's early Amsterdam period, are two of a group of four that depict details of the same pageant (Benesch 1973, II, nos. 365–68). The others are in the British Museum. The first of the British Museum drawings depicts two men mounted on mules: one striking two kettledrums and the other a commander (normally described as *Two Negro Drummers*, but Martin Royalton-Kisch [1992; no. 21] has pointed out that the Hungarian-style fur cap may identify its wearer as a commander, holding a mace rather than a drumstick). The second of the British Museum drawings depicts a mounted officer (Royalton-Kisch 1992, no. 22). All four drawings feature a similar use of red and yellow chalks, subtle tonal shifts from brown to reddish brown, and an impressively coarse line. In contrast to the Thaw drawing, white is used in the other three in addition to the media described above.

Rembrandt may have made these drawings after a pageant that included Africans and mummers, which, according to Benesch, might have taken place in Amsterdam in 1637. Van Regteren Altena has suggested a more precise date, February 1638, and a different place, The Hague, where, on the occasion of the wedding of Wolfert van Brederode and Louise Christine of Solms—sister of Amalia, princess of Orange—processions and competitions took place in which nobles and Moors in costume participated. The artist could have watched the events from the home of Constantijn Huygens (*Congrès* 1952, p. 39; Van Regteren Altena 1952, pp. 60–63). As Royalton-Kisch has noted, not only does the drawing style correspond to the period in which the event took place, but also the description of the pageant contains some details that match the information provided by the drawings: the presence of a mounted drummer striking two kettledrums, as depicted in one of the sheets in the British Museum, and black musicians, as represented here. He cautions, how-ever, not to take the connection for granted since "similar figures may have appeared at other events that Rembrandt could have witnessed, and his rare documented excursions from Amsterdam do not include one at this time" (Royalton-Kisch 1992, p. 71).

Provenance:
T. Hudson (Lugt 2434); J. Richardson, Sr. (Lugt 2184); J. Richardson, Jr. (Lugt 2170 as blind stamp); R. Houlditch (Lugt 2214); C. Rogers; T. Dimsdale (Lugt 2426); Andrew James; W. Russel; R. P. Roupell; H. M. Calmann, London; Victor Koch, London; Walter Feilchenfeldt, Zurich.

Bibliography:
Waagen 1857, p. 215; Benesch 1947a, no. 88, repr.; Van Regteren Altena 1952, p. 61, fig. 2; Calmann [1952], no. 10, repr.; Benesch 1960, p. 148, under no. 29; Benesch 1973, II, no. 366, fig. 441; Bernhard 1976, II, p. 233, repr.; Berlin and elsewhere 1991–92, under no. 14; Royalton-Kisch 1992, under no. 21.

Exhibitions:
London 1929a, no. 584 and *Commemorative Catalogue of the Exhibition of Dutch Art, 1929*, 1930, p. 200; Thaw III, no. 18, repr. in color.

PD

Rembrandt Harmensz. van Rijn

Leiden 1606–1669 Amsterdam

15

Three Studies for a Descent from the Cross

(Mark 15:42–46)

Quill and reed pen, and brown ink. Repair along upper margin. 7½ × 8⅟₁₆ inches (190 × 205 mm). Watermark: none.

Throughout his life, Rembrandt was concerned with the illustration of scenes from the life and passion of Christ, but he was particularly preoccupied with these themes in his drawings and etchings of the first half of the 1650s, the period to which this remarkably expressive sheet of studies is assigned. As is true of Rubens's *Descent from the Cross* (No. 11), it is possible here to trace the development and refinement of the artist's ideas, both formally and psychologically. He appears to have first drawn the right group of Christ and the compassionate supporter of his dead body, which is still suspended from the cross by one hand; he then seems to have revised the original position of Christ's left forearm and back, pressing heavily on the broad nib of his reed pen to produce the bold outlines. In the smaller sketch at the upper left, he incorporated the new position of the forearm and clarified that of the shoulder, at the same time altering the relationship of the two heads so that Christ's no longer overlaps the other. Finally, moving his pen to the lower left, he studied the new juxtaposition of the heads on a larger scale. As befits the nocturnal setting of the event, the sensitive face of Christ is now effectively illumined against the shadowed countenance of the young man, perhaps intended as St. John and possibly bearing a faint reminiscence of the features of Rembrandt's son Titus (cf. the portrait *Titus Reading*, Kunsthistorisches Museum, Vienna; Bredius-Gerson, no. 122).

The lightly indicated heads in the center of the sheet may have been first thoughts for spectators at the scene of the deposition, the two at the left possibly extraneous notations that were already on the sheet when Rembrandt began these moving studies of the dead Christ and his sorrowing young disciple, who performs his poignant task with infinite tenderness. Campbell's assertion that Rembrandt was inspired in this drawing by Marcantonio Raimondi's print after Raphael's *Deposition* is not as convincing as his association of *The Standing Old Man and Seated Young Man* (Benesch 1954–57, II, no. 3448, fig. 400; Benesch 1973, fig. 421) with Marcantonio's print after Raphael's *St. Paul Preaching in Athens*.

Critics have associated this drawing with the etching of 1654 (Bartsch 83) as well as with the *Descent from the Cross* in the National Gallery of Art, Washington, D.C., to which Gerson refers as the work of a "pupil who based himself on Rembrandt" (Bredius-Gerson, no. 584). Jakob Rosenberg always maintained that the painting is a "highly important" work from Rembrandt's own hand. It cannot be said that the Thaw drawing is directly connected with either work, although compositionally it would seem nearer to the painting than to the etching to which Benesch related it.

Provenance:
George Guy, fourth earl of Warwick (according to Benesch, no mark, see Lugt 2600); Thomas Halstead; Dr. A. Hamilton Rice, New York; Mr. and Mrs. Louis H. Silver, Chicago; M. Knoedler & Co., Inc., New York; Robert Lehman, New York; Norton Simon Foundation, Los Angeles; R. M. Light & Co., Inc., Boston.

Bibliography:
Valentiner 1925–34, II, no. 493, repr.; Benesch 1935, p. 55; Benesch 1954–57, V, 1957, no. 934, fig. 1145 (2d ed., 1973, V, no. 934, fig. 1211); Rosenberg 1959, p. 114; *Arts* 1960, p. 29, repr.; Campbell 1975, p. 28.

Exhibitions:
New York and Cambridge 1960, no. 68, pl. 57; Chicago 1969, no. 133, repr.; Thaw I, no. 30, repr.; Paris and elsewhere 1979–80, no. 72, repr.; Thaw III, no. 19, repr.

FS

Rembrandt Harmensz. van Rijn

Leiden 1606–1669 Amsterdam

16
The Finding of Moses

Quill and reed pen, and brown ink; correction in white in the area of the hands of the figure at the far left and possibly in the area of the left foot of Pharaoh's daughter. 7⅜ × 9¼ inches (188 × 235 mm). Numbered in brown ink at lower right corner, *15*.

As far as is known, Rembrandt drew the Finding of Moses only in this important sheet of the mid-1650s and an earlier one in the Rijksmuseum, Amsterdam (Benesch 1973, II, no. 475; Münz's attribution to Ferdinand Bol, which Benesch accepted, is rejected by most scholars). In the lively but slight sketch in Amsterdam, Pharaoh's daughter and her two attendants are depicted as bathers with little or no indication of the setting. Here, however, Rembrandt illustrates the biblical story with a full array of characters dramatically disposed at the water's edge, the great umbrella used to suggest the royal and exotic nature of the event. Pharaoh's daugher, richly garbed and arms akimbo, dominates the scene. Her elaborate hat, along with the inclination of her head, brings to mind—in reverse—the striking Flora of the Metropolitan Museum's painting (Bredius-Gerson, no. 114), a work not too far removed in date. Her peering maids focus with a telling variety of gazes on the two attendants lifting the infant Moses from the water. Boldly set down with broad, even crude, strokes of the reed pen as *repoussoir* figures, the attendants are imbued with the energy and purpose of their task; a pentimento may be observed in the arm of the figure in the corner of the sheet. Equally intense is the visage of the infant Moses' sister—somehow suggestive of concern even in its abbreviated notation—worriedly watching from behind the curving lines of the low chariot of Pharaoh's daughter.

Sumowski notes that a copy of the drawing sold at The Hague in 1912 shows that it has at some time been cut down on three sides. As Benesch remarked, the spokes of the chariot wheel, rendered in a more reddish brown ink than the rest of the drawing, appear to have been added at a later date.

Provenance:
H. Duval; sale, Amsterdam, Frederik Muller & Co., 22–23 June 1910, no. 302; Marignane; Dr. James Henry Lockhart, Jr., Rochester, New York; R. M. Light & Co., Inc., Boston.

Bibliography:
Valentiner 1925–34, I, no. 124; Benesch 1935, p. 56; Benesch 1954–57, V, 1957, no. 952, fig. 1163 (2d ed., 1973, V, no. 952, fig. 1225); Sumowski 1961, p. 17 ("Eine Kopie der Verst. C.O.C. Obreen, Den Haag, 18.12. 1912, Nr. 276 [Feder, 20:30 cm] erweist das Blatt als auf drei Seiten beschnitten."); Rotermund 1963, pp. 89, 109, 312, no. 70; Thaw III, p. 252, repr.

Exhibitions:
Pittsburgh 1939, p. 111; Thaw I, no. 29, repr.

FS

Rembrandt Harmensz. van Rijn

Leiden 1606–1669 Amsterdam

17

An Old Scholar at His Writing Table

Reed pen and brown ink, smudged by finger, some brown wash, corrections in white bodycolor. 5⅛ × 4³⁄₁₆ inches (129 × 105 mm). Watermark: illegible fragment (repr. in Paris and elsewhere 1979–80, watermark no. 57).

Between the middle of the 1650s and his death in 1669, Rembrandt made fewer drawings than he had in the first three decades of his career. His rare late sketches are distinguished by their unprecedented pictorial effects, which recall the broad, vigorous brushwork and luminous shadows of his paintings of the 1660s. In *An Old Scholar at His Writing Table*, Rembrandt summarized the structure of the figure, the table, the chair, and the globe with thick strokes of the reed pen, but when he smudged the ink with his finger and made corrections in white bodycolor, linear description gave way almost entirely to painterly impression. Otto Benesch placed this work at about 1661–62, comparing its style and technique with those of one of the studies for the *Syndics of the Cloth Drapers' Guild* of 1662 (Benesch 1973, no. 1178).

A scholar writing at his desk is the subject of many works by Rembrandt and his followers, including genre scenes, commissioned portraits, and, with the appropriate attributes, portraitlike representations of saints. The stacks of heavy books, the globe, and the pen poised to record the next thought are constant features of these paintings, drawings, and prints. Examples of the various types are found in Werner Sumowski (1983, I, nos. 62, 127, pp. 290, 521, 1979–92, I, 1979, no. 211[X]); Rembrandt's painting of 1634 (Bredius-Gerson, no. 432); and Rembrandt's etching *St. Jerome in a Dark Chamber* (Bartsch 105).

Provenance:
Friedrich August II of Saxony, Dresden (Lugt 971); A. & R. Ball, New York; L. V. Randall, Montreal; his sale, London, Sotheby's, 6 July 1967, no. 5, repr.

Bibliography:
De Groot 1906, no. 305; Singer 1921, no. 46; Freise and Wichmann 1925, no. 113; Hell 1930, p. 127; Benesch 1935, p. 67; Benesch 1954–57, V, 1957, no. 1151, fig. 1373 (2d ed., 1973, V, no. 1151, fig. 1447).

Exhibitions:
New York 1950, no. 39; Rotterdam and Amsterdam 1956, no. 252; New York and Cambridge 1960, no. 77, pl. 67; Paris and elsewhere 1979–80, no. 78, repr.; Thaw II, no. 8, repr.; Thaw III, no. 21, repr.

WR

35

Gerbrand van den Eeckhout

Amsterdam 1621–
1674 Amsterdam

18

A Seated Youth in a Hat, His Chin Cupped in His Hand

Brush and brown wash. Framing lines in pen and brown ink. $5\frac{5}{8} \times 4\frac{7}{16}$ inches (142×112 mm). Watermark: none.

This softly luminous study, executed entirely with the brush, belongs to a now-widely dispersed group of at least fifteen other drawings in exactly the same style and technique (Sumowski 1979–92, III, 1980, nos. 782[X]–97[X], repr.). In the majority of these drawings the model is male, although individual studies in the Rijksprentenkabinet, Amsterdam, and in the collection of Maida and George Abrams are of women, and one of two brush drawings of this type in the Frits Lugt Collection, Institut Néerlandais, Paris, represents a sleeping dog (Sumowski 1979–92, III, 1980, nos. 795[X]–96[X], repr., no. 797[X], repr., respectively). The same model as in the present sheet, in identical costume and very similarly posed, appears in another, somewhat larger drawing, formerly in the collection of Walter C. Baker and now in The Metropolitan Museum of Art, New York (Sumowski 1979–92, III, 1980, no. 783[X], repr.).

None of these drawings is signed or dated, which has led to considerable disagreement about the identity of the artist. For example, the *Boy Reading* in the Musée Cognac-Jay, Paris, was long attributed to Jean Honoré Fragonard, while other studies in the group have been ascribed to such Netherlandish draughtsmen as Ferdinand Bol, Quirijn van Brekelenkam, Nicolaes Maes, Caspar Netscher, Gerard as well as Moses Terborch, and Johannes Vermeer (Sumowski 1979–92, III, 1980, 3, p. 1686, under no. 782[X]). Current scholarship nevertheless subscribes to the opinion—first recorded in connection with the P. de Hollander and H. Verschuuring sales of 1770 and 1771, respectively, and reiterated by C. Ploos van Amstel, who included two of the drawings in his *Collection d'imitations de dessins d'après les principaux maîtres hollandais*—that the entire group is instead by Rembrandt's favorite pupil and close follower, Gerbrand van den Eeckhout.

Although this attribution cannot be proven, there is a good deal of evidence in support of it. As Sumowski has pointed out, the drawings in question are stylistically compatible with a number of other sheets that can be attributed to the artist, and similar figures appear in several of Eeckhout's paintings, among them his *Woman Drinking* of 1655 (formerly Buttery Gallery, London) and the 1653 *Portrait of a Twelve-Year-Old Boy* in the Musée des Beaux-Arts, Lille (Sumowski 1979–92, III, 1980, pp. 1686–88, under no. 782[X]). Another work that may be compared to the present sheet is a study of a sleeping boy in the Rijksprentenkabinet, Amsterdam, which is executed in black chalk and gray wash and is signed, *E. V. Eeckhout fec[it]* (Sumowski 1979–92, III, 1980, no. 634, repr.; see Paris 1974, p. 48, under no. 33, and New York and Paris

1977–78, p. 54, under no. 35. The connection is dismissed by Sumowski [1979–92, III, 1980, p. 1686, under no. 782[X]]). The series is usually dated about 1655.

Provenance:
J. de Vos Jacobszoon (Lugt 1450 on verso); sale, Amsterdam, Roos, Frederik Muller & Co., et al., 22 May 1883, no. 162; P. Langerhuizen; sale, Amsterdam, Frederik Muller & Co., 29 April–1 May 1919, no. 257, repr.; Adolf Goldschmidt; sale, New York, Christie's, 12 January 1995, no. 253, repr.; Bob P. Haboldt & Co.

Bibliography:
Henkel 1942, p. 77 n. 10; Rotterdam and Paris 1974, p. 48, under no. 33; New York and Paris 1977–78, p. 54, under no. 35; Sumowski 1979–92, III, 1980, no. 782[X], repr.

Exhibition:
Chicago and elsewhere 1969–70, no. 167, repr.

WMG

Stefano della Bella

Florence 1610–1664 Florence

19

A Feast at the Cascine, Florence, on the Banks of the Arno

Pen and brown ink, brush and water-color, accented with gum arabic, touches of white gouache, heightened with gold and silver, over traces of black chalk, on two sheets of paper joined vertically. Framing lines in pen and brown ink and brush and brown wash. 10⅞ × 31½ inches (276 × 799 mm). Watermark: none. Signed and dated in pen and brown ink, *SDB/1630.*

One of the most talented and prolific Italian draughts-men and printmakers of the seventeenth century, Stefano della Bella was apprenticed to a series of goldsmiths before entering the workshop of the Floren-tine painter Giovanni Battista Vanni, probably in 1623. About the same time, Stefano appears to have begun to study the prints of Jacques Callot, a native of Nancy who began his career in Florence in the atelier of Remi-gio Cantagallina and later entered the service of Grand Duke Cosimo II. Stefano was only eleven years old when Callot left Florence to return to Lorraine in 1621. It is therefore unlikely that the two ever met, but Callot's distinctive late mannerist style was to have a tremendous influence upon the work of the younger artist. Stefano's first etching is datable about 1627. Six years later, he traveled to Rome to continue his educa-tion, and by the time he left Florence for a ten-year sojourn in Paris in 1639, he was already an internation-ally acclaimed, stylistically independent printmaker.

Stefano della Bella produced more than a thousand etchings and several thousand known drawings—most of them relatively small, delicate pen studies made in preparation for his prints. This large, brightly colored, and highly finished drawing, executed on two pieces of paper joined vertically and heightened with gold and silver, is altogether exceptional in Stefano's oeuvre. Signed and dated 1630, and therefore made three years prior to the artist's departure for Rome, it is compara-ble in style and degree of finish to five drawings in Florence, Paris, and Rome, also executed toward the beginning of the artist's career, although on a smaller scale and in pen and ink on vellum (Florence, Uffizi, Gabinetto Disegni e Stampe, inv. nos. 5907–8 S; Paris, Musée du Louvre, Département des Arts Graphiques, inv. no. 292; Rome, Istituto Nazionale per la Grafica, inv. no. F.C. 116967; see Viatte 1974, nos. 2–3, repr.; Isola 1976, no. 7, repr.).

The large size and high finish of this sheet imply that it was made as a work of art in its own right, rather than as a study for a print, and its style reflects the breadth of Stefano's culture. The individual figures are very close in spirit to those of Callot and betray

Stefano's familiarity with that artist's prints. At the same time, however, Stefano's comparatively naturalistic approach to the representation of landscape and his interest in scenes from everyday life, evident in the picnickers on the left and the cardplayers on the right, suggests the influence of such contemporary Netherlandish printmakers as Esias van de Velde (Florence 1965, p. 48, under no. 15).

The drawing depicts a company of elegantly dressed men and their entourage engaged in a variety of pleasurable pursuits. In addition to eating, drinking, and playing cards, a number of men play pall-mall, a game somewhat similar to croquet that enjoyed great popularity in Italy and elsewhere in Europe during the sixteenth century; a strikingly similar depiction of a game of pall-mall by the Dutch artist Adriaen van de Venne is preserved in the British Museum, London (Royalton-Kisch 1988, no. 31, repr.). In Stefano's watercolor, the setting may be the Cascine, a park on the outskirts of Florence. If so, then the view would be toward Florence, with the Arno River on the right.

Provenance:
Carlo Lotteringhi della Stufa, Florence; Bob P. Haboldt & Co., New York.

Bibliography:
Nugent 1925–30, II, 1930, p. 314; Viatte 1974, p. 9; Haboldt 1995, no. 7, repr.

Exhibitions:
Florence 1922, no. 371; Florence 1931, no. 11; Florence 1965, no. 15, repr.

WMG

Claude Gellée, called Claude Lorrain

Chamagne 1600–1682 Rome

20

Heroic Landscape

Black chalk, pen and brown ink, brown, gray, and some blue wash. Verso: landscape with a coastal town in the distance, in black chalk. 10¹⁄₁₆ × 15¹¹⁄₁₆ inches (254 × 396 mm). Watermark: fragment of *tête de bœuf*.

This drawing, which Claude drew *en plein air* and probably reworked with washes in the studio, has much of the feeling of the artist's earlier nature studies, notably those in his Tivoli sketchbook, and, like those, it is fairly large. Since much the same sort of terrain can be seen on the verso, sketched only in black chalk, it may be assumed that he drew it on the same sketching excursion and the setting is taken from another vantage point at the same site. The imposing villa indicated in the background is typical of the region and also appears on the verso as seen from another viewpoint. The rendering of the building, however, is so summary and secondary to Claude's real subject, the landscape, that it has not been possible to identify it.

The drawing was recently removed from an album composed of Claude's best drawings that was assembled sometime shortly before or after his death. It has been surmised that Claude himself may have compiled the album between 1677 (the date of the last drawing in the album) and 1682, but it is also possible that his heirs put the album together after his death. Queen Christina of Sweden may have been the recipient of the album, which by 1713 had made its way into the Odescalchi collection in Rome. It remained with that family until 1960 when Georges Wildenstein acquired it (Roethlisberger 1962 and 1968). In addition to their consistent high quality, these drawings are remarkably fresh, owing to their preservation for almost three centuries in album format.

The Thaw drawing was one of the three largest in the album, which was originally made up of sixty leaves, containing twenty-four nature studies, twenty-one composition drawings, and fifteen figure drawings. It is clearly one of the most beautiful of the nature studies, close in composition to that of *The Journey to Emmaus*, which Claude painted in 1652, known today only from the artist's record drawing in the *Liber Veritatis*, British Museum, London (Roethlisberger 1961, LV 125, repr.). The framing trees of the foreground, as well as the view of the distant villa or castle, correspond well to the same elements in the *Liber Veritatis* copy. Only the figures of Christ and the apostles are not indicated in the drawing. The sketch on the verso was apparently not used by the artist in any known composition.

Provenance:
Queen Christina of Sweden (?) (1629–89), in Rome from 1655 to 1689; Cardinal Decio Azzolini (?) (1623–89), Rome; Don Livio Odescalchi, duke of Bracciano (1652–1713), Rome; by descent; Georges Wildenstein, Paris, 1960; Norton Simon, Pasadena, 1968.

Bibliography:
Roethlisberger 1962, pp. 6, 7, no. 35, repr. in color; Roethlisberger 1962a, pp. 144, 147, no. 7, repr. in color; Roethlisberger 1968, no. 709, repr.; Roethlisberger 1971, p. 7, no. 34, pl. 34 in color, verso repr., pl. 62.

Exhibitions:
Washington and Paris 1982–83, no. 47, repr.; Thaw II, no. 6, repr.; Paris and New York 1993–94, no. 23, repr. in color; Thaw III, no. 22, repr. (recto and verso).

CDD

Claude Gellée, called Claude Lorrain

Chamagne 1600–1682 Rome

21

Christ on the Road to Emmaus

Brush and deep brown wash over black and red chalk, heightened with white bodycolor, on paper tinted with a pale brown wash. Verso: same subject in pen and brown ink. 4⅞ × 8⅛ inches (123 × 206 mm).

Of Claude's two paintings of Christ on the Road to Emmaus only the second one, now in St. Petersburg, is preserved. The earlier picture, dated 1652, survives only in the copy that Claude made for the *Liber Veritatis* (see Roethlisberger 1968, no. 712) and two preliminary studies.

The Thaw drawing, in which the recto is traced through to the reverse, the only modification from one side to the other being the transposition of Christ's staff from his left hand to his right, is the earlier of the preliminary studies. In the other preparatory sheet, which is part of the Wildenstein Album, the articulation of gesture and placement of figures is identical to that in the final composition as recorded in the *Liber Veritatis*. This record drawing reveals that Claude placed his figures in the foreground of the painting in a beautiful Italian landscape before a river with a fortified hill town in the middle distance.

Provenance:
Jonathan Richardson, Sr. (Lugt 2183); Rev. Henry Wellesley; his sale, London, Sotheby's, 25 June 1866, no. 389; Pierre Dubaut, Paris; Walter Goetz, Paris.

Bibliography:
Roethlisberger 1962, under no. 13; Roethlisberger 1965, repr.; Roethlisberger 1968, p. 272, no. 710, repr.; Thaw I, no. 20, repr.; Thaw III, p. 257, repr.

CDD

43

Jean Antoine Watteau

Valenciennes 1684–
1721 Nogent-sur-Marne

22

Study of a Young Man Seen from the Back and Another Study of His Right Arm

Black, red, and white chalk on light brown paper; lower left corner made up. 8 3/16 × 9 inches (208 × 227 mm). Watermark: none visible through lining. Numbered in pen and brown ink on back of old lining, *43*.

Watteau's sketch of an elegantly disposed young man epitomizes his gift for effortless figure drawing. The assured execution of this rapid sketch is typical of the artist's work in the latter half of the second decade of the eighteenth century. Margaret Morgan Grasselli dates it 1716 because of its apparent connection to two paintings of that date, *La Gamme d'amour*, National Gallery, London, and *Plaisirs d'amour*, Dulwich Picture Gallery (Grasselli 1993, p. 116, under no. 10). The young man's pose is repeated in a full composition study in Dresden (repr. Washington and elsewhere 1984–85, D. 98). In the Dulwich painting, the artist modified the pose of this figure and appropriated the sketch of his right arm and shoulder, also on the Thaw sheet, for another young man who appears in the lower right, tête-à-tête with a young woman toying with a fan.

While Watteau executed the drawing *en trois crayons*—that special combination of black, red, and white chalk, which he perfected—here he worked primarily in black chalk, with some additions in red and far fewer in white.

Provenance:
Sir Thomas Lawrence (Lugt 2445); Miss James; her sale, London, Christie's, 22–23 June 1891, lot 300; Camille Groult, Paris; his descendant, Pierre Bordeaux-Groult; sale, Paris, Palais Galliéra, 30 March 1963, no. 17; Henri Farman; his sale, Paris, 15 March 1973, lot G; Otto Wertheimer, Paris and Zurich.

Bibliography:
Parker and Mathey 1957, no. 641, repr.; Grasselli 1987, pp. 97–98, 97 n. 11, fig. 5; Grasselli 1993, p. 116, under no. 10, p. 126 n. 23; Thaw III, p. 258, repr.

Exhibitions:
Washington and elsewhere 1984–85, D. 95, repr.; Thaw II, no. 9, repr.; Paris and New York 1993–94, no. 35, repr.

CDD

Jean Antoine Watteau

Valenciennes 1684–
1721 Nogent-sur-Marne

23

A Member of the Persian Embassy

Red and black chalk. 12½ × 6⅝ inches
(316 × 167 mm). Watermark: none
visible through lining.

The visit of the Persian embassy to Versailles in 1715 gave Watteau the opportunity to sketch several of its members in their exotic costume. The group included this slender young man wearing a peaked fur-trimmed cap and cloak, whom the artist sketched at least twice. He also can be seen, this time seated, in a drawing in the Victoria and Albert Museum, London (repr. Parker and Mathey 1957, no. 798). After Watteau's death Boucher was to engrave both studies for the *Figures de différents caractères*. The Thaw study appears in reverse as plate 4 in volume I, published in 1726, and two years later, the second and final volume of the *Figures* included Boucher's engraving of the London study of the young Persian as plate 215. A counterproof of the latter is in the Ashmolean Museum, Oxford. The overall impression of the Thaw sheet is one of great immediacy and freshness.

The back of the old mount of the drawing carries a clue to its early ownership in the inscription, *Claire Amélie Masson / 1795 née Falaize 1839.*

Provenance:
Claire Amélie Masson (according to back of old mount); Mme Chauffard, Paris; Mme Ader Picard Tajan; sale, Paris, Palais Galliéra, 7 December 1971, no. 5, repr.

Bibliography:
Parker and Mathey 1957, no. 796, repr.; *L'Œil* 1977, p. 43, fig. 8; Thaw III, p. 258, repr.

Exhibitions:
Thaw I, no. 33, repr.; Washington and elsewhere 1984–85, p. 57, D. 48, and under D. 47, repr.; Paris and New York 1993–94, no. 36, repr.

CDD

Jean Antoine Watteau

Valenciennes 1684–
1721 Nogent-sur-Marne

24
Seated Young Woman

Black, red, and white chalk on oat-meal-colored paper. Verso: various slight sketches in red chalk, including a sketch of a foot (not decipherable as David and Goliath, as previously described). 6⅞ × 8⅛ inches (174 × 206 mm). Watermark: grapes within a double circle (cf. Heawood 2431).

This sheet is one of at least seven surviving drawings grouped by Parker, and later by Engwall, as a series that eventually developed into *Woman at Her Toilet*, the painting of about 1719, now in the Wallace Collection, London. Donald Posner amplified the discussion of the group in his monograph on the Wallace painting, tracing how the idea for the picture evolved from the studio sketches. At first, the model was fully dressed, seated on a chaise longue (Paris, Fondation Custodia); then she was sketched partially undressed and apparently asleep on the chaise (PM 528, formerly Los Angeles, Norton Simon Foundation). The drawing in the Ganay collection and especially the one formerly in the Gould collection (PM 525; sale, New York, Sotheby's, 24 April 1985, lot 4, repr. in color) are closest to the Thaw drawing.

In all three sheets, the charming young model is clad only in her beribboned chemise. In the Thaw drawing, Watteau eliminated the chaise and brought the model into a heightened focus, concentrating on the play of light on the surface of her bare legs and shoulders. She is arranged in a somewhat complicated pose, leaning forward attentively, with her right leg folded beneath her. The drawing demonstrates Watteau's special affinity for drawing the female figure in relaxation—playful or pensive—but always elegantly posed.

The British Museum has two drawings belonging to this series. In one, the pose and nudity of the model, depicted in the act of pulling off her chemise, corresponds exactly to that of the young woman in the painting. Watteau adapted the painting from this sketch, adding luxurious touches to the composition, including a maidservant, a small dog, and a chaise longue with an elegantly carved headboard.

Provenance:
J. P. Heseltine (Lugt 1507); Adrien Fauchier Magnan; his sale, London, Sotheby's, 1935, no. 88, repr.; Mr. and Mrs. Siegfried Kramarsky, New York; Rosenberg & Stiebel, New York; Norton Simon Foundation, Los Angeles.

Bibliography:
[Heseltine 1900], no. 13; Guiraud 1913, no. 88, repr. in color; Engwall 1933, p. 7 (wrongly cited as plate 82 of Guiraud's catalogue of the Heseltine collection); Mongan 1949, p. 98, repr.; Noad 1950, p. 58, repr. (as included in the Montreal exhibition, see below); Parker and Mathey 1957, p. 75, no. 527, repr.; Posner 1973, p. 61f., fig. 28; Grasselli 1987, p. 98, fig. 7.

Exhibitions:
New York 1942, no. 119; Cambridge 1948, no. 43; Montreal 1950, no. 95, repr.; New York 1959, no. 93, pl. 337b; Thaw I, no. 35, repr. in color and on cover; Washington and elsewhere 1984–85, p. 57, D. 68, repr.; Thaw III, no. 24, repr. (recto and verso).

CDD

Etienne-Louis Boullée

Paris 1728–1799 Paris

25
Interior of a Library

Pen and black and some brown ink, gray wash, over faint traces of black chalk; ruled borders in pen and black ink at outer margin and framing design area. Full sheet, 15⅞ × 25⅝ inches (420 × 653 mm); design area, 15½ × 25⁵⁄₁₆ inches (394 × 644 mm). Watermark: none visible through lining.

Since most of his commissioned architectural works are no longer extant, the architect Boullée is best known for a group of 100 imaginative and rather grandiose designs that he left to the Bibliothèque Nationale, Paris. Most of these drawings are very large, and the group includes Boullée's design for the expansion of the royal library. Although he was commissioned in 1780, his rather startling and highly innovative plans for the project were never realized. Boullée set forth his ideas in 1785 in a short treatise, "Mémoire sur les moyens de procurer à la Bibliothèque du Roi les avantages que ce monument exige," in which he explained:

> My design would transform a courtyard, 300 feet long and 90 feet wide, into an immense basilica lighted from above. . . . For it seems that nothing could be more grand, more noble, more extraordinary, nor have a more magnificent appearance than a vast amphitheater of books. Imagine, in this vast amphitheater, disposed in tiers, attendants spread about so that they could pass the books, from hand to hand. Service would be as quick as the request, not to mention that this would avoid the dangers that often result from the use of ladders.

Also quite large, the present drawing—a variant of the design in the Bibliothèque Nationale—is about two-thirds the size of the other, which measures 24⅞ × 38⁹⁄₁₆ inches (630 × 980 mm). Although at first glance it appears to be an exact replica, a number of variations may be observed. For example, while most of the pages situated on the many levels of the library appear in both drawings, the present one includes two additional figures placed under the arch at the lower right corner. The skylight is different, and the books are neatly arranged in rows; for the most part they lean at odd angles in the Bibliothèque Nationale drawing. To accentuate the deep vaultlike space, Boullée used subtle gradations of gray wash, casting the lefthand side of the chamber in shadow while light, apparently emanating from the skylight, throws the righthand side into vivid, almost hyperreal, relief.

Given the grand scale of Boullée's late projects, it is not surprising that his designs were never executed. In fact Boullée never intended them to be more than the theoretical illustrations for his *Essai sur l'art*, the unpublished manuscript of which is also in the Bibliothèque Nationale (Fonds français No. 9153; for published edition, see Pérouse de Montclos 1968). From 1775 to 1777, Boullée, a pupil of J. F. Blondel as well as of J. L. Legeay, served as architect to the comte d'Artois, a brother of Louis XV. He designed a number of town-houses in Paris between 1761 and 1768. His first recorded work includes altars for St. Roch, Paris, between 1752 and 1754. A defender of the Louis XIV architectural style, he preferred the work of Mansart, Perrault, and Blondel to the excesses of the rococo as practiced by Meissonnier and other eighteenth-century architects. By the 1770s, however, when he designed the Hôtel de Brunoy in Paris, he had radically changed his style and was more directly influenced by the antique. In brilliant, large-scale designs, such as the present example, Boullée went beyond neoclassicism to the visionary—even futuristic—clarity for which his work is now so admired.

Provenance:
Possibly bequeathed to P. N. Benard; sale, Paris, Hôtel Drouot, 20 December 1982; private collection, Paris; sale, Paris, Drouot-Richelieu, 15 December 1993, no. 31, repr.; Bob P. Haboldt & Co., New York and Paris.

Bibliography:
Aaron 1985, p. 95, no. 98 (as private collection), repr. in color; Lévêque 1987, p. 274 (as private collection), repr. in color; Pérouse de Montclos 1994, p. 258.

Exhibition:
Thaw III, not in catalogue.

CDD

Jean Honoré Fragonard

Grasse 1732–1806 Paris

26

Interior of a Park: The Gardens of the Villa d'Este

Gouache on vellum. 7¾ × 9½ inches (197 × 242 mm).

In 1760 the Abbé de Saint-Non received permission from the Este family to spend the summer at the Villa d'Este at Tivoli and invited Fragonard to stay for a month and a half. Inspired by the beauty and picturesque neglect of his surroundings, the young artist turned out many red chalk views of the lovely old gardens during his stay. This is documented in Natoire's letters to the marquis de Marigny: "our young artist is creating some very lovely studies which can only be very useful to him and bring him much honor" (Montaiglon and Guiffrey 1887–1908, VI, 1896, p. 354, no. 5459). At least ten of these red chalk drawings were presented to the abbé after Fragonard had made counterproofs of them. The artist continued to work on subjects inspired by the Villa d'Este, including two highly finished red chalk drawings (Ananoff 1961–70, I, 1961, nos. 351 and 352, figs. 125, 126), followed by his etching *Le Petit parc* (Baltimore and elsewhere 1984–85, no. 46, repr.), most probably executed around 1763.

This small, rare gouache, last recorded in the Bryas sale, is a reduction of Fragonard's painting of the same subject, now in the Wallace Collection, London, which may also date from this time, although Wildenstein believes that it was the painting exhibited by Fragonard in 1785 in the Salon de la Correspondance. The artist added further details in the Wallace Collection painting and in this gouache, among them the figure of the boy with the wheelbarrow and the framing tree at the left. While Fragonard's view is generally impressionistic, David Coffin has suggested that it may be based in part on his recollection of the Dragon Fountain (Coffin 1969, p. 131).

The only other known gouache landscape by Fragonard is also a reduction of a large painting, *The Fête at Rambouillet*, in the Gulbenkian Foundation, Lisbon. The gouache in the Straus collection, New York (Paris and New York 1987–88, no. 1669, repr. in color, p. 358), and the present work were probably executed on special commission from clients sometime after the compositions they replicate.

Provenance:
Jacques de Bryas; his sale, Paris, 4–6 April 1898, lot 55; sold to Stettiner (4,650 frs.); Bernice C. Bowles; sale, New York, Sotheby's, 14 January 1987, no. 181, repr. in color.

Bibliography:
Réau 1956, p. 258; Ananoff 1961–70, III, 1968, no. 1575; Paris and New York 1987–88, under no. 66, p. 154, fig. 6 (exhibited in New York only, as New York, private collection); Ingamells 1985–92, III, 1989, under P379, p. 150 (as New York, private collection); New York 1990, under no. 35, p. 188 n. 5.

Exhibitions:
Paris and New York 1993–94, no. 73, repr. in color; Thaw III, no. 26, repr. in color.

CDD

Jean Honoré Fragonard

Grasse 1732–1806 Paris

27

Portrait of a Neapolitan Girl

Brush and brown wash over slight traces of black chalk. 14⁷⁄₁₆ × 11⅛ inches (367 × 282 mm). Watermark: Van der Ley (cf. Churchill 321). Inscribed, at lower right, in pen and brown ink, *Naples 1774–femme de / Ste Lucie.*

Ten years after his sojourn in Rome as a *pensionnaire* at the French Academy, Fragonard returned to Italy with his friend and patron, Bergeret de Grancourt. They set out in the autumn of 1773 and did not return to France until the summer of 1774. In addition to acting as a guide for Bergeret, who had never been to Italy, Fragonard made numerous drawings of the people and places they saw.

This beautiful wash drawing was executed in May 1774, when they visited Naples. Eunice Williams has noted that Fragonard's inscription indicates that the drawing was made on the *passegiata di Santa Lucia*, a favorite Sunday gathering place. Although not specifically mentioned in Bergeret's journal, the artist François-André Vincent, who had visited the two men earlier in Rome, must have accompanied them to Naples. He drew studies of the same young woman and eventually executed a painting of her, once owned by Bergeret and now on the art market in Paris (see Atlanta 1983, no. 35, repr. in color). The full details of the woman's distinctive costume can be fully appreciated in the painting. Since it was the feast of Januarius, she wore her best clothes—a black velvet jacket and a red skirt trimmed with gold lace.

Although it is a study of the young woman's head and shoulders, Fragonard's portrait concentrates on her face. Where Vincent's portrait has charm, Fragonard's drawing—worked almost exclusively in brush and wash—goes beyond her features and interesting costume to capture something of her psychological presence. It is one of the most memorable of the artist's drawings. On the same occasion, Fragonard made another study of the same young woman, seated and looking to the left, which is in the Städelsches Kunstinstitut, Frankfurt (inv. no. 1104, Ananoff 1961–70, I, 1961, no. 181, fig. 71). In that drawing, which is also in brush and wash, Fragonard inscribed the base of a plinth on which she rests her feet, *Naples 1774 fame de Ste / Lucie.*

Provenance:
Antoine Marmontel; sale, Paris, Hôtel Drouot, 28 March 1868, no. 24; E. M. Hodgkins; sale, Paris, Galerie Georges Petit, 30 April 1914, no. 28; Mrs. C. I. Stralem, New York; her son, Donald S. Stralem; his wife, Mrs. Donald S. Stralem, New York.

Bibliography:
Portalis 1889, p. 314; Shoolman and Slatkin 1947, p. 92, pl. 51; Grancourt 1948, p. 102, pl. XIV; Réau 1956, p. 215; Ananoff 1961–70, I, 1961, no. 119, III, fig. 495; Cuzin 1983, p. 110, fig. 12; Atlanta 1983, under no. 35, fig. III.6; Michel 1987, pp. 23–27, 106, 208, 210, fig. 248, repr. in color; Sutton 1987, fig. 8; Cuzin 1988, pp. 166, 255 n. 27, fig. 202 (as *Portrait of a Woman of Santa Lucia*).

Exhibitions:
Paris 1921, no. 173; Paris 1931a, no. 64; Paris 1958–59, no. 50, pl. 63; Rotterdam 1958, no. 50, pl. 66; New York 1959, no. 50; London 1968, no. 270, fig. 297; New York 1972, no. 20; Washington and elsewhere 1978–79, pp. 22–23, no. 33, repr.; Thaw II, no. 11, repr.; Paris and New York 1987–88, no. 192, and under no. 193, repr. in color; Rome 1990–91, no. 168, and under no. 173, repr. in color; Paris and New York 1993–94, no. 72, repr.; Thaw III, no. 27, repr.

CDD

Jacques Louis David

Paris 1748–1825 Brussels

28

Study for Exécution des fils de Brutus

Pen and black ink with some point of brush and wash over black chalk. 16⅜ × 23 inches (416 × 584 mm). Watermark: cluster of grapes within a circle and illegible letters (cf. Heawood 2395). Signed at lower left, with initials of both Jules David (Lugt 1437) and Eugène David (Lugt 839). Numbered in pen and brown ink on paper ticket affixed to original frame, *38* (its lot number in the 1826 sale).

David's painting of 1789, *The Lictors Returning the Bodies of the Sons of Brutus* (Louvre), depicts Brutus, the founder of the Roman republic, seated in his house while the bodies of his sons, whom he had condemned to death for plotting to restore the previous tyrannical government, are returned for burial. The drawing shows an earlier, more violent, idea for the painting: Brutus stoically observing the execution. Collatinus, the Roman consul seated next to him, cannot bear to watch and covers his face with his hand. A drawing in the Getty Museum, dated 1787, shows the artist's subsequent choice of subject (fig. 1). In a letter to his colleague Jean-Baptiste Wicar (14 June 1789), David described the scene, purely of his own invention, that he had decided to paint.

> Je fais un tableau de ma pure invention. C'est Brutus, homme et père, qui s'est privé de ses enfants et qui, retiré dans ses foyers, on lui raporte ses deux fils pour leur donner la sépulture. Il est distrait de son chagrin, au pied de la statue de Rome, par les cris de sa femme, la peur et l'évanouissement de la plus grande fille.

The composition and outdoor setting of the drawing are similar to David's *Horatius Defending His Sons* (Louvre). Arlette Sérullaz pointed out (Paris and Versailles 1989–90, p. 202) that the architecture of the Thaw and Getty drawings recalls David's first trip to Italy. The figure of Brutus was largely based on studies of antique sculpture that David had made during his sojourn in Rome when he visited the Vatican and Capitoline museums (see, for example, drawings in the *album factice*, now in the Département des Arts Graphiques, Louvre, as well as his studies of sculpture then in the Villa Giustiniani, the Villa Borghese, and the Palazzo Spada in *album factice 11*, private collection, New York).

Fig. 1 Jacques Louis David. *The Lictors Carrying Away the Bodies of the Sons of Brutus.* J. Paul Getty Museum, Los Angeles, 85.GA.8.

Provenance:
Jules and Eugène David (his sons; Lugt 839 and 1437); David sale, 17 April 1826, no. 38 (400 frs.); Baronne J. Meunier, Calais (his daughter); by descent; Galerie Hopkins-Thomas, Paris.

Bibliography:
Inventory of 25 February 1826, no. 17; David 1880, I, p. 655; David 1973, p. 244, no. 38; Bordeaux 1983, pp. 46ff., detail of Brutus and Collatinus repr.

Exhibitions:
Paris and Versailles 1989–90, p. 197, no. 87, repr.; Paris and New York 1993–94, no. 88, repr.; Thaw III, no. 30, repr.

CDD

Pierre Paul Prud'hon

Cluny 1758–1823 Paris

29
The Park at Malmaison

Black and white chalk on blue paper. 13¹/₁₆ × 10⁹/₁₆ inches (332 × 268 mm). Watermark: none.

Prud'hon rarely executed landscape drawings, and his subtle use of black and white chalk in this work created an exceptionally beautiful contrast between the light and shaded areas of the glade. White chalk was used to indicate the play of light on the trees and surrounding grassy areas in the foreground. The careful balance between detail and atmosphere was achieved by means of alternating fine and broad strokes of the same chalk, which he then stumped. Prud'hon finished the drawing with a detailed delineation of the wispy bush, executed in a few fine strokes of black chalk in the foreground.

H. J. Bourguignon, curator of Malmaison, where the Empress Josephine lived from 1798 to 1814, is said to have identified the subject as a glade in the park surrounding the château. The drawing is also known by titles assigned by the Goncourts, *Dessous de bois* and *Lisière d'un bois* (Goncourt 1876, pp. 307, 309). Two other landscape drawings by the artist were shown in the exhibition devoted to Prud'hon in 1958 (Paris 1958, nos. 225–26, not repr.).

Provenance:
Charles de Boisfremont (Lugt 353); Mme Power (née Boisfremont); her sale, 15–16 April 1864, no. 115; Baron de Clary; Baron de la Tournelle, Montpellier; David-Weill, Paris; Richard S. Davis, Minneapolis; Robert M. Light, Santa Barbara.

Bibliography:
Goncourt 1876, pp. 307, 309; Guiffrey 1924, no. 1307, p. 470; Henriot 1926–28, III, 1928, ii, p. 359, repr.

Exhibitions:
Paris 1874, no. 318; New York 1938, no. 129; New York 1944, no. 133; Paris 1958–59, no. 144, pl. 97; New York 1959, no. 144, pl. 89; Paris and New York 1993–94, no. 93, repr. in color; Thaw III, no. 31, repr.

CDD

Pierre Paul Prud'hon

Cluny 1758–1823 Paris

30
Female Nude

Black, white, and pale pink chalk, some stumping, on blue paper. 23³⁄₁₆ × 12⁷⁄₁₆ inches (589 × 316 mm). Watermark: none.

Working within the French academic tradition, Prud'hon brought a new refinement and finish to the drawing of the nude, working in black and white, and—in the case of this sheet—a pale pink, almost flesh-colored, chalk. When applied to the intense blue paper Prud'hon liked to use, the highly worked chalk stands out vividly, and the detailed modeling of the figure is very effective in terms of light.

This drawing is a study for the figure of Innocence in *L'Amour séduit l'Innocence, le Plaisir l'entraîne, le Repentir suit* (Guiffrey 1924, pl. II). It is clear that Prud'hon already knew how the figure of Innocence, if not that of Love, was to be posed and placed in the painted version. There, Love is personified by an Apollo-like youth whose left arm is draped around the shoulder of Innocence. With her eyes demurely downcast and her right arm slipped about Love's waist, Innocence stands to his right, her figure partially hidden by the drapery that is being pulled by a small cupid. In the drawing, Prud'hon has concentrated his attention on the nude figure of Innocence, and only Love's left hand on her shoulder is visible, although his form is suggested by the position of her right arm.

In his monograph on Prud'hon, Jean Guiffrey lists four paintings and two oil sketches of this subject as well as at least eleven preparatory drawings, including the present study. There is also an engraving of the subject by Barthélemy Roger (1767–1841), after Prud'hon's drawings.

Provenance:
Charles de Boisfremont (Lugt 353); Mme Power (née Boisfremont); her sale, 15–16 April 1864; Van Cuyck (400 frs.); George Farrow; sale, London, Sotheby's, 27 March 1969, lot 142, repr.; Camille Groult.

Bibliography:
Goncourt 1876, p. 144; Guiffrey 1924, p. 8, no. 14; Morgan Library, *Fellows Reports* XVII, 1976, pp. 148, 178, pl. 19; Morgan Library 1993, p. 300, no. 28, repr. in color.

Exhibitions:
Thaw I, no. 38, repr.; New York 1984, no. 91; Paris and New York 1993–94, no. 95, repr. in color; Thaw III, no. 32, repr.

Thaw Collection, The Pierpont Morgan Library, acc. no. 1974.71

CDD

Louis Léopold Boilly

La Bassée 1761–1845 Paris

31

Portraits of the Artist's Family and Servants

Black and white chalk on light brown wove paper. 17¹³⁄₁₆ × 11¹¹⁄₁₆ inches (450 × 297 mm). Watermark: none visible through lining.

The costumes in this drawing date it to about 1800. It is apparent from what we know about Boilly's family that the artist's second wife, née Adélaïde-Françoise-Julie Leduc, whom he married in 1795, and two of his sons are depicted. The man to the right of Boilly's wife is his friend Simon Chenard, the singer who also acted as tutor for the children of Boilly's first marriage. His features are well known from Boilly's many depictions of him, notably in the painting in the Louvre *Réunion d'artistes dans l'atelier d'Isabey*, exhibited in the Salon de l'An VI (1798; repr. Lille 1988–89, no. 21). The subjects of three of the four remaining portraits are most likely servants; the woman in the lower left corner remains unidentified.

Boilly must have begun his drawing with the likeness of his wife, which is the most carefully finished portrait of the eight on this sheet. She looks directly at us, and her features accord well with a known portrait Boilly made of her in 1796 (repr. Lille 1988–89, no. 28). Next he probably sketched in the profile of his friend Chenard, along with the portraits of his two sons by his first marriage—the elder, Félix, born in 1790, in the center of the bottom row, and the younger, Marie-Simon, born in November 1792, at the right in the top. Félix is the boy probably represented in the oil sketch now in Lille (repr. Lille 1988–89, no. 16). Félix and Marie-Simon were Boilly's children by his first wife, née Marie-Madeleine Josèphe Desligne, who died in 1795, the same year in which he married Adélaïde-Françoise. The first child of the second marriage, Julien-Léopold, who was born in 1796 and would have been around four years old when this sheet was executed, is not represented. His features, which are very like Boilly's, are known from the portrait exhibited in the Salon of 1808 (repr. Lille 1988–89, no. 38). Next the artist drew in the young woman with a cap at the upper left of the sheet, possibly the cook, and the young woman with the hoop earrings at the lower left. The sheet was likely completed with portraits of the older servant at the left of Mme Boilly and the young maid at the lower right.

Another example of Boilly working in this manner was recently on the art market (London 1994, no. 2, repr.). In this sheet, Boilly studied another family group, that of Jean Darcet, a prominent scientist and academician. While this sheet is oriented horizontally and not as fully worked, it is very similar in character, technique, and date to the Thaw drawing.

Têtes d'expression, a full sheet of portrait studies in a French private collection (repr. Lille 1988–89, under no. 50), is of similar date but entirely different character. In this drawing, Boilly was not interested in naturalistic portraiture. Instead, he indulged his aptitude for caricature, exaggerating the expressions and grimacing faces of eighteen different people.

Provenance:
Alfred de Rothschild; Almina, countess of Carnarvon, London; her sale, London, Christie's, 22 May 1925, lot 4; Thos. Agnew & Sons, London and New York; Mrs. John Magee Wyckoff, New York; George Magee Wyckoff; private collection, Connecticut.

Exhibitions:
Paris and New York, 1993–94, no. 96, repr.; Thaw III, no. 33, repr.

CDD

Giovanni Paolo Panini

Piacenza 1691/1692–1765 Rome

32

Piazza San Pietro and the Vatican Palace from the Colonnade of St. Peter's

Pen and brown ink, brush and brown wash, watercolor, and white gouache, over traces of black chalk. 9⅝ × 6⁹⁄₁₆ inches (245 × 166 mm). Watermark: none visible through lining. Inscribed in pen and brown ink on eighteenth-century mount, *J. P. Pannini.*, and in pen and black ink, *Sub porticibus S.ᵘ Petri plateam amplectentibus.*

The foremost Roman painter of real and imaginary architectural views, Panini produced a large number of pictures of St. Peter's and of Piazza San Pietro, located in front of the basilica. These include various views of the interior of the building (Arisi 1986, nos. 188, 200, 212, 217, 280–81, 309, 407, 447–50, 473, repr.) and of its atrium (Arisi 1986, nos. 399, 406, repr.) as well as a number of works depicting the piazza and its vast colonnade by Gianlorenzo Bernini, with the facade of St. Peter's, designed by Carlo Maderno at the beginning of the seventeenth century, in the background (Arisi 1986, nos. 308, 443, 445, 472, 476, repr.). Other views of Piazza San Pietro and the facade of St. Peter's, very similar to those in a number of the aforementioned paintings, appear in both versions of the artist's celebrated *Vedute di Roma moderna* in the Museum of Fine Arts, Boston, and The Metropolitan Museum of Art, New York (Arisi 1986, nos. 471, 475, repr.). The present watercolor, which exhibits numerous pentimenti, differs from Panini's other known depictions of the piazza in that the view is taken from beneath the colonnade, looking toward the Vatican Palace, rather than toward the facade of the basilica.

Although the blue mount would appear to be that of the eighteenth-century French amateur Pierre-Jean Mariette, the drawing does not seem to have been among the thirty-five sheets attributed to Panini in the catalogue of the 1775 sale of Mariette's legendary collection (Mariette 1775, nos. 548–74). Two other drawings by Panini from Mariette's collection—a pair of imaginary views of Roman ruins with figures standing amid well-known pieces of antique sculpture, both of which similarly retain their original eighteenth-century mounts—are also in the collection of The Pierpont Morgan Library (1982.18.1-2; see Stephanie Wiles in New York 1995a, nos. 43a–b, repr.; the drawings are fully described under lot number 567 in the Mariette sale catalogue).

Provenance:
Pierre-Jean Mariette (Lugt 1852 or 2097 and 2859, without cartouche); sale, Monte Carlo, Christie's Monaco, 20 June 1994, no. 4, repr.

Exhibition:
Thaw III, not in catalogue.

WMG

J.P. Pannini.

Antonio Canal, called Canaletto

Venice 1697–1768 Venice

33
Capriccio: Pavilion by the Lagoon

Pen and brown ink, gray wash, over black pencil lines prepared with compass and ruler. Verso: Venetian regatta in pencil. 14¹³⁄₁₆ × 9⁷⁄₁₆ inches (376 × 241 mm). Watermark: three crescents (Bromberg 1974, p. 185, no. 6). Signed on the wellhead in the right foreground with Canaletto's coat of arms, the chevron. Inscribed on verso, *oro*, and letters indicating colors, *n* (*nero*, black), *o* (*oro*, gold), *A* (*argento*, silver), *u* (*verde*, green).

This drawing depicts an imaginary Renaissance tower surmounted by the figure of Fortune—a copy, as Felice Stampfle and Cara Dufour Denison recognized when describing the sheet (Thaw I, no. 39), of that on top of the Dogana da Mar in Venice. In front of the tower is a smaller building in Renaissance style with an elaborate columned portal. Some staffage figures are also depicted in the foreground and on the nearest building.

This highly finished drawing—a work of art in its own right—was prepared in rough outlines on a smaller sheet (now in the Robert Lehman Collection, The Metropolitan Museum of Art, New York; Constable-Links 1976, no. 824). In the present drawing, the architectural outlines and measurements were prepared with a ruler and compass. The drawing on the verso records the faint outlines of barges—probably of a Venetian regatta—moving toward the left. Neither side of the sheet has been connected with an extant painting by Canaletto.

Provenance:
Sold in a London auction room, ca. 1925; with Robert Dunthorn; with Arthur Tooth & Son; Mrs. Dudley Tooth, London (according to Constable-Links).

Bibliography:
Constable 1962, no. 825, repr.; Constable-Links 1976, no. 825, repr.

Exhibitions:
Thaw I, no. 39, repr.; Thaw III, no. 35, repr. (recto and verso).

PD

Francesco Guardi

Venice 1712–1793 Venice

34
A View of Levico in the Valsugana

Pen and brown and black ink, brown wash, over black chalk. Verso: landscape with a fortified town. 16¹³⁄₁₆ × 25 inches (426 × 635 mm). Watermarks: letters *PS*; triple crescent (cf. Heawood 873); letters *BEA* (or *RBA?*) and countermark *PS*. Inscribed by the artist at lower left, in pen and brown ink, *Levego verso il Borgo di Valsugana dove la Brenta nazze*; illegible inscription in black chalk at lower right.

On a journey to his family home in the Trentino in the fall of 1778, Francesco Guardi, who traveled little, passed through Bassano on at least one leg of the trip. It was then that he made a series of large topographical landscape drawings. Six drawings of the sites are known today (see Thaw II, no. 22). The scene of the present sheet is identified by the artist as Levico, seen toward Borgo di Valsugana, near the origins of the River Brenta. Morassi is probably correct in assuming that the drawings were not made on the spot but after preliminary sketches made on site. The location depicted on the verso, a landscape with a fortified town on the left and a hill with poplars on the right, has eluded identification.

Provenance:
Marius Paulme (Lugt 1910); sale, Paris, Galerie Georges Petit, 13 May 1929, lot 101, pl. 69; Mrs. C. I. Stralem, New York; Mr. and Mrs. Donald S. Stralem, New York.

Bibliography:
Erdmann 1929, pp. 506–10; Pallucchini 1943, p. 49; Benesch 1947, no. 66, repr.; Byam Shaw 1951, pp. 35, 43, 65–66; Parker and Byam Shaw 1962, p. 78; Pignatti, no. 135, repr.; Pignatti 1967, no. XXIV; Morassi 1975, p. 153, no. 418, fig. 419; Morassi 1984 (reprint of Morassi 1973 and 1975; the drawings are mentioned on the same pages and illustrated on the same plates).

Exhibitions:
Buffalo 1935, no. 72, repr.; Springfield 1937, in addendum to catalogue, not numbered; Boston 1945, p. 9; Venice 1965, no. 46, repr. (recto and verso); New York 1971, no. 208, repr.; Thaw II, no. 22, repr.; Trentino 1993, p. 36, fig. 20 (as "collezione D. Stralem"); Thaw III, no. 36, repr. (recto and verso).

PD

Severo verso il Borgo di Valsugana dove la Branta nasse

69

Francesco Guardi

Venice 1712–1793 Venice

35
Venetian Courtyard

Pen and brown ink, brown wash, over faint traces of black chalk. 6¹⁵⁄₁₆ × 7⅞ inches (177 × 201 mm).

In this scene, as in a number of other architectural *capricci*, Guardi mingled the real and the imaginary with such conviction that the viewer is compelled to learn the identity of the spot. Licia Ragghianti Collobi finds it vaguely reminiscent of the courtyard of the Palazzo Pisani; Pignatti, on the other hand, speaks of architectural elements in the style of Coducci, recalling the Scuola Grande of S. Marco or the Palazzo Cappello a S. Zaccaria. When he first published the drawing in 1936, Byam Shaw treated it as a real view but later placed it in the category of the architectural *capricci*. The sketchier version of the subject in the Fondazione Horne in Florence, which lacks the effective frame created by the portico in the foreground, may have preceded the Thaw example, but both appear to be later rather than earlier drawings. As Byam Shaw first pointed out in 1936, Guardi utilized this courtyard motif in a painting in the Shtshoukin Collection, Museum of Fine Arts (now the Pushkin State Museum of Fine Arts), Moscow (see Lasareff 1925, pp. 58–63, repr.). The painting at first glance appears closer to the Horne drawing than the present one in that it lacks the portico, but at the same time it incorporates such features of the Thaw drawing as the series of three instead of four windows in the building at the rear, the building and its chimney pots visible above the wall at the left, and the figure of the man in a cloak walking into the courtyard. Very possibly when Guardi developed the Moscow picture from the quick jotting of the Horne sheet, he also more or less simultaneously created another independent work of art—the Thaw drawing. Guardi was not always precise in defining architectural relationships in his imaginary views, and here the attractive motif of the view through the doorway at the right is hard to reconcile spatially with the open arcade of the courtyard. Such inconsistencies are, as a matter of fact, not infrequently the hallmark of the *capricci*.

Provenance:
Dr. Henry Wellesley (according to 1963 Sotheby sale; no mark); Lieut. Col. William Stirling, Keir; Hon. Mrs. Stirling, Keir; sale, London, Sotheby's, 21 October 1963, lot 48 (bought by Cailleux); Galerie Cailleux, Paris; E. V. Thaw and Co., New York; Norton Simon Foundation, Los Angeles.

Bibliography:
Byam Shaw 1936, p. 47, pl. 43; Arslan 1944, pp. 1–28; Byam Shaw 1951, no. 57, repr.; Collobi 1967, p. 186, fig. 227; Pignatti 1967, no. 21, repr.; Morassi 1973, under no. 766; Morassi 1984 (reprint of Morassi 1973 and 1975; the drawings are mentioned on the same pages and illustrated on the same plates); Thaw III, p. 277, repr.

Exhibitions:
London 1953, no. 196; Venice 1962, no. 75, repr.; Venice 1965, no. 55, repr.; Thaw I, no. 50, repr.

FS

Giovanni Battista Piranesi

Mogliano Veneto 1720–
1778 Rome

36

The Temple of Isis at Pompeii

Quill and reed pen in black and some brown ink, black wash, over black chalk; perspective lines and squaring in graphite; several accidental oil stains. 20½ × 30⅛ inches (522 × 764 mm). Watermark: shield with bend, fleur-de-lis and sword between letters *F* and *M* (cf. Robison 1986, watermark 61). Inscribed along lower right edge, in pen and brown ink, *(on back) Veduta in angolo del tempio d'Isibe*, and numbered within the drawing by Piranesi from 1 through 23, in a different brown ink; on verso at upper center, *Tav. 12*, at lower left, *Part.2. / Tav. / 14*, at lower right, *veduta in angolo del tempio d'Iside*.

In the 1770s Piranesi undertook a number of trips to the ancient ruins around Naples to study and record them with the possibility of publishing a series of etchings. This view of the Temple of Isis at Pompeii is taken from inside the north colonnade of the sanctuary. The temple and its precincts are seen from an angle that allows for a full view of the temple proper, on its high podium, as well as the sacred enclosure with its colonnade, the Egyptian temple, and various altars and pedestals. Piranesi's drawings show that he studied the temple and its sanctuary from every point of view. Another drawing in the Morgan Library depicts the temple from the northeast corner (acc. no. 1963.12), and one in the British Museum shows a rear view. Four drawings in Berlin depict an interior view of the pronaos, the right side of the temple and adjacent courtyard, the Egyptian temple in the courtyard, and a view into one of the priestly dependencies of the temple (Thomas 1952–55, p. 23). In 1776, Piranesi made a small-scale drawing of the Temple of Isis. It can be found on page 97 of the *Album Amicorum*, which once belonged to the Dutch collector Arnout Vosmaer (1720–99) and is now in the Rijksprentenkabinet, Amsterdam.

Most of Piranesi's drawings of the ruins were eventually used, either directly or indirectly, by his son Francesco, who published the three-volume series of elephant folios, *Les Antiquités de la Grande Grèce*, in Paris between 1804 and 1807. The Temple of Isis is illustrated in plates LIX through LXXII of the *Antiquités*. A plate after the present drawing, reduced to approximately half its size, was engraved but apparently never used. The recto of this copperplate (Focillon 1091) depicts the *Dimostrazione dell'impluvio della casa medesima* that appeared in the *Antiquités* (Petrucci 1953, p. 305). On the verso of the plate, Maurizio Calvesi discovered the image that relates to the Thaw drawing. Proofs of this etched design and other such *roveschi* were pulled in the 1960s (Focillon 1963, pl. 254). Although the figures have been entirely changed in the plate, the architectural details correspond closely to the Library's drawing.

The attribution of the large Pompeii drawings to Piranesi has been doubted by some scholars. Arthur Hind, for example, pointed out that the architecture in both the drawings and etchings is worthy of Piranesi, but that the staffage has none of his characteristic style (Hind 1922, pp. 19–20). Hylton Thomas, however, followed the opinions of such scholars as Kurt Cassirer, Jakob Rosenberg, Karl Theodor Parker, James Byam Shaw, and others who attribute the drawings to

Piranesi with some reservations, particularly in regard to the figures (Thomas 1952–55, note 14).

Provenance:
H. M. Calmann, London; George Ortiz, Geneva; Sydney J. Lamon, New York; sale, London, Christie's, 27 November 1973, lot 314; R. M. Light & Co., Inc., Boston.

Bibliography:
Scott 1975, p. 249, fig. 295; Stampfle 1978, no. A-11, repr.

Exhibitions:
Thaw I, no. 56, repr.; Detroit and Chicago 1981–82, II, no. 89b, repr.; New York 1989; Montreal 1993–94, no. 45, repr.; Thaw III, no. 38, repr.

Thaw Collection, The Pierpont Morgan Library, acc. no. 1979.41

SW

Veduta in angolo del tempio d' Jube

Giovanni Battista Tiepolo

Venice 1696–1770 Madrid

37a

Bearded Oriental in Flat Cap and Striped Coat

Pen and brown ink, brown wash. 8 × 5⁵⁄₁₆ inches (204 × 135 mm).

Giambattista Tiepolo executed hundreds of pen-and-wash studies of single figures and of figural groups, which he evidently pasted into albums prior to his departure from Venice for Spain in 1762. The contents of these albums were organized by subject, so that each volume contained, for example, only drawings of single draped figures, of figures for ceilings, of the Holy Family, of heads, caricatures, or miscellaneous compositional studies. Although the albums have all been dismembered, several were acquired in their entirety by public institutions. These include the two volumes in the Victoria and Albert Museum, London, which are entitled *Vari Studi e Pensieri T:I:* and *Sole Figure Vestite T:I:*, as well as an album purchased by Charles Fairfax Murray and now in The Pierpont Morgan Library. The contents of a number of other volumes of Tiepolo drawings—notably an album of studies of the Holy Family, exhibited at the Savile Gallery in London in 1928, and *Tomo Terzo di Caricature*, formerly in the collection of Arthur Kay of Edinburgh—were recorded in some detail prior to being dispersed. Still others are known to have existed, but cannot be reconstructed with absolute certainty. Such is the case with the three albums that were acquired at Christie's by the dealer E. Parsons and Sons in 1914 and sold piecemeal to various collectors following the First World War (for a detailed history of these and all the other known volumes of Tiepolo drawings, see Knox 1975, pp. 3–9).

Nos. 37a–c may derive from one of those three albums. Although the contents of the albums are undocumented and their bindings have been lost, at least one of them seems to have been entitled *Sole Figure per Soffitti* and to have contained studies of figures seen from below. Another would appear to have been very similar to the album *Sole Figure Vestite* in the Victoria and Albert Museum and to have been made up of such drawings as these and two others, also now in the Thaw Collection. The present sheets were in all likelihood some of the twenty-odd studies of single draped figures that were purchased directly from E. Parsons and Sons by Dan Fellows Platt. Seven of these are now in the Art Museum, Princeton University (Gibbons 1977, nos. 590, 619–22, 626–27, repr.); the rest were sold in 1948 and are now in various other collections.

The early history of the album from which these drawings seem to have come is uncertain, but it and the other two volumes sold at Christie's in 1914 may have been among the nine volumes of Tiepolo drawings formerly in the collection of Edward Cheney of Badger Hall, Shropshire, which were sold as a single lot at Sotheby's in 1885. George Knox has established that Cheney purchased the volume containing studies of the Holy Family from Francesco Pesaro in 1842, and at least three, and possibly all eight, of the other albums were acquired from a Count Algarotti Corniani—probably Bernardino Corniani—ten years later. It has not been possible to determine exactly how and when the drawings came into the possession of the Algarotti Corniani family.

The reason for which Tiepolo made such studies as the present sheets remains to be satisfactorily established. While it is true that similar figures appear in pictures by Giambattista as well as in those by his son Domenico, few drawings of this type appear to have been directly preparatory for paintings, frescoes, or prints. Nevertheless, Tiepolo's luminous sketches in pen and wash on thin white paper, evidently preserved with great care during the artist's lifetime, rank among his most brilliant creations in any medium.

Provenance:
Dan Fellows Platt, Englewood; Austin A. Mitchell, New York; Mathias Komor, New York.

Bibliography:
Thaw III, p. 276, repr.

Exhibition:
Thaw I, no. 42, repr.

WMG

37b
Two Orientals

Pen and brown ink, brown wash. 7³⁄₁₆ × 5³⁄₁₆ inches (183 × 132 mm).

Although two men are represented, the drawing presumably came from the same album of studies of single draped figures as No. 37a. In this connection, it is worth noting that the album *Sole Figure Vestite T:I:* in the Victoria and Albert Museum, London, contains one sketch of three men and two compositional studies in addition to eighty-six drawings of single figures (see Knox 1975, p. 4).

Provenance:
Dan Fellows Platt, Englewood; Austin A. Mitchell, New York; Mathias Komor, New York.

Bibliography:
Benesch 1947, pl. 38; Thaw III, p. 276, repr.

Exhibitions:
New York 1960, no. 1; Thaw I, no. 43, repr.

WMG

37c
Oriental Seen from the Back

Pen and brown ink, brown wash. 8¹⁄₁₆ × 4⁹⁄₁₆ inches (204 × 115 mm).

See No. 37a.

Provenance:
Dan Fellows Platt, Englewood (Lugt S. 2066b); Austin A. Mitchell, New York; Mathias Komor, New York.

Bibliography:
Thaw III, p. 276, repr.

Exhibitions:
New York 1960, no. 7; Thaw I, no. 44, repr.

WMG

37b

37c

Giovanni Domenico Tiepolo

Venice 1727–1804 Venice

38

The Presentation of the Fiancé

Pen and gray-brown ink, gray and gray-brown wash, over black chalk. $14\frac{5}{8} \times 19\frac{11}{16}$ inches (371 × 499 mm). Numbered in black chalk at upper left, *74*.

Accustomed from his youth to borrowing from the works of his father and various other sources, Domenico Tiepolo, toward the end of his career, frequently recycled his own ideas in scenes of contemporary life, usually with a witty twist of caricature. The mincing couple and small spaniel in the Thaw drawing also appear in *Il Menuetto in Villa*, the fresco formerly in the salon on the ground floor of the Tiepolo family villa at Zianigo, near Mirano, and now with most of the other frescoes in the Ca' Rezzonico, Venice (repr. Mariuz 1971, no. 368). In the fresco, however, the couple is more or less realistically depicted in a garden setting of cypresses and umbrella pines, with no element of caricature. The pregnant woman in the enormous bonnet, perhaps the prospective mother-in-law of the diffident little suitor, appears in a drawing formerly in the Oppenheimer collection (repr. Hadeln 1929, II, no. 196) and again, this time in a feathered hat, as one of the singers in *Il Concertino*, a drawing in the Museo Correr, Venice (Mariuz 1971, fig. 27). Since the last two drawings are dated 1791, which is also the approximate date assigned to the fresco, the Thaw drawing, and the companion piece in the Heinemann Collection, *The Presentation of the Fiancée* (New York 1973, no. 112, repr.), must also be from this time, although the fresco surely preceded the Thaw drawing. Exceptionally, this drawing is not signed.

Provenance:
Sale, London, Sotheby's, 11 November 1965, lot 26, repr.; Galerie L'Œil, Paris.

Bibliography:
L'Œil 1967, p. 12, repr.; Thaw III, p. 279, repr.

Exhibitions:
New York 1971, no. 265, repr.; Thaw I, no. 60, repr.

FS

Giovanni Domenico Tiepolo

Venice 1727–1804 Venice

39
The Last Illness of Punchinello

Pen and brown ink, brown and some ochre wash (in the masks of several Punchinellos), over black chalk. Ruled border in pen and brown ink. 13¹³⁄₁₆ × 18⁵⁄₁₆ inches (351 × 465 mm). Numbered at upper left corner, in point of brush and brown ink, *99*, contemporary with and possibly by Domenico (according to Vetrocq 1983, p. 10). Signed at lower left, *Dom.o Tiepolo f.*

Giovanni Domenico Tiepolo, who at the beginning of his career was little more than a collaborator and imitator of his father, Giovanni Battista Tiepolo, developed a highly personal style later in life. He is most famous for the finished compositional drawings produced during his last years, such as this sheet, which belonged to a sequence, now dispersed, of a title page and 103 (originally 104) unbound drawings illustrating the life of Punchinello (Pulcinella, Polichinelle, or Punch), a character from the commedia dell'arte. The unnumbered title page depicts Punchinello reading DIVERTIMENTO PER LI REGAZZI [sic] CARTE *104 (Entertainment for Children, 104 Sheets)*. Seventy-seven of the sheets are known (see Gealt 1986), and *The Marriage Feast of Punchinello's Parents*, or *The Wedding Banquet* (Vetrocq 1983, no. 27; Gealt 1986, no. 101), and this sheet are in the Thaw Collection.

Much of the research and interpretation of the series has been done by Antonio Morassi (1941, pp. 251–62, 1941a, pp. 265–82), James Byam Shaw (1962), Adriano Mariuz (1971), M. Bonicatti (1971), and Marcia Ellen Vetrocq (1983). Most recently, Vetrocq surveyed the figure of Punchinello in comedy as well as in scenes from his life as depicted by the Tiepolos, starting with representations by Giovanni Battista Tiepolo prior to his departure for Madrid in 1762. Domenico's Punchinello frescoes in one of the rooms of the Tiepolo villa in Zianigo, now in the Ca' Rezzonico in Venice, are believed to date from 1793 to 1797. (One is said to have been dated 1793, although the date has vanished; Sack 1910, p. 315. The date 1797 was discovered in the course of restoration undertaken before 1969; Mariacher 1969, no. 2, pp. 22, 26.) The extensive series on paper was once thought to have followed these frescoes. None of the Punchinello drawings are dated; some, however, are based on drawings of Venetian life by the master, which are dated 1791 (Byam Shaw 1962, p. 57), and certain details of the latest costumes in the series point toward a date after 1800, at least for some of the sheets. Since Bonicatti's research, the series is no longer thought to have been drawn as a sequence from the beginning, and the dating could therefore be extended over a longer period, from the 1790s until Domenico's last days.

Morassi has suggested that the subject is based on Francesco Melosio's *Poesie e Prose* (Venice, 1688; see Morassi 1958, p. 21). However, since it has proved impossible to find any convincing narrative source, the sequence may well be an invention of the painter himself. As has been variously observed, there is certainly a mockery of Venetian life expressed in the drawings, perhaps even a response to the political events (Mariuz 1971, p. 88) and social upheaval of the time (Bonicatti 1971, pp. 24–35). The story begins with the birth of a Punchinello of an earlier generation from an egg hatched by a turkey; proceeds with his marriage and the birth of a later Punchinello; his childhood, youth, professional escapades—painting among them—his many and often unpleasant adventures, his aging, final illness, and death; and concludes with his burial and eerie resurrection as a skeleton. It is impossible to put them into any cogent biographical order, which has prompted Vetrocq to suggest that the series started as "a suite of 'idées pittoresches sopra Pulcinella' from which the outline of a biography precipitated once the drawings had reached a critical, suggestive number" (1983, p. 19).

In the *Last Illness*, Punchinello is visited by a doctor with donkey's ears, who takes his pulse; a similar donkey-eared figure of learning sits at a table at the left writing what might be a prescription, a testament, or even a death certificate. The patient, his bed, and the chamber pot are derived from a caricature by Giovanni Battista Tiepolo, also in the Thaw Collection (Thaw II, no. 21). The hat and cloak hanging on the rear wall also appear in *The Doctor's Visit of Pulchinello* [sic] (Vetrocq 1983, no. 31).

Punchinellos with an Elephant, a drawing that Pierpont Morgan acquired with the Fairfax Murray collection in 1910 (acc. no. IV, 151b), is probably one of the two sheets that were missing when the series appeared on the market in 1920.

Provenance:
Series possibly in the collection of Conte Algarotti (Morassi 1941a, p. 282 n. 16), anonymous collection; sale, London, Sotheby's, 6 July 1920, lot 41; P. & D. Colnaghi, London; Richard Owen, Paris, bought 13 January 1921 (from 1921/22, drawings sold in groups and individually); Léonce Suzor, Paris; sale, Paris, Hôtel Drouot, 1965, no. 69, repr.; Robert Lehman, New York (Bean [1966]); Galerie L'Œil, Paris.

Bibliography:
Veronesi 1951, repr. p. 139; Byam Shaw 1962, pp. 52–59, pl. 96; Bean [1966], under no. 103; New York 1971, under no. 283; Bonicatti 1971, p. 34, repr. p. 37; Vetrocq 1983, pp. 122–23, no. 32; Knox 1983, pp. 129, 146, repr.; Gealt 1986, pp. 172–73, no. 74, repr.

Exhibitions:
Paris 1921a (the whole series); Paris 1950a, no. 149, repr.; Paris 1952b, no. 57; Thaw I, no. 63, repr.; New York 1980a, no. 10, repr.; Thaw III, no. 40, repr.

PD

Alexander Cozens

Russia ca. 1717–1786 London

40

Fishing Boats in a Bay Below Cliffs

Brush and brown wash, traces of green watercolor, gum arabic throughout, over pencil. 19⅛ × 25⅝ inches (486 × 650 mm). Watermark: none.

The details of Alexander Cozens's early years are very sketchy. The sons of English parents living in Russia, he and his brother Peter apparently were sent to England to be educated in 1727. When their father, who was shipbuilder to Peter the Great, died in 1736, their mother petitioned the czarina for a pension to support the children still at home with her in Russia and to continue the education of her two elder sons in England, where it is believed Alexander was apprenticed to a painter or engraver. Kim Sloan suggests that he may have returned to Russia in 1740, upon completing his apprenticeship, and perhaps was then employed by the Art Department of the Academy of Science in St. Petersburg (Sloan 1985, pp. 70–75). Nonetheless, it is certain that he was in Italy in 1746, as this date appears on several of his Roman drawings.

In 1749, Cozens was appointed drawing master at Christ's Hospital in London (Sloan 1985, p. 74). He continued to earn his living as a teacher, both as private tutor and later as drawing master at Eton College. Perhaps it was his teaching experience that prompted him to develop several "systems" to assist his students in the drawing of landscape compositions. The often quoted statement by the Gothic novelist William Beckford that Cozens was "almost as full of systems as the Universe," aptly describes the artist's passion for methods. Cozens's best-known system, commonly called the "blot" method, instructed the student to freely apply black ink in blots to crumpled paper; these random marks could then be transformed into landscape compositions. This system, entitled *A New Method of Assisting the Invention in Drawing Original Compositions of Landscape* (ca. 1785), was, in fact, the culmination of many years of developing his methods. As early as 1759, he had published his ideas on this subject in *An Essay to Facilitate the Inventing of Landskips*, a copy of which is part of an album of various works by Cozens, presumably from William Beckford's collection, now in the Hermitage, St. Petersburg (see New Haven 1980, p. 7, and Sloan 1985a, p. 355).

Fishing Boats in a Bay Below Cliffs is such an invented scene. It belongs to a small group of large compositions by Cozens dating from the early 1760s. The artist has framed his composition with a darkened foreground of rocky cliffs and foliage, demonstrating the continuing preference for the idealized landscape prototype of Claude Lorrain along with the influence of Cozens's Italian sojourn in 1746. It has been further suggested that the artist, within his systems, wished to evoke certain "moralizing" tones and responses. The depiction of a harbor with fishing boats at rest conveys, perhaps, a feeling of safety and security (see Sloan 1986, p. 56ff., and London 1990, p. 32). Whatever the intended response, Cozens has produced a powerful work of the imagination.

Provenance:
Private collection; sale, London, Sotheby's, 15 March 1990, lot 39; Thos. Agnew & Sons Ltd., London.

Exhibitions:
New York 1992, no. 21; Thaw III, no. 41, repr.

EJP

Henry Fuseli

Zurich 1741–1825 London

41
Kriemhild at the Wake of Siegfried

Brush and gray and black wash, some watercolor, over pencil, heightened with white. Verso is reverse of drawing, strengthened in brush and gray and black ink, over pencil. 14 5/16 × 18 9/16 inches (364 × 471 mm). Watermark: J Whatman / 1801.

Fuseli first began to illustrate the *Nibelungenlied* between 1798 and 1802. He discovered the middle High German epic poem of more than 2,000 stanzas through his teacher, the influential writer and critic Johann Jacob Bodmer (1698–1783), in the 1750s. By 1805, Fuseli was totally absorbed in this legend, and he would continue to produce drawings, paintings, and even a poem based on this theme until 1820.

The year 1805, however, is the high point of his production on this theme and is the date given the Thaw drawing. The episode depicted here shows Kriemhild mourning the death of her husband, Siegfried. But Fuseli is subjective in his interpretation of the scene and includes three female figures, embodying Kriemhild's feelings of guilt for having caused the death of her husband, who torment her in her grief. Gert Schiff has described the Thaw drawing as the most beautiful of the *Nibelungenlied* series by Fuseli (Schiff 1973, p. 39). He also points out the relationship between the Fuseli drawing and a sculptural relief by Thomas Banks (1735–1805) entitled *Thetis and Her Nymphs Rising from the Sea to Console Achilles* (Schiff 1973, p. 319). Banks was one of the so-called Fuseli circle in Rome, where both artists lived from 1772 to 1778. The oval relief, which was begun in Rome, depicts Thetis rising from the sea with her nymphs, who, weeping, accompany her (see New Haven 1979, no. 53, p. 51). Much like the three figures of the Fuseli drawing, the entwined nymphs, arms stretching forward to clasp each other, create an encircling chain within the left side of the relief. As in the drawing, the drapery that billows out and around the heads of the upper female figures has been used as a unifying device. Although the purpose of the figures in the relief is to comfort rather than to accuse, the compositional structure of both depictions is very similar. Banks's marble relief, unfinished in his studio at the time of his death in 1805, was completed later from the original terra-cotta model, now in the Soane Museum, London (see New Haven 1979). The date of the model is uncertain, but believed to be sometime before late 1777. Fuseli visited Banks regularly during his final illness, and it is tempting to regard the *Nibelungenlied* sheet as a response to Banks's relief, which Fuseli would have seen in the artist's studio at this time.

Provenance:
Brinsley Ford, London; Stephen Spector, New York; John & Paul Herring & Co., New York.

Bibliography:
Federmann 1927, p. 180, pl. 56 (as unknown scene); Powell 1951, no. 19 (as *Mythical Scene*), repr.; Weil 1957, p. 39; Schiff 1973, I, pp. 319, 588, no. 1391, II, no. 1391, repr.

Exhibition:
Thaw III, no. 44, repr. (recto and verso).

EJP

John Robert Cozens

London 1752–1797 London

42

Rome from the Villa Mellini

Watercolor, over preliminary drawing in pencil. 20⅞ × 29¾ inches (531 × 757 mm). Watermark: none visible through lining. Signed (?) in pen and black ink along center lower edge, *Jn. Cozens*; quite abraded. Inscribed on original mount, in pen and black ink, *JNO COZENS 1791 / ROME, FROM NEAR THE VILLA MADAMA.* On verso at center of original mount, *Rome from near the Villa Madama*; at upper left, *Mr Annesley's* in pen and brown ink. Other illegible inscriptions in blue ink.

John Robert Cozens, the only son of Alexander, made two trips to the Continent. The first, through Switzerland and Italy, in 1776, was in the company of the critic and collector Richard Payne Knight (1750–1824). Cozens returned to England in April 1779, where he worked up a series of drawings for Knight, primarily Swiss views. He also worked on drawings for William Beckford (1759–1844), with whom he would travel in 1782 on a second tour of Italy. The wealthy and eccentric author of *Vathek*, William Beckford previously had been the pupil of Alexander Cozens and remained on intimate terms with the elder artist. During this second tour, Cozens filled several sketchbooks for Beckford, recording various views along the way. The seven existing volumes, purchased by the Whitworth Art Gallery at the 1973 sale at Sotheby's, London (*Catalogue of Seven Sketch-Books by John Robert Cozens*, Introduction by Professor Sir Anthony Blunt, K.C.V.O., November 29th), contain 193 sketches made by the artist. As the pages are identified and dated, the journey can be followed fairly closely. However, there is a gap of nine months, from 9 December 1782 until 15 September 1783, between the fifth and sixth volumes. It is believed that Cozens spent these months in Rome. (Beckford had returned to England in September 1782.) It is not known whether an intervening book (or books) has been lost or whether the artist chose to draw on single sheets of paper. Cozens habitually used these preliminary sketches to create finished drawings later; often several versions of the same view would be produced for various patrons.

Rome from the Villa Mellini is one of three known versions. The two other versions are both smaller and similar in size: one is in the Fitzwilliam Museum (17¼ × 23½ inches; 439 × 595 mm) and the second is in the British Museum (17⅛ × 23¼ inches; 436 × 591 mm). One is tempted to connect these drawings of Roman views with the Beckford tour. Ninety-four finished watercolors by the artist were auctioned from the Beckford collection in 1805 by Christie's (*A Catalogue of a Capital and Truly Valuable Collection of Original High-Finished Drawings, the whole executed by that eminent artist, The Younger Cozens, during a tour through the Tyrol and Italy . . .*, April 10th). But none is identified in the sale catalogue as a view of Rome from the Villa Mellini. A view of Rome from the Villa Madama is recorded, believed to be the version now in the Huntington Library, Art Collections, and Botanical Gardens, San Marino, California; a second version of this view is in the Whitworth Art Gallery, Manchester. The Thaw drawing had been identified at one time as a

view from the Villa Madama also, but it does not resemble the view depicted in these other drawings. A sketch of the Villa Mellini is recorded in volume one of the sketchbooks, dated 1 July (1782), but it is of the villa itself, not the view of Rome. This then merely places the artist at the site but does not show the preliminary sketch for these finished watercolors. Was the preliminary sketch made during the unrecorded nine months the artist spent in Rome from 9 December to 15 September 1783, or do these finished drawings go back to Cozens's earlier trip to Rome in the company of Knight? Since the artist often returned to earlier sketches for finished drawings years later (the Thaw drawing has been dated 1791), it is difficult to determine which tour and for which patron the finished work was completed.

As Andrew Wilton points out (New Haven 1980, p. 12), the later watercolors by Cozens are often characterized by the soft tones of gray and gray-green seen here, and the subdued palette enhances the calm, contemplative atmosphere of this beautiful drawing. Cozens's well-known concern for atmosphere is further displayed in the wide expanse of sky, with just the slightest tint of yellow of an early morning light. The sense of quiet solitude increases with the view of the city of Rome, sparkling in the distant sunlight.

Provenance:
Mr. Annesley (Alexander?, died 1813); Christopher Wood Gallery, London; purchased 1995.

EJP

William Blake

London 1757–1827 London

43
Christ Nailed to the Cross: The Third Hour

Pen and black ink, point of brush, and watercolor, with traces of black chalk and pencil. 13 1/16 × 13 5/8 inches (332 × 346 mm). Watermark: none visible through lining. Signed with initials in circle, at lower right corner, in pen and black ink, *inv / WB*. Inscribed on back of mount, in pencil, partially cut off . . . [w]*as the third hour, and they / [crucified] him"—Mark ch. 15 - v.25 – / 155.ff: Gilchrist's life of Blake.*

In a letter of 26 August 1799, Blake first speaks of a commission for illustrations of biblical subjects: "I am Painting small Pictures from the Bible . . . My Work pleases my employer, & I have an order for Fifty small Pictures at One Guinea each" (Butlin 1981, p. 317). Beginning with these "Fifty small Pictures," Blake would eventually produce over 135 illustrations for his most important patron, the civil servant Thomas Butts. The earlier illustrations are painted in tempera, on canvas or copper; the latter group of over eighty designs, begun in 1800, are in watercolor. Although the watercolors are of differing sizes, they appear to be intended as a series (Butlin 1981, p. 336). The Thaw watercolor, reflecting both the strong chiaroscuro of the earlier dating and the soft stippling effect of the latter, has been dated between 1800 and 1803.

Blake firmly believed that "spirit" could be expressed only through line and that mere imitation of nature was not the goal of art. Since his aim was the communication of his vision, his art is one of imagination rather than imitation. "No man of sense can think that an imitation of objects of nature is the art of painting, or that such imitation which anyone may easily perform is worthy of notice" (Blake, quoted in Keynes 1957, p. x). As Wilton points out, if Blake's art appears naive, it is the result of his personal vision and choice rather than his technical ability (Wilton 1977, p. 23).

Such personal vision and denial of physical reality are true of the Thaw drawing, in which the upright Christ all but floats upon a cross that stands both parallel and at an angle to the picture plane. It is hard to imagine the rocklike form beneath as capable of supporting either Christ on the cross or the three menacing figures above. The faces of the persecutors are masklike and caricatured. Blake is clearly not concerned here with representing physical reality but rather his vision of this event. His effective use of light on Christ and his mourners illuminates these figures with a divine presence and separates them from the figures held in darkness. Light and shadow along with space and perspective act out their own symbolic message instead of providing mere description of material form.

Provenance:
Thomas Butts; Thomas Butts, Jr.; sale, London, Foster and Sons, 29 June 1853, lot 138 (as *The Crucifixion*); bought by H. G. Bohn; presumably Col. Gould Weston; Alexander Anderdon Weston; his widow; sale, London, Christie's, 28 June 1904, lot 6; bought by E. Parsons; sold 1904 to W. Graham Robertson; sale, London, Christie's, 22 July 1949, lot 32; bought by Francis Neale for Lord Glentanar; his daughter, the Hon. Mrs. Jean Bruce; sale, London, Christie's, 4 June 1974, lot 134, repr.; Justin G. Schiller, New York; Barry Friedman, Ltd., New York; sold through the Fine Art Society to M. Koike, Tokyo; private collection, Tokyo; Thos. Agnew & Sons Ltd., London.

Bibliography:
Gilchrist 1863, under W. M. Rossetti, "Descriptive Catalogue," II, p. 227, no. 155 (as *The King of the Jews*), and 1880 edition, p. 240, no. 179; Richter 1906, no. 4, repr.; Robertson 1952, pp. 152–53, no. 57; Keynes 1957, p. 42, no. 138, repr.; Butlin 1981, I, p. 360, no. 496, II, pl. 599.

Exhibitions:
Thaw II, no. 28, repr.; Thaw III, no. 47, repr.

EJP

Francisco José de Goya y Lucientes

Aragon 1746–1828 Bordeaux

44
Solo porque le pregunta, si esta buena su madre se pone como un tigre
(Just because she is asked if her mother is well she acts like a tigress)
Verso: *Confianza* (Trust)

Point of brush and gray wash; traces of a pink paper mount. 9¼ × 5¾ inches (235 × 147 mm). Watermark: none. Inscribed by the artist along lower edge, in brush and gray wash, *solo p.ʳ q.ᵉ le pregunta, si esta buena su Madre-* (the dash in pen and brown ink); below (perhaps by Goya or by his son, Javier), in pen and brown ink, *se pone como un tigre.* Verso: inscribed along lower edge, in brush and gray wash, *confianza.* Numbered by the artist, at upper right, *69*; on verso, at upper left, *70*.

This sheet, numbered 69 and 70, was once part of the album of Goya's drawings generally known as the Madrid Album, or Album B. The Madrid Album designation was based on Valentín Carderera's observation that this suite of drawings was made by Goya either from nature or from memory in Madrid (Gassier 1973, p. 45). Carderera pointed out, however, that given the presence at the beginning of the album of scenes inspired by Andalusia, it is not certain that the album was actually begun in Madrid. Goya may have worked on them earlier, during the summer of 1796, when he lived with the duchess of Alba on her estate; the Sanlúcar Album, or Album A, was completed during this period. Both albums employ Netherlandish paper, with drawings on both sides of the sheet. These albums, along with all the artist's drawing books, were broken up by Goya's son, Javier, who then mounted the sheets in pink paper albums. For the Madrid Album, which probably dates to 1796–97, Goya selected a larger format than that used for the Sanlúcar Album, numbering each page in brush and gray ink at the upper right corner of the recto and at the upper left corner of the verso. Another sheet from this album, *A Young Man with Two Majas,* the verso of which depicts a *Majo Watching a Gallant Bowing to a Maja,* is also in the Thaw Collection (Thaw II, no. 29, repr.).

The subject matter and style of Goya's pictorial journals reflect what the artist saw and thought. In the Sanlúcar Album, his source of inspiration was clearly the duchess and the other young women he encountered on the estate. The first part of the Madrid Album again concentrates on the theme of woman, but now she is often surrounded by other figures and escorted by men. By about page 55 of Album B, Goya began to add captions to his drawings, initially using only single words, but, as the album progressed, phrases. Gassier has pointed out Goya's use of the stock pair of figures from the Spanish picaresque novel: the handsomely dressed young girl, or *maja,* and Celestina, an old bawd who observes her protégée (Gassier 1973, p. 123). The recto includes these two stock figures along with a young dandy. Given the trio, the caption is presumably intended to be ironic in its reference to the *maja's* mother. The verso depicts a priest, a *maja,* and a young man seen from the back. The gestures of the *maja* and the young man suggest that they are conspirators, and the juxtaposition of the image with the inscription, *Confianza,* undoubtedly hints at misplaced trust. As Gassier suggests, Goya's feeling for the language is evident in these captions, which, in the tradition of Spanish literature, often play upon the multiple meanings of a word.

Provenance:
Javier Goya; Mariano Goya; Valentín Carderera, Madrid; F. de Madrazo, Madrid; Mariano Fortuny y Madrazo, Venice; Henriette Fortuny, Venice; Otto Wertheimer, Paris; private collection, Basel; Hans M. Calmann, London; private collection, Switzerland.

Bibliography:
Crispolti 1958, pp. 181–205, pl. 24; Gassier and Wilson 1970, p. 175, nos. 429 and 430, repr.; Gassier 1973, B.69, p. 132 (recto), B.70, p. 133 (verso), repr. pp. 101 and 102.

Exhibition:
Thaw III, no. 48, repr. (recto and verso).

SW

Solo p.^r q.^e le pregunta, si esta buena su Madre —
se pone como un tigre.

recto

Confiama

verso

Francisco José de Goya y Lucientes

Aragon 1746–1828 Bordeaux

45
Dejalo todo a la probidencia
(Leave it all to Providence)

Brush and black wash. 10½ × 7¼ inches (268 × 185 mm). Watermark: none. Inscribed by the artist at lower center, in pencil, *Dejalo todo a la probidencia*; numbered by the artist at upper center, in pen and brown ink, *40*.

This is one of three drawings in the Thaw Collection from the so-called Black Border Album, or Album E (see No. 46 and Thaw III, no. 50). The Black Border Album, which is Goya's largest, dates to 1803–12 and is roughly contemporary with his celebrated etchings *Disasters of War*. The album was divided by Goya's son, Javier, into the two series that were sold in Paris in 1877. The present sheet was originally page 40 of the album. The same model, wrapped in a cloak and leaning against a tree trunk, appeared earlier in the album as *La resignacion* (Resignation). Here the broadly brushed figure stands, apparently resigned to her fate. Her passive attitude is in marked contrast with that of the man, depicted on page 39, who rails against his lot (private collection). The caption for the latter, "You won't get anywhere by shouting," and "Leave it all to Providence" on this sheet underscore the very different manner in which the subjects respond to their seemingly futile situations. This device of contrasts is one that Goya employed frequently in the album.

Provenance:
Paul Lebas, Paris; sale, Paris, Hôtel Drouot, 3 April 1877, lot 104 (as *Elle laisse tout à la Providence*); De Beurnonville, Paris; his sale, Paris, Hôtel Drouot, 16–19 February 1885, lot 50; Clément, Paris; Alfred Beurdeley, Paris (Lugt 421); his sale, Paris, Galerie Georges Petit, 2–4 June 1920, lot 169; Hector Brame, Paris; Edith Wetmore, New York; Karl Kup, New York; Helmut Ripperger, New York; T. Edward Hanley, Bradford, Pennsylvania.

Bibliography:
Lafond, p. 157, no. 88; Wehle 1938, p. 14; Sayre 1958, p. 136; Gassier and Wilson 1971, no. 1406; Gassier 1972, p. 116; Gassier 1973a, pp. 193, 217, E.40, repr.; Held 1981, p. 231, no. 22 E 40, repr.

Exhibitions:
Chicago 1941, no. 64, repr.; Buffalo 1960, no. 139; New York 1961, no. 67, repr.; New York and Philadelphia 1967, p. 68; Columbus 1968, no. 142, repr.; Thaw I, no. 66, repr.; New York 1981, no. 119, repr.; Thaw III, no. 49, repr.

SW

40

Dejalo todo a la providencia

Francisco José de Goya y Lucientes

Aragon 1746–1828 Bordeaux

46

Muy acordes

(They go well together)

Brush and gray and black wash; mounted on pink paper by Javier Goya, the artist's son. 10⁷⁄₁₆ × 7¼ inches (265 × 185 mm). Watermark: none. Inscribed by the artist at lower center in pencil, *Muy acordes*. Numbered by the artist at upper center in pen and brown ink, *50*; numbered by Javier Goya at upper right, *63*.

This masterful drawing of a blind couple, singing and playing on the street, is among the most powerful and moving of the Black Border Album (see also No. 45). Jutta Held observed that the blind singer, a common figure on the streets of Spanish cities, frequently acted as an information source for the underclasses (Held 1985, p. 125). Their songs encompassed a wide range of subjects, including romances, religious themes, and contemporary political events. Here Goya has portrayed the singers huddled together and lost in song. A hat, the symbol of begging, faces downward on the bench next to them, making it clear that at least on this occasion an audience is immaterial. Goya depicted the theme of blindness in yet another drawing in the Black Border Album, the *Blind Shoemaker* (Paris, private collection; Held 1985, p. 125; Gassier 1973a, E.d).

Provenance:
Paul Lebas, Paris; sale, Paris, Hôtel Drouot, 3 April 1877, no. 102 (as "Très-d'accord"); De Beurnonville, Paris; his sale, Paris, Hôtel Drouot, 16–19 February 1885, part of lot 50; Clément, Paris; Alfred Beurdeley, Paris (Lugt 421); his sale, Paris, Galerie Georges Petit, 2–4 June 1920, no. 172; Rosenthal.

Bibliography:
Lafond, p. 157, no. 93; Wehle 1938, p. 14; Sayre 1958, p. 136; Gassier and Wilson 1971, no. 1415; *Virginia* 1972, repr. on cover; Gassier 1973a, pp. 198, 218, E. 50, repr.; Held 1985, p. 107–131, fig. 34, repr.; Morgan Library, *Fellows Reports* XXI, p. 345, fig. 16; Thaw III, p. 261, repr.

Exhibitions:
Richmond 1972, no. 22, repr.; Thaw I, no. 67, repr.; Notre Dame 1980, no. 128, repr.

Thaw Collection, The Pierpont Morgan Library, acc. no. 1984.1. Gift in honor of Mr. Janos Scholz on the occasion of his eightieth birthday.

SW

Muy acordes

Wilhelm von Kobell

Mannheim 1766–1853 Munich

47
A Boy Asking Alms from a Man on Horseback

Watercolor, over pencil. Framing line in pen and black ink. 10¼ × 11⅛ inches (260 × 283 mm). Watermark: none visible through lining. Signed and dated at lower right, in pencil, *Wilhelm v Kobell / 1831.*

Wilhelm von Kobell, professor of landscape painting at the Munich Academy from 1813 to 1826, began his early training in Mannheim under his father, Ferdinand, and at the Mannheim drawing academy. He went to Munich in 1793 to be court painter to Crown Prince Ludwig of Bavaria. According to Wichmann (1970, pp. 114–16), the early influence of Dutch seventeenth-century painting acquired in Mannheim was soon replaced by the compositional style of such English artists as John Wooton (ca. 1686–1765) and George Stubbs (1724–1806), whose paintings of jockeys and hunters became known to the artist through the distribution of the English "sporting" print. Equestrian motifs, in which elegantly attired riders on horseback engage in chance meetings with a varying cast of characters, against a background of recognizable Bavarian locations, would come to dominate Kobell's work. The artist refined this compositional type, the so-called encounter, into a progressively more abstract form over the next thirty years.

The Thaw drawing, dated 1831, is typical of the later encounter type. The man on horseback and the young boy who confronts him are depicted in strict profile, silhouetted against the banks of the Isar, with the city of Munich in the distant background, on a clear, sunny day. This setting also appears in other encounter scenes, including a similar example of 1831 at the Nationalgalerie, Berlin, entitled *A Gentleman on Horseback and Peasant Girls on the Bank of the Isar, with Munich in the Background*. In the Thaw drawing, the friezelike composition is interrupted only by the dog that stands between the boy and the horses, listening attentively. The distinction between these two figures is emphasized not only through their dress (the elegantly attired rider is contrasted with the ill-clad boy) but also through spatial separation. The figures do not overlap, even the dog stands in isolation; only the two horses stand companionably side-by-side. Further, the elevated position of the man seems to point to his higher social standing.

As was the habit of the artist, the figures that decorate the background are based on earlier individual studies created as stock characters to be used in various works. For instance, both the wagon of hay seen at the far distant left and the woman carrying a basket on her head in the distant right appear in an earlier composition of 1822 (*Jäger mit Flasche und Reiter mit Glas*, present whereabouts unknown; see Wichmann 1970, no. 1278, repr.).

Provenance:
Galerie Biedermann, Munich.

Bibliography:
Thaw III, p. 272, repr.

Exhibition:
Thaw II, no. 30, repr. in color.

EJP

Caspar David Friedrich

Greifswald 1774–1840 Dresden

48
Moonlit Landscape

Watercolor. The moon is cut out and inserted on a separate piece of paper. Laid down on heavy cardboard. 9⅛ × 14⅜ inches (232 × 365 mm). Watermark: none visible through lining.

The full moon hovers above the densely wooded mountains in the background, casting a pale light on the clouds that is reflected in the pond in the foreground. The trees and statue in the left foreground are silhouetted against the sky and mountains with only a delicate shimmer of light at their edges. Börsch-Supan has called this sheet a "transparent," that is, a drawing intended to be lit from behind. In this case light could be filtered through the inserted piece of unpainted paper that represents the moon to make it the brightest point in the work. The statue has been called a *Mater Dolorosa*; however, the object which in such a depiction would be the sword in her bosom might also be interpreted as a cross.

Most of Friedrich's moonlit landscapes convey a totally different feeling. In *Two Men Contemplating the Moon* (*Zwei Männer in Betrachtung des Mondes*; Börsch-Supan and Jähnig 1973, no. 261) and other works, it is the communion between man and nature that is the focal point, and in some of his nocturnal landscapes the moon does not play such a prominent role as it does here (Börsch-Supan and Jähnig 1973, nos. 128, 215, 228, 281, 310, 381). Perhaps the lost moonlit landscape exhibited by the Dresden Academy in 1806 (Börsch-Supan and Jähnig 1973, no. 130) conveyed a feeling similar to the present sheet. Although, according to Börsch-Supan, it was a sepia drawing and not a watercolor like the Thaw sheet, it had the moon and water and may not have had figures since none are mentioned in the short description published by Johann Georg Meusel in 1808 (Meusel 1808, p. 260). Börsch-Supan and Jähnig proposed a dating of 1830–35, but an earlier date should not be ruled out. A drawing of 23 October 1800, now in Oslo, depicts the trees behind the statue and the fence of this sheet and indeed was used for it. If Friedrich's sister Catherina Dorothea Sponholz was really its first owner, this watercolor must have been made before her death in 1808.

Börsch-Supan has catalogued possible meanings of many components of Caspar David Friedrich's work. In his opinion the full moon illuminating the dark can be both a symbol of Christ and of death (Börsch-Supan and Jähnig 1973, p. 228). In considering the Thaw drawing, he sees in the broken dead tree behind the statue a symbol of Christ's death and in the birch tree and moon a symbol of his resurrection.

Provenance:
Catherina Dorothea Sponholz (1766–1808), the artist's sister (according to Thaw I, p. 96); Caroline Sponholz, the artist's niece (according to Thaw I, p. 96); F. Pflugradt, Zingst (a descendant of the Sponholz family, where it was known at least in 1941, according to Börsch-Supan and Jähnig); Galerie Meissner, Zurich.

Bibliography:
Pogge 1930; Sumowski 1970, pp. 159, 203; Börsch-Supan and Jähnig 1973, p. 453, no. 440, repr.

Exhibitions:
Thaw I, no. 107, repr. in color; Thaw III, no. 52, repr.

PD

Caspar David Friedrich

Greifswald 1774–1840 Dresden

49
Landscape on Rügen with Shepherds and Flocks

Graphite, pen and gray ink, brown wash and white heightening, point of brush in a deeper shade of brown. Borderline in black ink. 9⅝ × 12⅝ inches (245 × 326 mm). Watermark: none visible through lining. On the verso, in graphite, indications for mounting the drawing, *Ein Passep.* (Passepartout) *A mit Rückpappe;* two more lines now illegible because partly erased and, at lower left, *C. D. Friedrich.*

This topographical vista on the island of Rügen in the Baltic Sea is taken from southeast of Putbus with a view over the Goor and the Kollhof, in the middle-ground, toward the Grosse and Kleine Vlim. The same landscape, seen from a somewhat lower vantage point, appears in *Landscape with Rainbow* (*Landschaft mit Regenbogen;* Börsch-Supan and Jähnig 1973, no. 182), a painting formerly in Weimar, stolen and still untraced. The oak tree at the right edge of the drawing is moved to the left in the painting, thus forming the frame for the composition with the shepherd at the right. The horizon line in the painting is much lower than in the drawing, making the shepherd's figure reach into the sky, and a rainbow spans the entire scene.

Friedrich is documented as having been on Rügen in 1801, 1806, 1818, and 1826. A drawing of the Rügen landscape, made on 16 June 1801 and now in Cologne, has been thought to be preparatory for the painting (Hinz 1966, no. 269), but Sumowski has disagreed, maintaining that a lost drawing made the same day may have been used instead (Sumowski 1970, p. 94) and by extension was used for the Thaw drawing as well. Friedrich often employed on-site drawings for paintings and finished drawings such as this, and the present sheet is certainly based on the artist's knowledge of the place from one of his earlier stays. It would seem that the drawing antedates the painting, which is believed to have been acquired for Karl August, duke of Weimar, by Johann Wolfgang von Goethe in 1810. Two preparatory drawings for details of the Thaw sheet and the painting are known: one, in Dresden, for the barren limb of a tree in the right foreground and one, dated 9 June 1809 and now in Bremen, for the oak tree in the middleground (Hinz 1966, nos. 505 and 519; Sumowski 1970, figs. 160 and 132).

Although both the drawing and the painting appear to be simply views with the addition of a shepherd, a tradition dating to the mid-nineteenth century sees the painting as an illustration to Goethe's *Schäfers Klagelied,* a poem of 1802. This interpretation is improbable since a painter who knows mountains—as Friedrich did—would hardly depict the shepherd on such a modest hill overlooking a rolling countryside when Goethe's text describes him as high aloft a mountain and descending into the valley. Nor is the poem applicable to the drawing, which lacks the rainbow described in Goethe's text.

Provenance:
Private collection or art market, Weimar (prior to 1945); private collection, Berlin; C. G. Boerner, Düsseldorf; Seiden and de Cuevas, New York.

Bibliography:
Börsch-Supan and Jähnig 1973, p. 307, no. 181; Boerner 1976, pl. 13.

Exhibitions:
Düsseldorf 1976, pp. 154–55, no. 95, repr.; Thaw III, no. 53, repr. in color.

PD

Philipp Otto Runge

Wolgast (Pomerania) 1777–1810 Hamburg

50
The Child

Pen and black ink, over pencil. Framing line in pen and brown ink, over pencil. 5 ¹³⁄₁₆ × 8 ¹⁄₁₆ inches (147 × 205 mm). Watermark: none. Inscribed on verso along right edge (in the hand of the artist's brother Daniel?), *Original von Philipp Otto Runge 1809*, in pen and light brown ink.

Runge's north German pietism and love of nature had been nurtured by the pastor and poet Ludwig Theobul Kosegarten, who was his teacher in Wolgast from 1789 to 1792. This religious view of nature was the principle behind Runge's best-known theme, the *Times of Day* cycle, which the artist began in 1802. The initial four compositions—*Morning*, *Evening*, *Day*, and *Night*—were symmetrical designs in which flowers, children, and light were used to symbolize Runge's religious philosophy of landscape. The arabesque, linear quality of these early drawings was influenced by the artist's exposure to engravings of scenes from Homer, Aeschylus, and Dante by the English artist John Flaxman, sent to him by his brother Daniel in 1801. The fluid, neoclassical, linear style of these engravings transformed the scenes into their "hieroglyphic" form; it was this symbolic approach to subjects that appealed to the artist. Runge produced engravings for his *Times of Day* drawings in 1805 and 1807, a set of which is in the Morgan Library (acc. no. [P]1985.70:1–4). In 1807, Runge began making further studies for a painted version of the series. However, he would complete only two oils before he died—one sketch known as the *Small Morning* (fig. 1) in 1807 and in 1808, the *Large Morning* version, which was cut up some time after his death and then reassembled in 1927. Both paintings are now in the Hamburg Kunsthalle.

The Thaw sheet is a preparatory sketch for the baby who appears in the *Small Morning* oil. As Traeger points out, here the child lies on his back, feet raised and together, hands apart. The sheet is devoid of indication of the vegetation that is included in the subsequent painted sketch. The child appears in further studies in the Hamburg Kunsthalle, including a compositional study for the middle section of the oil. There are slight variations in the placement of the baby's feet and hands, but the basic pose remains the same. Runge's artistic theories encompass many levels of interpretation of his work. According to the pantheistic reading, the baby both witnesses and represents the new day; within the tradition of Runge's north German Protestant heritage, the child symbolizes the Christ Child, or Redeemer.

Provenance:
The artist's estate; his son Otto Sigismund Runge; given by the son to the Hamburger Künstlerverein; sale, Leipzig, C. G. Boerner, 19 June 1937, no. 183, pl. III; sale, Munich, Sotheby's, 27 June 1995, no. 60, repr.

Bibliography:
Isermeyer 1940, p. 131; Waetzoldt 1951, pp. 127, 142, fig. 46 (cited in Traeger and auction entry); Krafft and Schümann 1969, p. 285; Traeger 1975, p. 424, no. 392, repr.

Exhibition:
Hamburg 1935, no. 112 (according to sales catalogue, Munich, Sotheby's, 27 June 1995, p. 23).

EJP

Fig. 1 Philipp Otto Runge. *Small Morning.* Hamburger Kunsthalle.

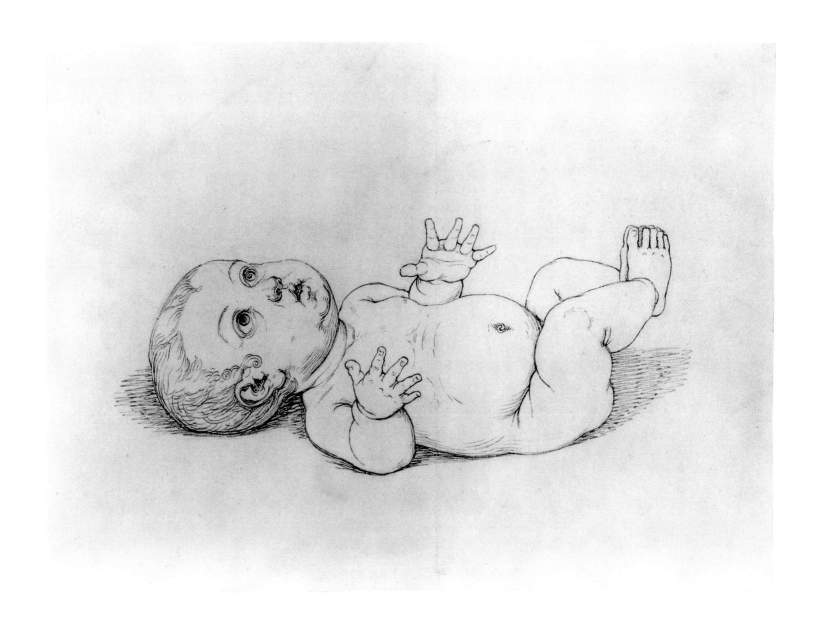

Thomas Girtin

Southwark 1775–1802 London

51

The Eruption of Mount Vesuvius

Brush and gray wash, over some pencil. 12⅝ × 18⁵⁄₁₆ inches (320 × 465 mm). Watermark: none. Inscribed on verso, *Girtin / Drawn in the House of R. K. P. / 1800.*

Thomas Girtin was an essential link between J. R. Cozens (No. 42) and the succeeding generation of English landscape watercolorists through his participation in the "Monro Academy." There, in the Adelphi Terrace home of Dr. Thomas Monro (1759–1833), Girtin spent many evenings copying the drawings by Cozens in the doctor's collection. Perhaps motivated by this experience with the Monro Academy, Girtin subsequently joined the earliest known of the London sketching societies, often referred to as Girtin's Sketching Club. The first meeting, which was at the house of Robert Ker Porter, has been recorded by François Louis Thomas Francia on the back of his drawing entitled *Landscape Composition—Moonlight,* now in the Victoria and Albert Museum, London. He records the date, *Monday, May the 20th, 1799,* and describes the group of young artists as *a small and select Society of Young Painters under the title (as I give it) of the Brothers* [who have] *met for the purpose of establishing by practice a school of Historic Landscape, the subjects being original designs from poetick* [sic] *passages.* Francia then lists the artists present, Thomas Girtin among them.

The Thaw drawing has a more concise inscription on the back, *Girtin / Drawn in the House of R. K. P. / 1800,* leading us to believe that it, too, is a product of a meeting of the "brothers." In addition, there is an entry in the sketching society minute book for Saturday, 2 November 1799, which notes that "Mount Vesu[vius]" was the topic for the evening (see New Haven 1986, p. 20). The minute book, now in the Henry E. Huntington Library, San Marino, California, was kept by the society's secretary, George Samuel. Samuel records that this meeting was at the house of Robert Ker Porter and further notes that Girtin was among those present. Although the evening's theme was usually suggested by a "poetick passage," no lines of poetry are recorded for the November 2d meeting (see Winter 1974, p. 135). Among the names of poets that recur in the minutes is that of James Thomson, the Scottish poet best known for his four poems comprising *The Seasons.* Each season, testifying to the sublime power of nature, would certainly inspire these brother artists sufficiently in their imaginative drawings. In fact, for the meeting of 5 October 1799, Girtin selected a quotation from Thomson's poem *Winter.*

It appears that the Girtin drawing is the only one for the November 2d meeting that has survived. It is puzzling that the inscription on the back dates the drawing 1800 rather than 1799. There are two possibilities for this discrepancy. One, that the inscription was added later and the date remembered incorrectly; or perhaps

Girtin re-created this marvelously finished work, based on his earlier drawing, which, according to the rules of the sketching society, would have been handed over to the host for the evening, Robert Ker Porter.

Provenance:
Dr. Thomas Calvert Girtin; his daughter, Mrs. Cooper; her sale, Sherborne, 2 December 1884, lot 43; Mr. Davis of Castleton; B. de le Bullock; his sale, London, Sotheby's, 20 July 1978, lot 171; Christopher Norris; his sale, London, Sotheby's, 19 November 1987, lot 71; Thos. Agnew & Sons Ltd., London.

Bibliography:
New Haven 1986, p. 20 n. 28 (not exhibited).

Exhibitions:
New York 1992, no. 48, fig. 15, pp. 30, 33, and 42; Thaw III, no. 57, repr.

EJP

Joseph Mallord William Turner

London 1775–1851 Chelsea

52

Interior of St. Peter's Basilica, Rome

Point of brush and watercolor, over traces of pencil, on board. 11 7/16 × 16 5/16 inches (290 × 414 mm). Signed and dated at lower left, in brown ink, *JMW Turner 18* [cut off].

Turner made two trips to Rome: the first in 1819 and the second in 1828. During the course of his travels, he filled nineteen sketchbooks, recording the popular sites and monuments he visited and carefully indicating on the covers the names of the principal places he had recorded (Wilton 1979, pp. 140, 141). He later referred to these sketchbooks when working up finished watercolors and paintings at home in his studio.

The Thaw watercolor belongs to a group of seven or eight drawings that the artist created upon his return from Rome in 1820 for his patron, Walter Fawkes. Cecilia Powell states that the Rome drawings reflect both the 1819 sketches and the "works of art which had shaped Turner's attitudes to Rome before his own visit" (Powell 1987, p. 105). These works of art not only directed Turner's attention to specific monuments and sites but also may have suggested the angle from which he drew them. Such a combination of influences is certainly present in this work. While the sketches Turner made of St. Peter's in 1819 (St. Peter's sketchbook, Turner Bequest clxxxviii-83, Tate Gallery) are all rapid notations, this watercolor is far more detailed and composed. As Powell points out, there is a strong connection between this work, particularly the contrived perspective and view, and eighteenth-century oil paintings of the interior of St. Peter's by Giovanni Paolo Panini. Turner also may have referred to Giovanni Battista Piranesi's etchings of the subject (Powell 1987, p. 109).

Turner, of course, adapted his eighteenth-century models to his own style and medium. He applied delicate shades of ochre, brick-red, and green-blue watercolor with a dry, fine brush, allowing him to depict this great interior in exacting detail. The overall subdued, linear treatment is in direct contrast to the tumultuous and fluid display of color in *The Pass at Faido* (No. 53). The two drawings reveal Turner's wide-ranging control of the difficult watercolor medium in creating the effect he chooses, whether it be topographical accuracy or emotionally charged display.

Provenance:
Walter Fawkes, acquired from the artist in 18.1; Rev. F. H. Fawkes; sale, London, Christie's, 2 July 1937, lot 57; bought by Polak; Mrs. E. L. Hedley; sale, London, Sotheby's, 7 July 1965, lot 45; bought by Spink; Mrs. O. R. Edwards; sale, London, Sotheby's, 11 July 1990, lot. 83.

Bibliography:
Caldesi 1864, pl. 33 (according to auction house sale catalogue); *Athenaeum* 1879, p. 502; Armstrong 1902, p. 274; Finberg [1912], p. 14, no. 191, pl. V; Finberg 1961, p. 272, no. 497; Wilton 1979, p. 148, pl. 159, and no. 724; Wilton 1982, p. 44, under no. 38; Powell 1987, p. 109, pl. 120.

Exhibitions:
Leeds 1826, no. 264 (according to auction house sale catalogue); Leeds 1839, no. 27 (according to auction house sale catalogue); London 1902, no. 73; York 1980, no. 96; Thaw III, no. 58, repr. in color.

EJP

Joseph Mallord William Turner

London 1775–1851 Chelsea

53
The Pass at Faido, St. Gotthard

Watercolor, point of brush, scratching out, over traces of pencil. 11¹⁵⁄₁₆ × 18½ inches (303 × 469 mm). Watermark: none.

Turner made six trips to Switzerland: the first in 1802; the next in 1836; then four successive journeys in 1841, 1842, 1843, and 1844. As was his long-established practice, he filled many sketchbooks, copiously recording what he saw. The sketches in the 1802 notebooks were primarily monotone notations, often pencil on washed or gray paper. Turner used these sketches as reference material for larger, more finished compositions created in the studio. However, during his 1836 trip he began introducing touches of color to his preliminary sketches, and paper-covered sketchbooks, which he could roll and put in his pockets, gradually replaced the smaller stiff-backed notebooks (Russell and Wilton 1976, p. 26). These color studies became more elaborate in the 1840s, watercolor being a most appropriate medium for Turner to convey the atmosphere of Switzerland.

It was after the 1841 tour that Turner first presented selected examples of these color studies to his dealer and agent, Thomas Griffith, not for the purpose of sale but as sample subjects to submit to potential buyers. Although the results of this approach were not wholly successful—Griffith obtained only nine commissions from three patrons—Turner repeated this procedure twice more, in 1842/43 and again in 1845. The Thaw sheet is a commission from the second offering (Turner Bequest ccclxiv-209, Tate Gallery). The commission came from the artist's most ardent patron, John Ruskin, who reproduced this watercolor as an etching in his *Modern Painters*. In addition, Ruskin created a watercolor copy which is also in the Thaw Collection (fig. 1).

The Pass at Faido shows Turner at his best in evoking the overwhelming power of nature. At first, we are not even aware of the small, vulnerable figures and carriage (at lower right) that dare to travel this route. Rather, Turner forces our attention upon the rush of water over rocks and the merging of sky and mountains, giving form to the concept of the sublime. As Ruskin would discover when visiting the same site on his trip to Switzerland in 1845, Turner's depiction is as much invention as reality.

Provenance:
John Ruskin; Kennedy collection (according to Cook and Wedderburn 1903–12, XIII, 1904, p. 456 n. 2); George Coats (1901); by descent; private collection, United Kingdom; Thos. Agnew & Sons Ltd., London.

Bibliography:
Cook and Wedderburn 1903–12, XIII, 1904, p. 456, no. 66, and p. 484, no. 5; Russell and Wilton 1976, pp. 110, 139, checklist no. 82, p. 139, repr. p. 161; Wilton 1979, p. 243, fig. 253, p. 484, no. 1538; *Dealer's Record* 1981, p. 176, repr. in color; Wilton 1982, p. 68, under no. 107; *Turner Studies* 1983, p. 64; Phimister 1992, p. 965, pl. IX; London 1993, under no. 30; London 1995, under no. 40, fig. 34.

Exhibitions:
London 1878 and 1900 (see Cook and Wedderburn 1903–12, XIII, 1904, pp. 456, 484); London 1974, no. 612; Toronto and elsewhere 1980–81, p. 179, no. 104, pl. 24, color; Thaw II, no. 32, repr.; New York 1992, no. 103, pp. 23, 39, 43, and 44, fig. 23; Thaw III, no. 59, repr.

EJP

Fig. 1 John Ruskin. *Rocks in Unrest.* Thaw Collection, The Pierpont Morgan Library.

Joseph Mallord William Turner

London 1775–1851 Chelsea

54
Lucerne from the Lake

Watercolor, some gouache, scratching out, over traces of pencil. 11⅝ × 18⅝ inches (296 × 474 mm). Watermark: none visible, drawing laid down.

This later watercolor is based on a sample study (Turner Bequest ccclxiv-386, Tate Gallery) made on the artist's final trip to Switzerland in 1844. In 1845, Turner again provided the dealer Griffith with a set of Swiss watercolor samples to show to prospective buyers (see No. 53). And, once again, only a few patrons, including Ruskin, responded favorably to the artist's late style.

Turner produced three different sample studies of Lucerne from his last three trips to Switzerland. These studies demonstrate the artist's concern with the changing effects of light and atmosphere. The 1842 sample depicts the town in broad daylight; in the 1843 study, a moonlit Lucerne is cast in evening shadow; and the 1845 sheet renders the town at early dusk. The finished watercolor in the Thaw Collection delicately glows with the passing of sunset into early twilight. The town of Lucerne casts a blue reflection onto an ochre lake, the mountains to the left and right also taking on these colors. Pale washes and thin brushstrokes create a delicate, glimmering overall effect enlivened by accents of dark reds and a touch of green in the foreground.

In 1845, Turner's obligations to the Royal Academy (he stepped in for the ailing president, Sir Martin Archer Shee) prevented his making more trips to Switzerland. Later that year, the artist's own deteriorating health would keep him at home until his death in 1851.

Provenance:
John Ruskin; sold in 1865 to Mrs. Newall; by descent in Newall family until 1978; Thos. Agnew & Sons Ltd., London; private collection, Germany; Rudolph Zwirner, Cologne.

Bibliography:
Thornbury 1862, II, p. 395; *Athenaeum* 1873, p. 408; Armstrong 1902, p. 263; Cook and Wedderburn 1903–12, III, p. 552, VI, pp. 277, 361–62, figs. 72, 106, 107, XIII, pp. 201, 476n., 556, 602, XXXV, p. 380 n., XXXVIII, p. 363; Russell and Wilton 1976, p. 139, no. 88; Wilton 1979, no. 1544, repr. p. 485; Wilton 1982, under no. 115; Thaw III, p. 255, repr.; London 1995, under no. 24, fig. 23.

Exhibitions:
London 1899, no. 161; London 1929, no. 7; London 1951, no. 120; London 1967, no. 94; London 1975, no. 97, repr.; Thaw II, no. 33, repr.; New York 1992, no. 104, p. 44; Brussels 1994, no. 111, repr. in color.

EJP

111

John Constable

East Bergholt 1776–1837 London

55

View of Cathanger Near Petworth

Pencil, on two sheets of paper pasted together. 8 1/16 × 13 5/8 inches (205 × 347 mm). Watermark: none visible through lining. Inscribed by the artist, in upper left corner, in pencil, *Petworth Sepr. 12 / 1834 Cat Hanger.*

In a letter of 16 July 1834, to his dear friend and future biographer, Charles Leslie, Constable described his reaction to the Sussex countryside. Writing from Arundel, he noted:

> The Castle is the cheif [*sic*] ornament of this place—but all here sinks to insignificance in comparison with the woods, and hills. . . . I never saw such beauty in *natural landscape* before. I wish it may influence what I may do in the future, for I have too much preferred the picturesque to the beautifull [*sic*]—which will I hope account for the *broken ruggedness of my style* (*Constable* 1965, p. 111).

A "broken ruggedness" aptly describes Constable's masterful handling of this soft pencil drawing. Cathanger was a farm located on the Petworth estate of Lord Egremont, who had invited the artist to spend a few days there in July, when Constable was in Sussex (*Constable* 1965; Leslie 1937, p. 315). He turned down the invitation, however, hoping to arrange for a future visit in the company of Leslie. On 10 September, Constable finally joined Leslie at Petworth. In his biography of Constable, Leslie relates how Lord Egremont, "with that unceasing attention" of a good host, ordered a carriage ready for Constable each day to carry him to the surrounding areas (Leslie 1937, p. 319).

Constable remained at Petworth for two weeks, during which time he filled a large sketchbook with pencil and watercolor drawings. The Thaw work, the earliest known dated drawing of Constable's visit, is composed of two sheets of paper pasted together. It was the artist's habit to apply an isinglass fixative to his pencil drawings, which has preserved all the richness of his pencil work. However, the year of the inscription, *1834*, is faint where the fixative has not taken, on the seam joining the two sheets of paper (Reynolds 1984, p. 262).

Provenance:
Edward Seago; Baskett & Day, London.

Bibliography:
Reynolds 1984, I, p. 262, no. 34.31, II, pl. 938.

Exhibitions:
London 1976, no. 315, repr., and under no. 316; New York 1981, no. 124, repr.; Thaw II, no. 35, repr.; New York 1992, no. 12, p. 46, repr.; Thaw III, no. 60, repr.

EJP

113

Samuel Palmer

Newington 1805–1881 Redhill

56
Pear Tree in a Walled Garden

Watercolor and gouache, over preliminary indications in brush and gray wash, on gray paper; traces of pencil. 8¾ × 11⅛ inches (222 × 281 mm). Watermark: none.

In October 1824, the nineteen-year-old Samuel Palmer was introduced to the visionary artist William Blake (No. 43) by John Linnell, his future father-in-law. This meeting has been described as the "single most important event" in the artist's life (Detroit and Philadelphia 1968, p. 260). Palmer had experienced "visions" of his own, and the meeting was one of mutual recognition of two similar minds. It should be noted, however, that Palmer had already developed a personal and emotionally charged style of his own prior to this meeting and, as Grigson points out, Palmer's style during his "Shoreham period" actually intensified after Blake's death in 1827 (Grigson 1947, p. 30). Palmer moved to the village of Shoreham in Kent in 1826/27. Blake visited him at least once in Shoreham, while Linnell and other friends were frequent visitors. However, Palmer's Shoreham years were primarily a time for introspection and communion with nature, carried out in the artist's own singularly spiritual way; the art created during this period reflects that communion.

In this work, the pear tree dominates the garden not only through its relatively large size, but also through its burgeoning white blossoms and glossy black branches with yellow, orange, and green leaves. The tree is truly "alive" but in a mystical, otherworldly way. The superabundant growth depicted here takes this garden beyond the ordinary. This drawing is closely related to another by Palmer in the Victoria and Albert Museum, London, *In a Shoreham Garden*, which also depicts an extravagantly blossoming fruit tree. Both have been dated to about 1829, and both reflect an artist enthralled with the revitalizing force of spring.

Palmer's son suggested that this study depicts either the garden of Waterhouse, the artist's home in Shoreham, or perhaps the rich and fertile garden of a Mr. Groombridge referred to in Palmer's letters.

Provenance:
A. H. Palmer, Tilford, Surrey, and Vancouver, B.C.; sale, London, Christie's, 4 March 1929, lot 45; Victor Rienacker; Mrs. K. T. Parker, Oxford; Mrs. Paul J. Sachs, Cambridge, Massachusetts; Mr. and Mrs. Victor O. Jones (née Elizabeth Sachs); R. M. Light & Co., Inc., Boston.

Bibliography:
Grigson 1937, pp. 11, 13, and 14, repr.; Grigson 1947, p. 90ff., 174, no. 77, pl. 33; Grigson 1960, p. 32, under no. 45; Sellars 1974, p. 58, fig. 54; Egerton 1979, no. 42, repr.; Lister 1985, pl. 17; Lister 1988, p. 70, no. 102, repr.; Phimister 1992, p. 965, pl. XII.

Exhibitions:
London 1926, no. 56 (as *Study of a Wall Fruit Tree in Blossom*); Amsterdam 1936, no. 223, repr.; Paris 1937a, no. 114; Paris 1938, no. 216; New York 1949, no. 11; London 1957, no. 29; Detroit and Philadelphia 1968, no. 181, repr.; Thaw I, no. 112, repr.; New York 1992, no. 66, fig. 9, pp. 23, 24; Thaw III, no. 61, repr.

Thaw Collection, The Pierpont Morgan Library, acc. no. 1980.37

EJP

Jean Auguste Dominique Ingres

Montauban 1780–1867 Paris

57
Portrait of Hippolyte-François Devillers (1767–1837)

Pencil on wove paper. 9 × 6⁹⁄₁₆ inches (228 × 166 mm). Watermark: none. Signed, inscribed, and dated at lower right, *Ingres. a rome / 1812.*

A student of Jacques Louis David, Ingres was the winner of the Prix de Rome in 1801, a prize he did not claim until 1806. He remained in Rome until 1820, earning his livelihood chiefly by making portrait drawings. In the years before Waterloo, Ingres developed a clientele among the French officers of the Napoleonic administration in Rome. His work proved popular in that city but initially did not fare as well in Paris. It was not until 1824, with *The Vow of Louis XIII*, that Ingres was critically acclaimed in France, at which time he returned to Paris, confident of success.

His first client in Rome had been Charles Marcotte d'Argenteuil, who befriended the artist while he sat for him as well as introduced him to other officials. Among these was Hippolyte-François Devillers, *directeur de l'enregistrement*, whom Ingres praised in later years for his helpfulness and solicitude in Rome. Ingres painted Devillers's portrait, now in the Bührle collection in Zurich, in 1811 and made two drawings of him. One, dated 1811, was in the collection of Mme Jacques Dubourg, Paris, as of 1977; the second, dated 1812, is in the Thaw Collection. In the earlier drawing, Devillers is depicted in a relaxed pose—seated and leaning back with his sword in hand. In this later drawing, he is portrayed standing, his right hand inside his coat, his left hand in his pocket. Devillers was forty-five when he posed for this portrait. He is represented as a man of position, even though his uniform lacks the insignia featured in the painting—notably the ear of wheat on his collar and the sword at his side. His eyes convey the kindness that Ingres mentioned, along with a certain rigidity of character. The artist's pencil captured not only his physiognomic likeness but something of his character as well.

Devillers left Rome before 1820 to assume a similar position in Vesoul for the Haute-Saône. There, he was also a member of the municipal council and eventually performed the mayoral duties of the town. He seems to have enjoyed a very comfortable life, and his family remained in Vesoul until the middle of the nineteenth century. He married Anne Chaton, who was thirty years his junior. The couple had four children prior to the marriage and two more afterward.

Provenance:
Mme de Gorsse; Alfred-Louis Lebeuf de Montgermont by 1913; his sale, Paris, Galerie Georges Petit, 16–19 June 1919, no. 121, repr.; Comtesse Bernard de Laguiche (the Princess Clotilde de Broglie); Armand de Laguiche (her son); art market; Robert H. Smith, Washington, D.C.; Feilchenfeldt, Zurich.

Bibliography:
Naef and Lerch 1964, pp. 5–16; Naef 1977–80, I, 1977, ch. 29, pp. 255–61, fig. 3, IV, 1977, p. 144, no. 78, repr., and under no. 77.

Exhibitions:
Paris 1913a, no. 335; Rome 1968, no. 36, repr.; Thaw II, no. 36, repr.; Thaw III, no. 64, repr.

CDD

Jean Auguste Dominique Ingres

Montauban 1780–1867 Paris

58
Odalisque with Slave

Pencil, black and white chalk, white gouache, gray and brown wash, especially on the Moor's face, hands, and cuffs; surface scratched in places to produce highlights; on cream-colored wove paper. Design area, 13³⁄₁₆ × 18¼ inches (335 × 462 mm), on sheet measuring 19¼ × 24¼ inches (488 × 616 mm). Signed, inscribed, and dated at lower left, *J. Ingres / Rom. 1839*.

The subject of the odalisque held an almost lifelong fascination for Ingres. Although the painting on which this drawing is based was commissioned by Charles Marcotte d'Argenteuil and executed in Rome in 1839, Ingres made the drawing that set the pose of the odalisque (now preserved in the Musée Ingres, Montauban) as early as 1809, in preparation for *La Dormeuse de Naples*, a painting, now lost, that had been purchased by Murat. In an inscription, Ingres identified the model as *Mariuccia blonde belle-via Margutta 106*.

The painting *Odalisque with Slave* is now in the Fogg Art Museum, Harvard University (fig. 1). There is also a replica, dated 1842, in the Walters Art Gallery, Baltimore. While the composition of both paintings and this highly finished drawing is nearly identical, the same background is used in the drawing and the Fogg painting. (The background depicted in the Walters replica is a landscape rather than an interior.)

Even though the Thaw drawing replicates the Fogg painting, it is evident from its meticulous finish that the artist spent a good deal of time on it. While he clearly intended the drawing to be an independent work, its painstaking—almost lithographic—technique suggests that it also served as the model for Réveil's engraved version of the subject (Magimel 1851, no. 64). It has been suggested (Cohn and Siegfried 1980, p. 118) that the drawing may be the *Odalisque with Slave* recorded in J.-Ch. Thévenin's estate sale of 1868 as *Odalisque. Magnificent drawing after Ingres*. This, however, is not the case. Almost twenty years after he completed the present work, Ingres made a copy for Emile Galichon in 1858 and finished it in the same combination of washes and gouache. This copy was bequeathed to the Louvre in 1918 (Paris 1952a, no. 14, repr.).

Provenance:
Gustave Pereire, Paris; Sir Philip Sassoon (according to Louvre catalogue); Georges Seligmann, New York; Dr. and Mrs. T. Edward Hanley, Bradford, Pennsylvania; E. V. Thaw and Co., New York; The Norton Simon Foundation, Los Angeles.

Bibliography:
Paris 1967–68, p. 268 n.; Radius 1968, p. 107, no. 128 n.; Cambridge 1969, p. 116, no. 85 n.; Cohn and Siegfried 1980, p. 118, under no. 41; Louisville and Fort Worth 1983–84, p. 242 (as U.S.A., private collection).

Fig. 1 Jean Auguste Dominique Ingres. *Odalisque with a Slave.* Fogg Art Museum, Harvard University Art Museums, 1943.251.

Exhibitions:
Philadelphia 1957; New York 1961, no. 77, not repr.; Midland and Denver 1967, no. 93; New York and Philadelphia 1967, no. 32, repr.; Columbus 1968, no. 79; San Francisco 1973, no. 15, repr.; Thaw III, no. 66, repr.

CDD

Théodore Géricault

Rouen 1791–1824 Paris

59
Head of a Black Man

Black chalk, stumped. 9¹³⁄₁₆ × 6⅞ inches (248 × 175 mm). Watermark: illegible fragment.

This impressive head, very sculptural in its execution, is a study for a figure in Géricault's famous *Raft of the Medusa*, painted 1818–19.

The history of the *Medusa* and Géricault's painting has been fully told elsewhere by Lorenz Eitner (1972). In what was a clear case of ineptitude, the *Medusa* foundered in the sea off Senegal in 1816, and those who were unable to fit into the crowded lifeboats were forced to build a raft, which was to be towed by the boats. The cables broke, and, adrift for thirteen days, only fifteen of the original total of 150 passengers were eventually rescued by the *Argo*. In the painting, Géricault shows the moment when the survivors sight the rescue ship. In 1817, two of the survivors, Alexandre Corréard and Henri Savigny, published *Naufrage de la frégate la Méduse*, detailing the horrors of their travail, from cannibalism to murder, from thirst to famine and death. The French public was shocked and opinion ran high against the monarchy.

It is not known exactly when Géricault made the decision to paint the incident, but it was to occupy him fully for one and a half years, the longest period he had ever worked on a single project. As the son of wealthy and rather indulgent parents, he had previously followed a highly personal course of studies, characterized by its irregularity and interrupted by distractions, among them his passionate love of horses and sportsmanship as well as an involvement with a married woman who was a distant relative.

He threw himself into his new project, researching the disaster and making studies of cadavers and severed limbs along with many figural and portrait studies, including those of Corréard and Savigny. The subject of the Thaw drawing is probably the famous model Joseph, whom Géricault used several times (Eitner 1983, p. 176). It is a study for the black man recorded as being on the infamous raft. In the painting he appears by the mast, next to Corréard and Savigny.

The rise of abolitionism in France was just beginning, and Géricault was sympathetic to that struggle. There had been no recognition of the role blacks had played in the *Medusa* incident, and Géricault wanted to rectify that, though in typical romantic fashion he exaggerated the truth by portraying three on the raft, including the figure who waves to the *Argo* and forms the dramatic apex of the painting. As was natural for the time, Géricault considered blacks to be exotic, as he did Turks and other non-Europeans, romanticizing them in costume and pose.

The evident sympathy between artist and subject has resulted in an indelible likeness of the model. Bazin's intuitive rejection of this extraordinary portrait study from Géricault's oeuvre is not convincing.

Provenance:
Pierre Dubaut (Lugt S. 2103b); James Lord, Paris.

Bibliography:
Berger 1952, p. 72, pl. 50; Aimé-Azam 1956, repr. facing p. 208; Lem 1962, pp. 24, 39, pl. 2; Prokofiev 1963, p. 208, repr.; Testori 1963, p. 59; Berger 1968, p. 81, figs. 54, 177; Berger and Johnson 1969, n.p., fig. 14; Eitner 1972, p. 172, no. 107, pl. 106; Prat 1990, p. XVI; Noël 1991, p. 64; Bazin 1987–94, V, 1992, pp. 119, 308, no. 1910, repr. (as unknown artist).

Exhibitions:
Paris 1950, no. 52, repr.; Paris 1952, no. 69; London 1952, p. 172, no. 55; Zurich 1953, p. 46, no. 171; Paris 1954, no. 59; Recklinghausen 1962, no. 201; Baltimore 1980, no. 6, repr.; Thaw II, no. 37, repr.; Paris 1991–92, no. 216, fig. 270; Thaw III, no. 68, repr.

CDD

121

Théodore Géricault

Rouen 1791–1824 Paris

60

Mustapha

Watercolor over pencil. 11¹⁵⁄₁₆ × 8½ inches (302 × 216 mm).

This drawing and various others—notably the fully realized watercolor in the Louvre—have been identified as portraits of Géricault's servant Mustapha, a shipwrecked Turkish sailor whom Géricault encountered most likely in 1819 (cf. Zurich 1953, nos. 210, 215–16). His subsequent employment was one manifestation of the artist's predilection for Orientalism. Mustapha is known to have posed in exotic dress, some items of which were borrowed from the artist-dilettante Jules-Robert Auguste (1789–1850), a prominent member of the circle of artists that included Baron Gros and Delacroix—both of whom were also lent pieces from M. Auguste's collection of costumes and weapons.

It seems likely that Mustapha was dismissed from Géricault's service in 1821, when the artist went to London. Contact, however, must have been renewed after Géricault's return to France, for Mustapha was conspicuous among the group of mourners at his funeral.

This drawing was one of a number of Géricault's studies of Orientals in costume owned by Delacroix's friend, Baron de Schwiter (his sale, Paris, Hôtel Drouot, 20–21 April 1883, nos. 41–49). Bazin, who doubts Géricault's authorship of this drawing, cannot refute its early provenance. His comparison of this rapid but touching sketch of Géricault's servant with the masterful and fully worked watercolor of a black soldier in the Fogg Art Museum is not at all persuasive.

Provenance:
Baron de Schwiter (Lugt 1768); his sale, Paris, Hôtel Drouot, 20–21 April 1883, no. 43; P.-A. Chéramy, Paris; A. Stroelin, Paris; probably (according to Bazin) sale, Paris, Hôtel Drouot, 14–16 April 1913; Pierre Dubaut (Lugt S. 2103b); Walter Goetz, Paris.

Bibliography:
Bazin 1987–94, V, 1992, pp. 116, 298–99, no. 1884, repr. (as artist unknown).

Exhibitions:
Paris and Rouen 1924, no. 266; Paris 1931, p. 39; Paris 1937, no. 157; Paris 1942, no. 93; Paris 1950, no. 66 (as 1822–23); London 1952, no. 43 (as 1808–16); Zurich 195₃, no. 214; Paris 1954, no. 65; Paris 1964, no. 87; Los Angeles and elsewhere 1971–72, p. 154, no. 110, repr.; Thaw I, no. 72, repr.; New York 1984, no. 102; New York and elsewhere 1985–86, no. 102, repr.; Kamakura and elsewhere 1987–88, p. 84, fig. 1; Paris and New York 1993–94, no. 105, repr.; Thaw III, no. 69, repr.

CDD

Antoine Louis Barye

Paris 1795–1875 Paris

61

Tigress on Her Back

Watercolor. 8¼ × 10⅞ inches (205 × 275 mm). Signed in pen and brown ink at lower right, *Barye*.

Unlike his friend Delacroix, Barye did not travel. Until he went to Barbizon in 1849, he had barely been away from Paris or gotten close to animals in the wild other than those in the Jardin des Plantes. There he was a frequent visitor and acute observer, as his drawings, clay models, and bronzes of animals attest. In his drawings and paintings, he often placed the animals against colorful landscape backgrounds, which in their contours sometimes echo the animals' forms; later he occasionally depicted the animals in a Barbizon setting. Most often creating scenes of ferocity—animals stalking prey or locked in mortal combat—Barye made numerous studies of lions and tigers (and even an elephant) rolling on the ground, such as this one of a playful young tigress.

Provenance:
P.-A. Chéramy, Paris; his sale, Paris, Galerie Georges Petit, 5–7 May 1908, no. 273 (1,940 frs.); Alfred Beurdeley, Paris; his sale, Paris, Galerie Georges Petit, 2–4 February 1920, no. 15 (9,100 frs.); André Schoeller, Paris; Jacques Zoubaloff, Paris; his sale, Paris, Galerie Georges Petit, 16–17 June 1927, no. 9; Gerson; Galerie Alfred Daber, Paris.

Bibliography:
Zieseniss 1955, p. 64, pl. ii, B-14; Thaw III, p. 263, repr.

Exhibitions:
Paris 1889, no. 746; St. Petersburg 1912, no. 17; Paris 1913, no. 5; Paris 1929, no. 59; Paris 1931, p. 37; Paris 1936, no. 130; Paris 1956, no. 9; New York 1964, no. 3, repr.; Thaw I, no. 76, repr.; Paris and New York 1993–94, no. 107, repr.; New York 1994, no. 24, repr.

CDD

Camille Jean-Baptiste Corot

Paris 1796–1875 Paris

62

Portrait of a Man

Pencil, partly stumped, on wove paper. 10½ × 8½ inches (265 × 216 mm). Signed and dated at lower right, *C. Corot. / octobre. 1844.*

In this work, Corot, the painter of landscapes and romantic Barbizon pieces, is revealed as a portrait draughtsman of unusual strength and psychological penetration. The drawing was executed in 1844, some twelve years after Ingres's portrait of M. Bertin, the celebrated picture that had such impact on contemporary and later portraiture. There is something of the visual power of Ingres's portrait in this work, with its crisp execution and close observation, somehow suggestive of his sitter's character and inner life. According to a label on the back of the old mount, this is a portrait of Théodore Rousseau's grandfather. This suggestion, however interesting, does not seem tenable inasmuch as the sitter appears to be too young to be the grandfather of Rousseau. The great Barbizon painter was born in 1812, the son of a tailor. Although Rousseau's maternal grandfather, Guillaume-Etienne Colombet, a marble worker, was still alive in 1844, he was ninety-four years old. This man, whose quizzical countenance immediately engages the spectator's curiosity and sympathy, appears to be in his sixties or seventies, much closer to the age of Rousseau's father, who was born in 1787.

Provenance:
Abbé Constantin; sale, Paris, Hôtel Drouot, 6 April 1914, lot 16; André Desrouges (all according to back of old mount); M. R. Schweitzer, New York.

Bibliography:
Art Journal 1964–65, p. 187, repr. in advertisement of M. R. Schweitzer, New York (as M. Rousseau); Thaw III, p. 263, repr.

Exhibitions:
Thaw I, no. 78, repr.; Paris and New York 1993–94, no. 108, repr.

CDD

C. COROT.
octobre . 1844

127

Ferdinand-Victor-Eugène Delacroix

Charenton-Saint-Maurice
1798–1863 Paris

63
Royal Tiger

Pen and brown ink, and watercolor, over pencil. 7 × 10⁹⁄₁₆ inches (178 × 268 mm). Signed in pen and brown ink at lower right, *Eug Delacroix*.

A keen student of animal anatomy, Delacroix was a frequent visitor to the Paris Museum of Natural History, where he often was accompanied by the sculptor Barye. Tigers were especially fascinating to Delacroix. Alfred Robaut, who compiled the earliest catalogue raisonné of the artist's work, listed more than fifty renderings of tigers in various poses. This sleek watercolor of the powerful animal depicted in an open landscape is close to the artist's lithograph *Royal Tiger*, 1829 (Delteil 80; fig. 1) but closer still to *Crouching Royal Tiger*, the painting at Princeton (acc. no. 61-140; see Mras 1962, pp. 16–24).

A sheet of studies of a flayed tiger includes one small figure in a pose almost identical to that in the Thaw watercolor (repr. Moreau-Nélaton 1916, I, fig. 78). Although Delacroix was occupied with similar subjects over a period of many years, the restrained style of this work is compatible with that of his drawings of the late 1820s.

"Royal tiger" is not a scientific designation but a popular term; however, in this case it may refer to the animal's size. There is a similar watercolor depiction of a tiger in the Rosenwald Collection, National Gallery of Art, Washington, D.C. (inv. no. 1943.3.3375; repr. Frankfurt 1987–88, no. I 12, p. 200).

Provenance:
Private collection, New York.

Bibliography:
Johnson 1981–89, I, 1986, p. 12, under no. 176; Frankfurt 1987–88, under no. I 12, p. 200; Thaw III, p. 264, repr.

Exhibitions:
Thaw I, no. 79, repr.; New York 1984, no. 103, repr.; Paris and New York 1993–94, no. 110, repr. in color.

CDD

Fig. 1 Ferdinand-Victor-Eugène Delacroix. *Royal Tiger*. The Art Museum, Princeton University, x1970-120.

Ferdinand-Victor-Eugène Delacroix

Charenton-Saint-Maurice
1798–1863 Paris

64
Mephistopheles Appears Before Faust

Pen and brown ink, brown wash, over pencil. 8⅛ × 6½ inches (206 × 165 mm). Signed at lower margin, in pen and brown ink, *Eug. delacroix*.

The first part of Goethe's *Faust*, which appeared in 1808, was soon performed throughout Europe and became an inspiration for both composers and artists. In 1821, Delacroix was impressed by the outline etchings of Moritz von Retzsch, which were first published in 1816. Upon seeing a musical production of *Faust* in London in 1824, he decided to create his own illustrations of the text. Although these originally were planned for special publication as an album, when the series of seventeen lithographs was completed some three years later, they were published in a French edition of *Faust* (translated by Albert Stapfer and published by Charles Motte & Sautelet in Paris in 1828). By 1826, Delacroix's work was sufficiently advanced for Goethe to see some of the illustrations, to which he responded enthusiastically:

> Mr. Delacroix is a man of great talent, which in "Faust" has found its true nourishment. He will, I hope, go through all "Faust." We can see that he has a good knowledge of life, for which a city like Paris has given him the best opportunity. . . . I observed that these designs greatly conduce to the comprehension of the poem.

Delacroix based *Mephistopheles Appears Before Faust*, the fifth text illustration, on the composition by Von Retzsch. In both renderings, Faust appears at the left, seated at his desk in his study. While he is in the garb of a Renaissance scholar, which includes a flat cap and handsome cape, his opposite is outfitted in the latest fashion and wears a rakishly tilted cap. Although this drawing is similar to the artist's lithograph and painting (now in the Wallace Collection, London), it may actually precede both, for here the figures are in reverse of how they appear in the print and the painting, where Mephistopheles is at the left and Faust at the right. The earlier date for the present drawing is supported by the pencil sketch for the same subject, apparently an even earlier rendering, in which the figures also occupy the same positions as in the drawing (Houghton Library, Harvard University, inv. nr. FLH 424; see Frankfurt 1987–88, no. E 9). The psychological intensity conveyed by the Thaw drawing resulted from Delacroix's imaginative conception of the meeting of two such diametrically opposed and formidable personalities as Faust and Mephistopheles.

Provenance:
Art market, Paris; private collection, Paris; Jill Newhouse, Fall 1986, catalogue VII.

Bibliography:
Johnson 1981–89, VI, 1989, p. 194, fig. 77.

Exhibitions:
Frankfurt 1987–88, no. E8, repr.; New York 1991, no. 23, repr.; Thaw III, no. 70, repr.

CDD

Ferdinand-Victor-Eugène Delacroix

Charenton-Saint-Maurice
1798–1863 Paris

65

Forest View with an Oak Tree

Watercolor over black chalk.
12¼ × 8⅞ inches (310 × 225 mm).

As Maurice Sérullaz (1975) remarked, Delacroix paint-ed very few landscapes, not because he was indifferent to nature, but because he regarded landscape as back-ground for composition paintings and not as an end in itself. He did make a number of drawings in the forest of Sénart, near his country house in Champrosay, south of Paris, including a study of an oak tree, which is dated 10 May 1853 and is now in the collection of Mrs. Karen B. Cohen (repr. New York 1991, no. 67). This was dur-ing the period when the artist was busy working on the wall paintings of *Jacob Wrestling with the Angel* and *Heliodorus* in the Chapel of the Holy Angels at Saint Sulpice, Paris. The lower branch of a tree to the right of the central group in *Jacob Wrestling with the Angel* is gnarled in precisely the same manner as is the tree in the Thaw watercolor, which possibly was made around the same time. A rather small oil study, also depicting a forest scene (possibly in the forest of Sénart), in a pri-vate collection in Paris, may well be contemporaneous with the Thaw sheet (Johnson 1981–89, III, 1986, no. 482a, repr.).

A similar watercolor, *Landscape at Nohant*, formerly in the collection of the late John S. Thacher, is now in the National Gallery of Art, Washington, D.C. (*Master Drawings* 1978, repr. p. 94).

Provenance:
Delacroix atelier sale, 1864 (Lugt 838); A. Beurdeley (Lugt 421); 9th Beurdeley sale, Paris, Galerie Georges Petit, 1–2 December 1920, no. 121; Boutet; Roulier.

Exhibitions:
Paris 1990, n.p., repr. in color; New York 1991, no. 68, repr. in color; Thaw III, no. 72, repr. in color.

CDD

Honoré Daumier

Marseilles 1808–
1879 Valmondois

66

The Reading (La Lecture)

Black chalk, pen and black ink, gray wash. 9½ × 11⅞ inches (241 × 303 mm). Watermark: none visible through lining. Signed in pen and black ink at lower right, *h. Daumier*.

Daumier made at least a half-dozen drawings (Maison 1968, nos. 353–58) and several paintings of a man reading to one or two others (Maison 1968, nos. 1–99 and 101). All were straightforward, serious studies concentrating on the differences in pose and expression of reader and listener. The only finished composition among the drawings, the Thaw sheet is analogous in general configuration, and especially in lighting, to the painting in the Stedelijk Museum, Amsterdam (Maison 1968, no. 1-100), that Daumier recorded he sold on 18 March 1877 to M. Tabourier for 1,200 francs. Both the middle-aged reader and his older, probably somewhat deaf listener, leaning slightly forward to catch every word, are absorbed by the tale that is being unfolded— with some suspense, one would judge. Like the painting, such a finished drawing was no doubt made for sale.

Provenance:
Mme Hecht, Paris; Pontremoli; Trenel; Wildenstein and Co., New York; Norton Simon, Los Angeles.

Bibliography:
Klossowski 1923, no. 341; Maison 1956, p. 203, fig. 25; Maison 1968, I, p. 105, under no. 1-100, II, no. 358, pl. 111; Thaw III, p. 265, repr.

Exhibitions:
Paris 1901, no. 213; Paris 1934, no. 77; Los Angeles 1958, no. 200; Thaw I, no. 86, repr.; Paris and New York 1993–94, no. 114, repr.

CDD

135

Honoré Daumier

Marseilles 1808–
1879 Valmondois

67

The Schoolmaster and the Drowning Child

(L'Ecolier et le pedant)

Pen and brush, black ink and water-color, heightened with white, over black chalk. 11¹⁵⁄₁₆ × 9⁵⁄₁₆ inches (287 × 256 mm). Signed, at lower right, in pen and black ink, *h. Daumier.*

In 1855, at one of their regular Saturday evening gatherings at Théodore Rousseau's house in Barbizon, a group of artists and writers decided to produce a volume illustrating La Fontaine's fables. Each artist—Narcisse-Virgile Diaz de la Peña, Jules Dupré, Daumier, Jean-François Millet, Antoine Barye, Félix Ziem, and presumably Théodore Rousseau—was to contribute a certain number of subjects designated on that occasion. Daumier, who was "en verve rabelaisienne," was to illustrate *"Le Villageois et son seigneur," "Le Cygne et le cuisinier," "L'Ecolier et le pedant," "L'Astrologue (qui se laisse tomber dans un puits)," "Le Savatier et le financier," "L'Huître et les plaideurs,"* and *"L'Ivrogne et sa femme"* (Sensier 1872, p. 231).

The project was never realized, but according to Maison (1968, p. 137), Daumier executed six drawings for three different subjects, of which only two are finished watercolors: the present drawing and *Les Deux médecins et la mort* in the Reinhart Collection, Winterthur. Of the remaining four drawings, two are preparatory for *L'Ecolier et le pedant*. One of these, present location unknown (Laughton 1991, fig. 9.9), is clearly preparatory for this illustration. As Bruce Laughton noted, Daumier must have known the 1646 edition of the fables, which Fessard illustrated, because all the compositional elements are the same, including the placement of the figures: The pedant on the right looks down at the child, who has just fallen into the Seine and clings for dear life to the branch of a pollarded willow.

Provenance:
Mme Paul Meyer; Andrew Lawrence; Schweitzer; Lord Rayne; Hazlitt, Gooden & Fox, London.

Bibliography:
Klossowski 1923, no. 318b; Maison 1968, II, no. 398, pl. 133; Alfrey 1985, p. 555, fig. 62; Provost 1989, p. 23 (mentioned); Laughton 1991, pp. 144f., 207, repr. in color p. 146.

Exhibitions:
Paris 1901, no. 234; London 1985, no. 12, frontispiece in color, pl. 15; Paris and New York 1993–94, no. 115, repr.; Thaw III, no. 73, repr.

CDD

Honoré Daumier

Marseilles 1808–
1879 Valmondois

68

Two Lawyers Conversing

Black chalk and gouache in white and
gray, with some pale pink, yellow,
and brown watercolor. 8¼ × 10⅝
inches (209 × 270 mm). Signed in
pen and black ink, at lower right, *h.
Daumier.*

There is a considerable group of Daumier drawings
representing two, sometimes three or more, lawyers
engaged in various kinds of interchange, often seen
full-length but also half-length. Frequently, the lawyers
are contrasting physical types, as in the present drawing, where the bulky, bullnecked man leans over
to convey some bit of strategy or comment to his
thin colleague, whose saturnine countenance remains
enigmatic.

This important work was among the 147 drawings
and watercolors assembled by Daumier's friends for the
exhibition held on the artist's behalf at the Galerie
Durand-Ruel, Paris, in 1878, shortly before his death.
The exhibition was an artistic success but, unfortunate-
ly, a financial failure. When the drawing, which had
remained in the family of the lender, was sold in Paris
in 1973, it was accompanied by two letters by Daumier's friend Jules Clarétie relating to its loan to the 1878
exhibition.

It is usually maintained that the 1860s saw the peak
of Daumier's artistic powers, and it is to this period that
one would assume that this impeccably preserved drawing belongs. Yet it is in these late watercolors that Daumier was presenting themes he had explored earlier
within a journalistic context to a new and sophisticated
audience of connoisseurs (see Frankfurt and New York
1992–93, p. 175).

Provenance:
Jules Clarétie, Paris; sale, Paris, Palais Galliéra, 27 March
1973, no. 17.

Bibliography:
Not in Maison 1968.

Exhibitions:
Paris 1878, no. 195; Thaw I, no. 88, repr. in color; Frankfurt
and New York 1992–93, no. 89, repr.; Thaw III, no. 74, repr.

CDD

Jean-François Millet

Gruchy 1814–1875 Barbizon

69

The Potato Harvest

(La Récolte des pommes de terre)

Black chalk, stumped with some white. 9 × 13¾ inches (229 × 349 mm). Signed in black chalk at lower right, *J. F. Millet.*

Moreau-Nélaton placed this carefully composed and executed drawing around 1857, a period in which Millet was struggling desperately to support his family at Barbizon and often sent drawings of this kind off to such friends as Alfred Sensier and Théodore Rousseau in Paris, in hopes that their sale might bring him a few hundred francs to pay the grocer and baker. Sober in mood and style, these finished drawings depict scenes of simple peasant life and labor—a shepherd, men spading in a field, women washing at the edge of a stream, others cooking and tending their children. The Thaw drawing was probably that sold as lot 558 in the sale of Théodore Rousseau, which may mean that it was he who bought the drawing, not only to help Millet as he did on many occasions but also because he esteemed Millet's work. Among the almost five hundred Millet drawings in the Louvre is a vigorous sketch (RF 23591; Bacou 1975, no. 26, repr.) that must have been the raw material from which Millet developed this finished work; it is in the reverse direction of the Thaw sheet. Robert L. Herbert found a small, somewhat damaged painting in the Davis Museum and Cultural Center, Wellesley College, that appears to duplicate the composition almost exactly (fig. 1). There is, in the Louvre, another drawing of peasants digging potatoes (RF 5769; Bacou 1975, no. 62, repr.) and, in the Ashmolean Museum, Oxford, a small sketch of a peasant woman gathering potatoes, but these, like Millet's painting of peasants gathering their potato crop, now in the Walters Art Gallery, Baltimore, the picture he sent to the Universal Exhibition of 1867, are not related to the composition of the Thaw drawing.

Provenance:
Théodore Rousseau (?); probably his sale, Paris, Hôtel Drouot, 27 April–2 May 1868, no. 558 ("Une Moisson; paysans chargeant une charrette. Dessin rehaussé."); Alfred Sensier (?); probably his sale, Paris, Hôtel Drouot, 10–12 December 1877, no. 232 ("La Récolte des pommes de terre. Dessin au crayon noir. 22.0 × 34.0 cm"); Antoine Marmontel; his sale, Paris, Hôtel Drouot, 28–29 March 1898, no. 155 ("La Récolte des pommes de terre. Dans un champ, à la nuit tombante, un paysan et sa femme chargent des sacs de pommes de terre sur une champ, à la nuit tombante, un paysan et sa femme chargent des sacs de pommes de terre sur une brouette. Beau dessin. Signé en bas et à droite: J. F. Millet. 22.0 × 34.0 cm." Bought by Le Senne); Camille Le Senne; Blumenthal; Count Pecci-Blunt, Rome; Hazlitt Gallery, London.

Fig. 1 Jean-François Millet. *The Potato Gatherers*. Davis Museum and Cultural Center, Wellesley College, 1966.28.

Bibliography:
Moreau-Nélaton 1921, II, p. 37, fig. 114 ("vers 1857"); Bacou 1975, p. 206, under no. 26; Laughton 1991, p. 215 n. 17; Thaw III, p. 266, repr.

Exhibitions:
Paris 1887, no. 143 (lent by Marmontel); Thaw I, no. 89, repr.

CDD

141

Théodore Chassériau

Limon, near Ste.-Barbe-de-
Samana, Santo Domingo
1819–1856 Paris

70

Portrait of Mme Charles Damour

Pencil, with touches of white chalk in
the lace of the sleeves. 13^{15}⁄₁₆ × 10^{9}⁄₁₆
inches (355 × 268 mm). Inscribed,
signed, and dated at lower right, *A
mon ami- / Ch-D'Amour / Th^{re}-
Chasseriau/ 1852-.*

This portrait of the wife of Chassériau's friend Charles
Damour is as complete and fine an example of the finished Ingres-manner portrait drawing as can be found
in the artist's oeuvre. Although he died at the age of
thirty-seven, he left an extraordinarily large number of
drawings, many of which, thanks to the legacy of his
cousin, Baron Arthur Chassériau, are preserved in the
Louvre.

Chassériau's talent as a portraitist manifested itself
when he was still a youth. In the early 1830s, between
his eleventh and fifteenth years, he had already made
successful portraits of members of his family. He pos-
sessed above all the gift of being able to express something of the interior life of his sitters. In this rendering
one sees his manner of indicating the features of the
face: not in one smooth pencil line but in a series of
delicately curved, rather short strokes, always modeling, suggesting the softness and mobility of the countenance. A bit of chalk evokes the foamy white lace that
trims the sleeves of his subject's fashionable dress. Her
somewhat faraway gaze possibly conveys the reserve or
shyness associated with the experience of sitting for a
portrait.

By 1852, the date with which the artist inscribed this
work, he had been producing for some time his version
of the type of finished pencil portrait produced by his
teacher, J. A. D. Ingres. An artistic prodigy, Chassériau
had entered the master's studio when he was twelve
years old. Ingres considered him his best student and
always admired him. It has been said that Chassériau's
sensibilities and place as an artist put him somewhere
between Ingres and Delacroix. His biographer, J. L. Vau-
doyer, observed that his art marked "le passage de l'hél-
lenisme à l'exotisme dans l'art du XIXe siècle."

Charles Damour, like Chassériau, was also an artist.
Born in 1813, he entered the Ecole des Beaux-Arts and
became Ingres's pupil in 1831, about the same time as
the youthful Chassériau. After spending two years in
Rome and Sicily, he returned to France but was not
very successful as a portraitist and landscape painter
and eventually turned to printmaking. Not much else is
known about Charles Damour, not even the date of his
death. Chassériau drew the likeness of Damour when
both men were students in Ingres's atelier, between
1831 and 1834 (Prat 1988, repr.), and this early drawing
was sold in Monaco (sale, Sotheby's, Monaco, 8 December 1990, no. 313, repr.).

Provenance:
M. and Mme Charles Damour; Galerie Odermatt-Cazeau,
Paris; John & Paul Herring & Co., New York.

Bibliography:
Daulte 1987, p. 66, fig. 1; Prat 1988, no. 178, repr.

Exhibitions:
Paris 1987; Thaw III, no. 75, repr.

CDD

Hilaire-Germain-Edgar Degas

Paris 1834–1917 Paris

71
Sketchbook (Notebook 29)

21 drawings on 43 leaves. Chiefly pencil with touches of charcoal, a few leaves executed in blue chalk, on wove paper, mostly white, with some light brown, tan, and gray toward the back of the book. Leaves measuring approximately 9⅞ × 13⅜ inches (249 × 339 mm) in linen-clad boards measuring 10⅛ × 13½ inches (258 × 345 mm). Watermark: none. Inscribed by Halévy throughout, notably on first leaf in pen and black ink, *Tous les croquis de cet album / ont été faits chez moi par Degas. / Années 1880 et suivantes.*

Thirty-eight of the sketchbooks (or notebooks, as Reff calls them) of Edgar Degas have survived essentially intact. They cover the period between 1853 and 1886 and constitute the most significant sustained record of any impressionist artist. The full publication of these sketchbooks involved the comprehensive study of approximately 2,000 sketches (and 500 pages of notes) concerning the chronological order of their use, the subject of more than fourteen years of study by Theodore Reff. The majority of the notebooks are the twenty-nine in the Bibliothèque Nationale in Paris that were donated in 1920 by Degas's brother René shortly after the artist's death. Of the nine remaining, two were purchased by the Cabinet des Dessins of the Louvre in 1922, while another was acquired by The Metropolitan Museum of Art, New York, in 1973. An early sketchbook (notebook 8), which the artist used when he was in Italy in the late 1850s, entered the collection of The Pierpont Morgan Library in 1985 (1985.47; Purchase: The Board of Trustees of The Pierpont Morgan Library in honor of Mr. and Mrs. Eugene Victor Thaw). The other five are in private collections or on the art market.

The present book is one of two large sketchbooks bound in linen-clad covers that were in the possession of the playwright and librettist Ludovic Halévy (1834–1908) and his family until quite recently. Although most of the Degas notebooks are highly portable, it is obvious from their relatively large size that the Halévy notebooks were not meant to be carried about.

According to Mme Halévy's reminiscence, written in 1924, when these notebooks (Reff notebooks 28 and 29) were first exhibited (Paris 1924, no. 188), she and her husband had a few of their closest friends to dinner every Thursday evening. The group included Halévy's fellow playwright Henri Meilhac, the composer Ernest Reyer, Jules Lemaître, Anatole France, and Degas. These dinners were either in the Halévy's apartment in Paris on rue de Douai or at their summer residence at St. Germain-en-Laye. After dinner, Degas, who rarely participated in the conversation, often sketched on little scraps of paper. Halévy finally decided to buy the two albums for his friend's use on these occasions, later inscribed many of the leaves, and, at the beginning of this volume, noted that all of the sketches were made in his home by Degas in 1880 and the following years. It was also Mme Halévy's recollection that while the first album (notebook 28) was begun in 1877, the second was started, but never completely used up because of Degas's steadily failing eyesight, at St. Germain-en-

Laye in 1880. This account is confirmed by her son, Daniel Halévy, in his preface to the facsimile of both notebooks in 1949. He remarks that after 1881 or 1882 Degas never drew in the evening because of his eyesight. The date assigned by the Halévy family to the Thaw sketchbook is supported by Ronald Pickvance.

Writing in 1983 after the publication of Reff's monumental catalogue, Pickvance differs with him as to the chronology of the sketchbook. Reff dated the book between 1877 and 1880, based on the evidence of what he plausibly took to be preparatory sketches for some of the key works that engaged Degas during those years, such as *Les Deux danseuses* (Lemoisne 599), painted ca. 1878–80; *Miss Lala at the Cirque Fernando* (Lemoisne 522), now in London, on which Degas was working between January and April of 1879; as well as *Scènes de ballet* (Lemoisne 610), of ca. 1880. He reasoned that since one page illustrates the scene in which a model poses as a laundress for an artist in *La Cigale*, Halévy and Meilhac's play, which was first produced on 6 October 1877, the book must also date from that time.

Pickvance, on the other hand, feels that the book must postdate July 1879, when the first of what were to become weekly dinners took place at the Pavillon Henri IV; an identified view of the restaurant is on the first drawn leaf in notebook 29. He argues that the evidence put forth by Reff for an earlier dating is not so much a record of works in progress as a recollection of these paintings that may have been elicited by the artist's friends during the course of their after-dinner conversations. Looked at this way, the leaf with the sketch of Miss Lala, for instance, with the detail of the metal bit, which she held onto with her teeth, might be regarded as the answer to a question from one of Degas's friends as to how she had managed such a feat of strength. The book also includes a number of sketches, often satirical, of friends and acquaintances, many of whom are identified in Ludovic Halévy's inscriptions.

Among the satiric drawings, one of an Oriental lounging in a seragliolike setting is of William Busnach, a man who always claimed to be of Arabian origin. Pickvance goes further than Reff in identifying the café-concert singer, whose slim figure appears a number of times in the book, as Mlle Emélie Bécat, the subject of No. 73. If the book can be said to have a theme, Pickvance feels it is self-indulgence and pleasure, that it essentially represents "an all-male view of the world, with its broad robust humor and mocking in-jokes." That Degas executed these works for the benefit of his male companions is further corroborated by the open-

fol. 2

145

ing, which depicts a prostitute and her pimp, inscribed *une grue* (a French slang expression for a woman of easy virtue) at the upper left.

Provenance:
Ludovic Halévy, Paris; by descent to Daniel Halévy, Paris.

Bibliography:
Halévy 1949, published in facsimile with another sketchbook (nb. 28) with the same provenance; Reff 1976, I, pp. 2f., 10f., 17, 30, 31, 131 ff., II, repr., n.p., under nb. 29; Reff 1985, I, pp. 2, 11 n. 10, 12 n. 9, 16, 28 n. 1, 30 ns. 3 and 5, 131–33, II, repr., n.p., under nb. 29; Thaw III, pp. 267–68, repr.

Exhibitions:
Paris 1924, no. 188 (with nb. 28), not repr.; London 1983, no. 21 (lent by Mr. and Mrs. Thaw), six leaves repr.; Thaw II, no. 45, repr.; Thaw III, not in catalogue.

CDD

fol. 4

147

fol. 13

148

fol. 14

149

Hilaire-Germain-Edgar Degas

Paris 1834–1917 Paris

72
Seated Dancer

Essence over pencil, on pink paper.
10¹⁵⁄₁₆ × 8¹¹⁄₁₆ inches (279 × 222 mm).
Watermark: none.

This remarkable drawing, which is dated to 1872, is one of the artist's studies for *Dance Class at the Opera*, now in the Musée d'Orsay, Paris. Both this drawing and a companion sheet in the collection of Thomas Gibson, London, are studies for the figures in the foreground of that painting. Both are executed in essence on vivid pink paper, the medium emphasizing the three-dimensionality of the figures. The dancer's face, hands, and legs are shaded by bluish gray tones; Degas used the pink paper to suggest her exposed upper back and shoulders. She is seen at a slightly different angle in the painting.

The standing dancer studied in the Gibson sheet (see Paris and elsewhere 1988–89, no. 108, repr.) is identified by Degas's inscription on the sheet, *93 rue de Bac / d'Hugues*, which gives her name and address. The identity of the dancer represented in the Thaw sheet is not known. She resembles one Joséphine Gaujelin, whose name appears in an inscription written in Degas's hand on a drawing now in The Boijmans Van Beuningen Museum, Rotterdam (Browse 1949, no. 12, repr.). If she is Mme Gaujelin, her features may be studied in Degas's portrait of her, painted in 1867 and now in the Isabella Stewart Gardner Museum, Boston (Hendy 1974, p. 74, repr. p. 75). The young woman is certainly a familiar type in Degas's drawings of dancers. Perhaps the same dancer is depicted standing at the barre in the drawing that was in the collection of Mme Roger Nathan, Paris (sale, London, Sotheby's, 30 March 1977, no. 112, repr. in color). Here, too, the artist used essence and the pink paper.

Other drawings for *Dance Class at the Opera* include one of M. Mérante conducting the class (Louvre; repr. Browse 1949, no. 16) and a study of dancers at the barre, in Rotterdam (repr. Browse 1949, no. 16a).

Provenance:
Atelier Degas, Vente Degas II, 11 December 1918, no. 231b, repr.; René de Gas, Paris, sale, 10 November 1927, no. 23b, repr.; Rodier; Galerie Georges Petit, Paris; Wildenstein and Co., New York; John Nicholas Brown, Providence; deposited with Joslyn Art Museum, Omaha, 1941–46; heirs of John Nicholas Brown to 1986; David Tunick, New York.

Bibliography:
Rouart 1945, p. 71 n. 28; Lemoisne 1946, I, p. 150, no. 299, repr., p. 151, fig. 299; Browse 1949, pp. 53, 340, no. 15, repr.; Pickvance 1963, p. 258 n. 24; Russoli and Minervino 1970, no. 295, repr.

Exhibitions:
Cambridge 1929, no. 22; Providence 1931, no. 22 (of drawings); Philadelphia 1936, no. 74, repr.; Rotterdam and elsewhere 1958–59, no. 164, repr.; Cambridge 1962, no. 8, repr.; Boston 1974, no. 76, repr.; San José 1981, no. 59, repr.; Tübingen and Berlin 1984, no. 83, repr. in color; Paris and elsewhere 1988–89, p. 178, no. 109, repr. in color; Thaw III, no. 77, repr. and on cover (in color).

CDD

Hilaire-Germain-Edgar Degas

Paris 1834–1917 Paris

73
Mlle Bécat at the Café des Ambassadeurs

Pastel over lithograph. 9 1/16 × 7 7/8 inches (230 × 200 mm). Signed and dated at lower right, in pastel, *Degas / 85*. Watermark: none.

Whereas Degas is recognized as one of the greatest printmakers of the nineteenth century, the artist himself regarded the process essentially as a private means to explore new techniques and create a variety of images. Since most of his prints were never published, few besides his friends and fellow artists knew this aspect of his art.

In 1885 Degas took his lithograph of about 1877 and enlarged it by adding two strips of paper to the side and lower edge. He then worked up the image in pastel and added the three women spectators and the framing column at the right. This effectively changed the perspective of the original print, moving Mlle Bécat's figure from the immediate foreground to the middle of the composition. Although Degas manipulated the tonal values of black and white in the lithograph, here he added color to striking effect, especially in the contrasting hues of the same colors that indicate the effect of different kinds of light. The performer is illuminated by pink gaslight, a pale but warm color that is repeated in her gown. A bright, fresh green is used for the wooden framing elements as well as the bits of foliage in the background, while clear pinks and blues light up the fireworks in the summer night. In marked contrast to the vivid theatrical light and the fireworks, the three female spectators are cast in shadow, illuminated only by an unflattering half-light that gives their faces a blue tinge. For these figures, the artist chose a muted palette of blue-greens, purples, and ochres, using color in a way that suggests the difference between the mundane and the magical world of the theater.

In 1891 Lucien Pissarro, then living in London, wrote his father about a paper on impressionism he had delivered at an artists' club: "after the meeting . . . Sickert—a young man who knows Degas—asked me to lunch. I went to his place; he has Degas's little lithograph finished in pastel that we saw at Clauzet's" (Meadmore 1963, p. 60). Sickert apparently gave the print to his wife's sister, Mrs. Fisher Unwin, who lent it to the first exhibition of the International Society of Sculptors, Painters and Gravers, held in London in 1898.

Degas frequented the theater, the ballet, and these informal open-air concerts at the Café des Ambassadeurs in the Champs-Elysées, where Mlle Emélie Bécat was the star. She was the subject of three other lithographs by Degas, as well as a number of other works (Boston and elsewhere 1984–85, nos. 26, 30, 31). There are numerous sketches of her in his notebooks, including several in the Thaw sketchbook (No. 71).

Provenance:
Clauzet, Paris; Mr. and Mrs. Walter Sickert (by May 1891); Mrs. Fisher Unwin (Sickert's sister-in-law; by 1898); Mrs. Cobden Sickert (by 1908); M. Knoedler & Co., Inc., New York; Mrs. Ralph King, Cleveland (by 1947); Mr. and Mrs. Robert K. Schafer, Mentor, Ohio (until 1982); David Tunick, Inc., New York.

Bibliography:
Rewald 1950, p. 239; Wilson 1983, p. 713, fig. 64; Brame and Reff 1984, no. 121, repr.

Exhibitions:
London 1898, no. 119 (as *Café Chantant*); London 1908, no. 87; Cleveland 1947, no. 44 (as *At the Music Hall*); London 1983, no. 26, repr. in color; Boston and elsewhere 1984–85, no. 31b (exhibited in Boston only), repr. in color; Thaw II, no. 46, repr. in color; Paris and elsewhere 1988–89, no. 264, repr. in color; Thaw III, no. 78, repr.

CDD

Hilaire-Germain-Edgar Degas

Paris 1834–1917 Paris

74
At the Theater: The Duet

Pastel over monotype printed in black ink. Plate: 4¹¹⁄₁₆ × 6⅜ inches (118 × 161 mm); on sheet, irregularly trimmed at lower right, 5⁵⁄₁₆ × 7¹⁄₁₆ inches (136 × 179 mm). Signed at left, in black chalk, *Degas*.

Usually, at least two impressions can be taken from the monotype process, which, by definition, is limited. The artist draws by brush, finger, or rag onto a glass or metal plate, then applies a dampened piece of paper to the plate and runs the two together through a press. Since so much of the ink comes off in the initial printing process, only enough for one more impression may be left. *At the Theater: The Duet* is known in only one version.

In this work the star performer, Mlle Bécat, appears with another of Degas's favorite performers, Thérésa (Emma Valadon). Thérésa, who was famous for the *Song of the Dog*, is easily identified by the pawlike pose of her hands. (Mlle Bécat is also the subject of No. 73.)

Degas began by drawing on the plate in black ink. After printing, he reworked the impression with pastel in vivid shades of pink and red, especially noticeable in the costume of Mlle Bécat, who wears a pink dress with a bodice checkered with fine black and red pastel lines that suggest a plaid. The red is echoed in the bright red ribbons of her black hat and is picked up in turn in the curtain and loges in the hall. Thérésa, her face garishly illuminated by the footlights, is dressed in a light greenish blue garment. A third chanteuse may be indicated by a gloved hand at the right margin, or it may only be another black ribbon on Thérésa's dress.

Provenance:
John Lewis Brown, Paris; sale, Paris, Hôtel Drouot, 22 May 1919, lot 41, repr.; purchased by Durand-Ruel, Paris and New York; M. Knoedler and Co., Inc., New York; purchased by Robert von Hirsch in 1919, no. 606 in his collection, according to old label on back of frame, sale, London, Sotheby's, 26–27 June 1978, no. 825, repr.; private collection, United States.

Bibliography:
Lemoisne 1946, II, no. 433, repr.; Cooper 1952, pp. 12, 14, 19, no. 9, repr.; Shinoda 1957, p. 80 f., no. 71, repr.; Russoli and Minervino 1970, no. 418, repr.; Adhémar and Cachin 1973, p. 63; Terrasse 1981, no. 275; Wilson 1983, p. 713; Sutton 1986, p. 225, no. 212.

Exhibitions:
Basel 1943, no. 218; Cambridge 1968, p. 72 n. 8, p. 76 n. 24, no. 227, repr.; London 1983, no. 15, repr.; Tübingen and Berlin 1984, no. 124; London 1985a, no. 15, fig. near no. 21; Thaw III, no. 79, repr.

CDD

Hilaire-Germain-Edgar Degas

Paris 1834–1917 Paris

75
Group of Four Jockeys

Pencil with some stumping, on tracing paper faded and mounted. 17¹¹⁄₁₆ × 16⅜ inches (449 × 416 mm).

Degas executed many studies of loosely grouped horses and jockeys from which he might use single figures or groups in later compositions. The studies are fascinating for the strong characterization of both men and animals as well as for the way in which they convey the tension and frequent conflicts in the paddock before a race. The present drawing, with its play of intersecting lines of movement, has strong similarities to the painting *Jockeys Before the Race* (Lemoisne 1946, II, no. 649, repr.).

As at the ballet, Degas was a frequent spectator at the races, and it might be said that his treatment of horses was generally more sympathetic than that of dancers. Paul Valéry says of Degas's remarkable perception of horses:

> Le cheval marche sur les pointes. Quatre ongles le portent. Nul animal ne tient de la première danseuse, de l'étoile du corps de ballet, comme un pur-sang en parfait équilibre, que la main de celui qui le monte semble tenir suspendu, et qui s'avance au petit pas en plein soleil. Degas l'a peint d'un vers: il dit de lui: 'Tout nerveusement nu dans sa robe de soie' dans un sonnet fort bien fait où il s'est diverti et évertué à concentrer tous les aspects et fonctions du cheval de course: entraînement, vitesse, paris et fraudes, beauté, élégance suprême (Valéry 1938, pp. 69–70).

Provenance:
Fourth Degas atelier sale (Lugt 657–58), Paris, Galerie Georges Petit, 2–4 July 1919, III, p. 154, lot 178a, repr.; Lord Howard de Walden, London; sale, Sotheby's, London, 22 April 1971, lot 26.

Bibliography:
Thompson 1979, p. 674, fig. 92; Thaw III, p. 267, repr.

Exhibitions:
Thaw I, no. 96, repr.; Edinburgh 1979, no. 9 and under nos. 2, 8, 10, repr.; Tübingen and Berlin 1984, p. 47, no. 63, fig. 63; Paris and New York 1993–94, no. 120, repr.; Thaw III, not in catalogue.

CDD

157

Ignace-Henri-Jean-Théodore Fantin-Latour

Grenoble 1836–1904 Bure

76

Portrait of (Jean-Nicolas) Arthur Rimbaud (1854–1891), 1872

Brown and gray wash, with white bodycolor mixed with the wash in some places and used as heightening in others, on light brown paper, lined with a heavier paper or board. Full sheet: 7 1/16 × 5 5/8 inches (177 × 143 mm); reduced by artist with framing line to 5 3/8 × 4 5/8 inches (138 × 151 mm). Signed at upper left in pen and black ink, *Fantin. 72*; also below framed area and partially effaced by wash at lower right, *F. Latour/F. Latour*.

In 1872 Fantin-Latour exhibited his now famous painting, *Coin de table*, at the Salon. This work was a continuation of the series Fantin had begun in 1864 with *Hommage à Delacroix*; both are now at the Musée d'Orsay, Paris. Before executing *Coin de table*, Fantin had conceived and carried out a number of preparations for yet another painting—*Le Repas*, or *Le Toast*—a sort of allegorical work depicting painters he admired. The artist, however, was dissatisfied with the finished work and destroyed it. *Coin de table* also may be considered an homage since Fantin assembled a number of writers he admired, including Verlaine and Rimbaud, in this group portrait. Fantin's original conception of this work was as an homage to Baudelaire, who died in 1867. There are numerous sketches in which a portrait of Baudelaire is prominent at the center of the work, but it seems that eventually Fantin's focus shifted: Both Verlaine and Rimbaud, seated together, are isolated from the rest of the group. It is rather fascinating that Rimbaud occupies about the same place that Fantin (who depicted himself) does in *Hommage à Delacroix*, since they occupy approximately the same position in the paintings. In *Coin de table* Rimbaud gazes dreamily into the middle distance, his right elbow leaning on the edge of the table, his face cupped in his right hand, while in *Hommage à Delacroix* Fantin is conspicuous as the only member of the group not properly attired— he appears in his shirtsleeves holding a palette. Both Fantin and Rimbaud are bathed in a misty half-light as if to convey the isolation of young, creative people from their elders. While Fantin was twenty-seven or twenty-eight in 1864, Rimbaud would have been only seventeen in 1872. Verlaine wrote (on the corrected galleys of his *Hommes d'Aujourd'hui*, devoted to Rimbaud) of Fantin-Latour's depiction that Rimbaud had "Une sorte de douceur luisant et souriant dans ces cruels yeux bleu clairs et sur cette forte bouche rouge au pli amer; mysticisme et sensualité, et quels!" When Verlaine read Rimbaud's *Illuminations* in 1871, he invited the youthful poet to come to Paris; it is well known that the two quickly entered into a passionate relationship. The present drawing is dated 1872, the same year as the painting depicting Rimbaud in an identical pose. The close connection between the painting and drawing makes it highly likely that Fantin executed this sensitive portrait after Rimbaud's painted image, a hypothesis put forth by the authors of the Paris 1991 exhibition catalogue. Reduced on all four sides, the image probably was made for a book illustration, as the presence of brown and gray wash—a combination often used at the time in preparatory designs

for prints—suggests. However, the earliest known publication of the image was in Paterne Berrichon's 1897 edition of *Œuvres de Rimbaud*.

Provenance:
Louis Barthou; Léon Barthou; by whom presented to Georges Duhamel in 1936 (according to old autograph inscription in pen and black ink on label in back of frame, *A Georges Duhamel, qui a dit/de Rimbaud: "exception héroique/et inquietante" le portrait que/lui offre un admirateur et/ami/Léon Barthou/19 déc. 1936.*); M. Viardot; Alain Clairet, Paris.

Bibliography:
Carré 1939; *Labyrinthe* 1945, no. 2 (according to Ruchau 1946, q.v.); Ruchau 1946, no. XII (as in Georges Duhamel collection), pl. XII; Rimbaud 1955, repr. on cover.

Exhibition:
Paris 1991, no. 35, repr. in color.

CDD

Paul Cézanne

Aix-en-Provence 1839–
1906 Aix-en-Provence

77
Sketchbook

73 drawings on 48 leaves, rebound in
linen-clad boards (while it was in the
Block collection). Pencil, with watercolor on one leaf only, on wove paper,
four sheets of blue interleaved.
Leaves measuring approximately
4¹⁵⁄₁₆ × 8½ inches (126 × 216 mm), in
binding measuring 5⁵⁄₁₆ × 8⅝ inches
(134 × 221 mm). Watermark: MONT-
GOLFIER S A.

As compared with Degas, Cézanne drew relatively little. Chappuis lists eighteen sketchbooks in his catalogue
raisonné, many of which are represented only fragmen-
tarily (Chappuis 1973, p. 20 ff.). Five sketchbooks,
including the one now in the Thaw Collection,
remained in the possession of the artist's son until the
1930s, at which time they were sold as a group,
through the Parisian dealer Maurice Renou, to a collector in Lyons. In 1950 all five of these books were
acquired by Sam Salz, a dealer in New York, who presented one to the Louvre and sold the others to American collections, including one to the Art Institute of
Chicago and two to Mr. and Mrs. Ira S. Haupt of New
York. The Thaw sketchbook was sold at that time to Mr.
and Mrs. Leigh Block of Chicago. In 1987 Walter and
Leonore Annenberg gave the two sketchbooks that they
had acquired previously from the Haupt collection to
the Philadelphia Museum of Art. The entire group was
published by John Rewald in 1951.

It is generally acknowledged by scholars that the
sketchbooks were executed between 1870 and 1885 and
date to a period when Cézanne was most concerned
with drawing. Like many of his impressionist contemporaries, Cézanne was primarily a colorist and did not
need to draw in the usual sense to realize his artistic
conceptions, which he visualized in terms of color, light,
and volume. Nevertheless, at a stage of his development
dating from around 1870, he wanted to further explore
light and the representation of space in terms of black
and white, rather than color, and concentrated on drawing in an attempt to sort out the relationship between
the structural qualities of line and the naturalistic prop-
erties of color. While in the early sketchbooks his notations are sometimes awkward, gradually he developed
into an assured draughtsman. Eventually—having
worked out his problems in the process of drawing—he
all but abandoned pencil drawing and continued in col-
or alone.

The sketchbooks, which should be regarded essentially as technical exercises, contain a variety of images
not usually connected with works in progress. In several Cézanne made copies of the works of earlier masters,
such as his studies after Rubens and Delacroix, which
appear in the earliest book (now in Philadelphia), or of
sculpture in the Louvre (now in the Cabinet des
Dessins).

Most Cézanne authorities agree that the artist used
the Thaw sketchbook between 1875 and 1885. It offers
an especially broad range of subject matter, including
sketches of the Provençal landscape, and concentrated
drawings of an assortment of items, often domestic in

origin and occasionally extraordinary, such as the suit
of armor (probably seen at Emile Zola's house). Most
often, however, it is the back of a chair, a vase of flowers, or a mantel clock that is studied. Cézanne put so
much energy into these works that they almost may be
considered small still lifes in their own right.

The book also contains a number of informal portrait studies, including one of Camille Pissarro at work
before his easel, two of Zola, a self-portrait, several
studies of Cézanne's wife, and one of a sleeping child,
possibly their son, on one of the blue leaves. It is
believed that, besides the suit of armor, Cézanne
sketched a number of other items in Zola's house. An
early sketch for *The Bathers* (which Rewald dates to
1875) is of particular interest for the study of the
work's development. Occasionally, the juxtaposition of
images on a leaf can be startling. This is the case in several instances where one or more portrait sketches
appear on a page or a head is drawn on a page otherwise occupied by a piece of furniture, atop which sits a
vase.

Although most of Cézanne's essays in pure
draughtsmanship are confined to the relatively small
size of sketchbook leaves, there are a few large-scale
pencil drawings, notably *The Card Player*, which Mr.
and Mrs. Thaw presented to the Morgan Library in
1975 (No. 78). Usually, however, "once the artist began
to draw on a good-sized piece of paper, he seems to
have felt the urge to animate these lines with touches
of color" (Rewald 1983, p. 20).

Provenance:
The artist's son, Paul Cézanne, Paris; Maurice Renou, Paris;
Poyet collection, Lyons; Maurice Renou, Paris; Sam Salz, New
York; Mr. and Mrs. Leigh Block, Chicago.

Bibliography:
Rewald 1951, for general discussion of all five, repr.; Berthold
1958, no. 333 (f. 13), repr.; Chappuis 1973, pp. 9f., 16, 20f., 22
(no. 16), nos. 550, 551; Rewald 1982, discussion of the Thaw
sketchbook and facsimile; Thaw III, p. 269, repr.

Exhibitions:
Thaw II, no. 47, repr.; Thaw III, not in catalogue; Paris and
elsewhere 1995–96, "Les Carnets," pp. 516–17, figs. 1, 2, 4, 5,
pp. 520–21, repr. (notebook pp. XII, XIII), figs. 1, 2 (exhibited
in Philadelphia only).

CDD

fol. 11 verso

fol. 12

fol.13 verso

fol. 15

Paul Cézanne

Aix-en-Provence 1839–
1906 Aix-en-Provence

78
The Card Player

Pencil. 21¾ × 17⅛ inches (552 × 430 mm).

This powerful drawing is one of Cézanne's figure stud-ies for *Card Players*, of which five versions are known, dating from 1890 onward. While it is closest to the fig-ures at the right of the Musée d'Orsay and Courtauld paintings, it is not specifically a study for either. A drawing of the same model's head, wearing the familiar soft crushed hat and smoking a cigarette, is in The Boij-mans Van Beuningen Museum, Rotterdam (inv. F II 225; see Chappuis 1973, no. 1094). In Chappuis's opin-ion the Morgan Library's drawing could be one of the earliest in the series of figure studies. The sheet, one of the largest of Cézanne's drawings, gives an impression of great solidity, which the artist built up with a series of light strokes, repeatedly going over the contours. The figure verges to the right of the sheet, but this effect is counterbalanced by the lightly indicated table and the power of the player's concentrated gaze. It is fairly cer-tain that Cézanne's model was Alexandre Paulin, a gar-dener who posed for him at his country house in 1891.

Provenance:
Ambroise Vollard, Paris; F. Matthiesen, London; Paul Rosen-berg and Co., New York; M. Knoedler & Co., New York; Dr. and Mrs. T. Edward Hanley, Bradford, Pennsylvania; E. V. Thaw and Co., New York; Norton Simon Foundation, Los Angeles.

Bibliography:
Vollard 1924, p. 72, repr.; Badt 1956, p. 61, fig. 15; Moskowitz and Sérullaz 1962, p. 101, repr.; Andersen 1970, no. 250 (as 1890–92), repr.; Chappuis 1973, I, p. 250, no. 1093 (as 1892–96), II, repr.; Sutton 1974, p. 99; Morgan Library, *Fel-lows Reports*, XVIII, 1978, p. 257; Badt 1985, p. 120, fig. 15; Thaw III, p. 268, repr.

Exhibitions:
Philadelphia 1957 (unnumbered checklist); Buffalo 1960, no. 55; New York 1961, no. 43; Ann Arbor 1962, no. 31, pl. XIVc; New York and Philadelphia 1967, p. 61, repr.; Midland and Columbus 1967–68, no. 51; Newcastle-upon-Tyne and Lon-don 1973, p. 164, no. 67, repr.; Tokyo and elsewhere 1974, no. 125; New York 1974, p. 56; Thaw I, no. 98, repr.; Tübingen 1978, no. 62, repr.; Paris and New York 1993–94, no. 121, repr.; Thaw III, not in catalogue; Paris and elsewhere 1995–96, no. 135, repr. in color (exhibited in Philadelphia only).

Thaw Collection, The Pierpont Morgan Library, acc. no. 1975.39

CDD

Paul Cézanne

Aix-en-Provence 1839–
1906 Aix-en-Provence

79
Trees

Watercolor over pencil. 18¾ × 12⁵⁄₁₆
inches (476 × 313 mm).

Cézanne's elaborate pattern of brushstrokes breaks this stand of trees into a kaleidoscopic scene of color. Each stroke retains its chromatic autonomy—one sees blue, green, yellow, orange—even as it interacts with the others in the dominant blue tonality. It is this breaking down of form, the elements to be reworked into a pattern, that to some critics suggests parallels with cubism in Cézanne's work after about 1900. But his depiction of the scheme of volume and voids is perhaps not so much an intellectual translation of nature as a recording of the natural optical effect of light in moving foliage, rendered with a brilliantly authoritative watercolor technique. Theodore Reff notes that this compact arrangement, with the wedge of foliage hanging above the small ravine, is unique among Cézanne's hundreds of tree-and-foliage studies (Reff 1960, p. 118).

Provenance:
Paul Vallotton, Lausanne; private collection, Switzerland; Wildenstein and Co., New York; Lazarus Phillips, Montreal; Georges Bernier, New York.

Bibliography:
Reff 1960, p. 118, fig. 27; Elderfield 1971, p. 56, repr.; Rewald 1983, no. 538, repr.; Thaw III, p. 268, repr.

Exhibitions:
Neufchâtel 1956; New York 1959b, no. 76, repr.; New York 1963, no. 62, pl. LVIII, repr.; Washington and elsewhere 1971, no. 55, repr.; Tokyo and elsewhere 1974, no. 80; Thaw I, no. 99, repr.; New York and Houston 1977–78, pl. 101; Paris and New York 1993–94, no. 122, repr. in color; Thaw III, not in catalogue; Paris and elsewhere 1995–96, no. 194, repr. in color (exhibited in Philadelphia only).

CDD

Paul Cézanne

Aix-en-Provence 1839–
1906 Aix-en-Provence

80

*The Terrace of the
Garden at Les Lauves*

Watercolor over pencil, on white
wove paper. 17 × 21 1/16 inches (432 ×
534 mm). Watermark: none. Numbered in blue pencil on verso at upper
right, *39*. Mostly effaced inscription
in French in pencil at lower left of
verso, directions for a frame, *gros
cadre feuille / [C]arte [gris] ou bleu.*

In some respects Cézanne's watercolors develop in a
way that is parallel to his pencil drawings. The earlier
watercolors rely more heavily on clear outlines and recognizable forms than do the later ones. In the artist's
more mature works, the contours tend to disappear and
modeling and the concretion of form are accomplished
in the layering of color.

It is clear that Cézanne found in watercolor an
expressive medium that filled a different set of aesthetic
needs than did oil. The oil paintings are massive in
effect, whereas the watercolors are light and vibrant. In
watercolor the artist could apply successive layers of
color, allowing each to dry before painting the next.
Since each layer was diluted so extensively that it left
only a sheer tint, it created a "splendid variety of
nuances" that is "accompanied by a delicate contrast of
textures" (Rewald 1983, p. 31). There is, moreover, an
almost wistful, poetic quality to the watercolors, which,
as Meyer Schapiro has observed, "permits us to dwell
on the intimacy of Cézanne's sensing of a pictorial apt-
ness in things; we experience . . . his attentiveness, his
fine hesitations and scruples, his delicacy of touch . . ."
(New York 1963, p. 12).

Although it is often difficult to fix precisely the
chronology of Cézanne's watercolors, Rewald dates this
work to the four-year period between 1902 and
Cézanne's death in 1906. The mood is especially poetic
and the artist's use of pale color suggests that he painted it in the spring when greens are at their freshest.
The predominant greens and blues are complemented
by the pale washes of rose madder and ochre used to
depict the flowerpots and the play of sunlight on the
stone terrace. Although Cézanne had a remarkable view
from his terrace of the range of mountains known as
the Châine de l'Etoile—rendered here in summary
fashion with a curving blue line—he gave his full
attention to the terrace itself (Rewald 1983, no. 621).

Provenance:
Ambroise Vollard, Paris; Georges Bernheim, Paris; Knoedler
Galleries, Paris and New York; Mrs. Thalia Malcolm; Knoedler
Galleries, New York; Sam Salz, New York; Erich Maria
Remarque, Ascona; Feilchenfeldt, Zurich.

Bibliography:
Venturi 1936, no. 1072; Jewell 1944, p. 21, repr.; Rewald 1983,
no. 621, repr. in color, pl. 36; Thaw III, p. 269, repr.

Exhibitions:
Columbus 1939–40, no. 14; New York 1943a, no. 33; New
York 1947, no. 86; Chicago and New York 1952, no. 103, repr.;
The Hague 1956, no. 89, repr.; Zurich 1956, no. 142, repr.;
Munich 1956a, no. 110, repr.; Rotterdam 1958, no. 155, pl.
159; Paris 1958–59, no. 155, pl. 172; New York 1959, no. 153,
pl. 170; New York 1963, no. 63, repr. pl. LXI; New York and
Houston 1977–78, no. 108, pl. 104; Paris 1978, no. 74, repr.;
Thaw II, no. 48, repr. in color; Paris and elsewhere 1995–96,
no. 207, repr. in color (exhibited in Paris only).

CDD

169

Paul Cézanne

Aix-en-Provence 1839–
1906 Aix-en-Provence

81

Still Life with Pears and Apples, Covered Blue Jar, and a Bottle of Wine

Watercolor over black chalk. Verso: landscape sketch with Mont Sainte-Victoire and trees in black chalk with touches of watercolor. 18¾ × 24¹⁵⁄₁₆ inches (476 × 617 mm). Paper embossed: MONTGOLFIER S.A. Numbered on verso, in black chalk, *69.* and *1984.*

It was often remarked by those who knew him that Cézanne cared little for his watercolors. Yet, he spent a good deal of time working in the medium, and at least 651 of his watercolors have been documented (Rewald 1983, p. 10). During his lifetime, they were admired and collected by a significant minority that included such artists as Degas and Renoir. While a few were exhibited in Cézanne's first retrospective at Vollard's newly opened gallery in 1895, the full range of water-colors produced over decades was finally exhibited, again by Vollard, in the spring of 1905, by which time Cézanne's reputation among artists had grown signifi-cantly. Nevertheless, it was not until 1907—the year following Cézanne's death—when Bernheim-Jeune held a large memorial exhibition devoted solely to the artist's watercolors that they began to attract their wide audience. They had an immediate effect on the cubists, who admired them for their abstract volumetric quali-ties. One of the most prominent figures in the move-ment, Delaunay, declared: "The watercolors of Cézanne announce cubism . . . the colored or rather luminous planes destroy the object" (New York 1963, p. 15).

The rudimentary sketch of a mountain and tree indicate that a Mont Sainte-Victoire landscape had been Cézanne's first plan for this sheet. For whatever rea-sons, he abandoned it and used the other side for this remarkable still life, a perfect example of Cézanne's later watercolor manner, which John Rewald has characterized as "bold and large, superbly fluent and self-assured" (Rewald 1983, p. 37). The subject matter, as well as the close viewpoint and strong color values and the handling of the brushwork, suggested to Rewald a date of about 1902–6. Cézanne chose an unusual starting point for this work, beginning almost one third up the page. While a faint chalk sketch is visi-ble, the artist has addressed the white paper directly with his brush, using patterns of bright color to mold forms that are almost abstract and retracing many of the contours with a broken blue brushline.

Here his palette is dominated by bright, cool blues and reds. Gold and pink tones model the pears at the left, and the apples are indicated in yellow and green. The process of ripening is suggested by the faint bluish-pink apparent in some of the apples. The blue jar or pot at the left is similar to the blue enamel coffeepot that appears in a number of Cézanne's watercolors (Rewald 1983, nos. 554, 571, 572), but (as Rewald notes) it is so much smaller here, it may not be the same object.

Provenance:
Ambroise Vollard, Paris; Henri Manguin, Paris; Lucile Manguin-Martinais, Paris; Norton Simon, Los Angeles; Norton Simon Inc. Museum of Art, Pasadena.

Bibliography:
Murphy 1968 (detail used as front endpaper); Daulte 1968, no. 8, repr.; Rewald 1983, no. 567, pl. 40 in color.

Exhibitions:
New York 1943a, no. 33; London and elsewhere 1946, no. 43; New York 1947, no. 86; Chicago and New York 1952, no. 103; The Hague 1956, no. 89; Zurich 1956, no. 142; Munich 1956, no. 110; Paris 1958a, no. 31; Vevey 1962, no. 33, repr.; New York 1963, no. 63, pl. LXIII; Los Angeles 1965; New York and Houston 1977–78, no. 108; Paris 1978, no. 74; Thaw II, no. 49, repr. in color; Thaw III, no. 82, repr. (recto and verso); Paris and elsewhere 1995–96, no. 198, repr. in color (exhibited in Paris and Philadelphia only).

CDD

Odilon Redon

Bordeaux 1840–1916 Paris

82
Cavalier

Charcoal pencil on paper prepared with a light brown tone. 21⅛ × 14¾ inches (535 × 375 mm). Signed at lower left, *ODILON REDON.*

Born in the same year as Monet, Redon did not aspire to the naturalistic goals of the impressionists. The artist was more interested in the mysterious than the mundane. A prodigious reader, his imagination was stirred by many literary sources, especially classical myths and medieval legends. Horses recur in his art, whether the winged Pegasus of Greek mythology or those of the chivalric legends. He also executed a number of Oriental subjects that were inspired by Delacroix's many studies of Arabian horsemen. Redon prepared at least nine etchings of cavaliers, or riders, between 1865 and 1866 that demonstrate both his debt to his master, Rodolphe Bresdin, and his admiration of Delacroix. Although they are conventional works, they reflect the strong influence of the romantic movement.

About twenty years later, Redon returned to the thematic material of his earlier etchings and produced a series of drawings and lithographs suggestive of the Middle Ages. As noted by Agnes Mongan, the subject of the Thaw drawing resembles one of the earlier etchings, *Porte-étendard franchissant un gué* (New York 1959, no. 177). It appears in Redon's account book as no. 144 under the year 1882. *Cavalier* is one of Redon's best-known charcoal renderings and was shown in the retrospective exhibition of his work in 1926, ten years after his death. As is true of all his works, its content is enigmatic. Even though it is related to his medieval etchings, it is not really clear from the unspecified nature of the rider's costume whether he is truly a medieval figure. Redon delighted in challenging the viewer's imagination through unconventional, dreamlike imagery.

Introduced to a wider public in J. K. Huysmans's controversial and highly popular 1884 novel of decadence, *A Rebours*, Redon aroused much interest in those who wished to identify with the avant-garde. Before this he was appreciated only by the very small circle of symbolist artists and writers, among them Stéphane Mallarmé and Huysmans himself. The symbolists saw in Redon's art a visualization of their ideas. On 10 November 1891, Mallarmé wrote to Redon in appreciation:

> Vous agitez dans nos silences le plumage du Rêve et de la Nuit. Tout dans cet album me fascine, et d'abord qu'il vous soit tout personnel, issu de vos seuls *Songes*: l'invention a des profondeurs, à l'égal de certains noirs, ô lithographes et démon; et, vous le savez, Redon, je jalouse vos légendes (*Lettres* 1960, p. 141, no. XVI).

Despite the considerable public interest in Redon, his art remains essentially mysterious. Since the Art Institute of Chicago plans to publish some previously unavailable documents by Redon's contemporary and biographer, André Mellerio, it is hoped that more light will be shed on the artist's intentions and an accurate chronology of his work will be established. For the present catalogue, Douglas Druick has kindly provided the chronology as well as invaluable information concerning this work as well as the two following *noirs* provided by Mellerio's unpublished transcription of Redon's account book.

Provenance:
Sold, by the artist, to the dealer Bailly in 1892; Gustave Fayet, Béziers, possibly Bourgat collection; Alexander M. Bing, New York, ca. 1927; sale, New York, Christie's, 17 May 1984, lot 110, repr. in color.

Bibliography:
Parnassus 1931, p. 37 (according to Wildenstein 1992–94); Berger 1966, p. 228, no. 623 (as *Rider*); Wildenstein 1992–94, II, 1994, no. 1030, p. 136f., repr. in color; Chicago and elsewhere 1994–95, p. 452; MRC, no. 144.

Exhibitions:
Paris 1926a, no. 208; New York 1928, no. 60; New York 1952, no. 8; Rotterdam 1958, no. 177, pl. 169; Paris 1958, no. 177, pl. 183; New York 1959, no. 177, pl. 169; Thaw II, no. 52, repr.; New York 1992c, no catalogue; Paris and New York 1993–94, no. 123, repr.; Thaw III, no. 85, repr.

CDD

Odilon Redon

Bordeaux 1840–1916 Paris

83

Mephistopheles (il montre son ongle),
also known as
The Fool or *Intuition*

Various charcoals with some black and white chalk for heightening, wiped, stumped and erased, on paper prepared with a golden tone. 15½ × 13½ inches (394 × 343 mm). Watermark: none. Signed at lower right, *Odilon Redon*; inscribed in pencil on verso at upper left, *Mephistophéles*; at lower left center, *91*.

Redon worked almost exclusively in black from the late 1860s through the 1890s. It was probably through Corot that he discovered charcoal, "that powder which is volatile, impalpable, and fugitive. It expressed me best, and I kept to it." Redon loved these black pictures, or "mes noirs," as he referred to them. "One must respect black. . . . It does not please the eye, and it conveys no sensuality. It is the agent of the mind far more than the most beautiful colors of the palette or the prism" (A.S.M. 1922, p. 125). Redon produced between four and five hundred charcoal pictures and worked in lithography as well. In the 1870s he began what was to be the most intensely creative period of his life. From rather conventional beginnings he gradually evolved an idiosyncratic canon of symbolic motifs and achieved the most profound blacks. He developed a series of imaginary portraits often characterized by a weird, secret imagery meaningful only to himself.

The key to the interpretation of the imaginary portraits may be found in the following passage from one of Redon's letters: "The sense of mystery consists in existing always under some aspect of ambiguity. This may be a double or triple aspect or even suspicions of such aspects; for example, images within images, forms that are becoming or will come into accord with the viewer's state of mind" (A.S.M. 1922, p. 97). *Mephistopheles*, or *Intuition*, which dates to 1877, illustrates this sort of ambiguity. It is interesting to contrast it with another imaginary portrait of the same date called *Mephistopheles* (repr. in Roger-Marx 1956, opp. p. 21; formerly collection of Claude Roger-Marx, now Paris, Musée D'Orsay) that also was meant to be interpreted on various levels of meaning and to evoke a "sense of mystery" in the viewer's mind. The heads of both subjects are emaciated and masklike. Mephistopheles is dressed in cap and bells, while the fool wears a cap trimmed with a feather, the angle of which complements his knowingly crooked finger. The characterizations of the eyes differ: Those of Mephistopheles are huge, vacuous, melancholic, and unfocused, while those of the fool are knowing and perceptive, as if to reflect *Intuition*, the alternative aspect of the title.

That Redon admired the works of Poe and Baudelaire is evident from *A Edgar Poe*, 1882, and *Les Fleurs de mal*, 1890, his lithographic suites inspired by their works. Both writers found aesthetic meaning in distortion as well as the unnatural and in the concept that there is beauty in evil. Redon invested these portraits with several seemingly contradictory aspects. From his inscriptions we know that the artist had Delacroix's Mephistopheles in mind—the elegant, smiling devil

introduced in Goethe's *Faust*, which was so vividly depicted in the artist's suite of seventeen lithographs.

Provenance:
Ernest Redon, Bordeaux; returned to the artist by 1891; on consignment with Boussod et Valadon (Théo van Gogh), Paris, 1891; on consignment with Librairie de l'Art Indépendant (Edmond Bailly), Paris, 24 May 1891; sold to Ambroise Vollard, Paris, 10 February 1899; Jacques Dubourg, Paris; René Malamoud, Zurich; Hazlitt, Gooden & Fox, London.

Bibliography:
Pigeon 1881 and 1881a; Berger 1950, no. 51, repr.; Roger-Marx 1950, no. 2, repr.; Bacou 1956, I, p. 71 n. 1, II, cited under no. 41; Paris 1956–57, p. 45, fig. 43; Berger 1964, no. 578, pl. 43; Selz 1971, p. 33, repr.; Vialla 1988, repr. p. 68; Wildenstein 1992–94, I, 1992, no. 417; Thaw III, p. 269, repr.; MRC, no. 53.

Exhibitions:
Possibly Paris 1878a (according to Chicago and elsewhere 1994–95) or Paris 1887a; Paris 1881; Vienna 1903, no. 246; Bern 1958, no. 19, repr.; London 1959, no. 6, repr.; Venice 1962a, no. 35; London 1977, no. 66, pl. 64; Thaw II, no. 50, repr.; Paris and New York 1993–94, no. 124, repr.; Chicago and elsewhere 1994–95, no. 43, fig. 43, p. 94, repr. in color, fig. 5:7, p. 128.

CDD

Odilon Redon

Bordeaux 1840–1916 Paris

84

Lady Macbeth (prêtesse d'Egypte)

Charcoal and some black chalk, erased or gone over in areas with stump, on pink paper. 19 7⁄16 × 12 1⁄8 inches (495 × 307 mm). Signed at lower left: *Odilon Redon.*

In this highly charged work, the subject is dramatically illuminated by candlelight, her features schematized into a mask and her face reduced nearly to cubist forms. While her costume is brightly lit, her face—especially her expressive eyes, staring upward, away from the viewer—provides the true focus of the work. Redon simplified all forms here and contrasted the tones of the rich charcoal with the warm but pale tones of the pink paper to create a powerful chiaroscuro effect. He also added some black chalk to the charcoal and sharpened some of the outlines with a finely pointed eraser.

There is no strict textual illustration here. Indeed, as Redon's title indicates, he interpreted the subject alternatively as Lady Macbeth or as an Egyptian priestess. For Lady Macbeth, Redon effectively suggested the moment after the murder of Duncan rendered in the lines "Out, out, brief candle. Life's but a walking shadow . . ." (Act V, verse 17). Redon may have considered a series inspired by the works of Shakespeare, judging from a number of the artist's works, including Bottom from *A Midsummer Night's Dream*, another charcoal in the Thaw Collection (Thaw I, no. 102, repr.), and Caliban from *The Tempest*, now in the Louvre (Département des Arts Graphiques, fonds du Musée d'Orsay, Paris, Inv. RF 35.820).

Redon later produced a pastel of the same subject, which he sold to Ambroise Vollard in 1899 (Wildenstein 1992–94, no. 408, repr.).

While the present work follows a large series of mysterious frontal portraits that Redon produced, Lady Macbeth bears some resemblance in both type and mood to the woman depicted in *La Voile*, an oil on paper (Wildenstein 1992–94, no. 409, repr.).

Provenance:
Baron Robert de Domècy in April 1896 (according to Redon's account book as "Un dessin prêtesse égyptien, rigide avec un flambeau devant elle [elle fut exposé sous le titre Lady Macbeth]"); The Artemis Group, London.

Bibliography:
Chicago and elsewhere 1994–95, fig. 94, p. 182, repr. in color; MRC, no. 46.

Exhibition:
Thaw III, not in catalogue.

CDD

Berthe Morisot

Bourges 1841–1895 Paris

85

A Young Woman and Child Seated on the Grass

Watercolor over pencil. 6½ × 8¹¹⁄₁₆ inches (164 × 221 mm). Signed at lower left, in pen and ink, *Berthe Morisot.*

Although all three Morisot sisters studied drawing as children, only Berthe and Edma would become artists. When they expressed an interest in landscape painting, their teacher, Joseph-Benoit Guichard, introduced them to Achille Oudinot, who in 1860 brought them to the attention of Corot, the leading French landscape painter of the time. It is not surprising that Corot's influence on their painting style during the following decade was great. From Corot Berthe learned her pale palette and brush technique and acquired a taste for small landscape studies featuring simply rendered figures. But it was also in this decade, when both sisters were in their twenties, that they were introduced to the circle of Edouard Manet, where they met, among other artists, Degas, Puvis de Chavannes, and Fantin-Latour. Berthe spent a great deal of time in Manet's company and absorbed much of his manner, as this very free and confident watercolor study reveals.

After her marriage in 1869, Edma gave up her serious interest in art and devoted herself instead to her family. Berthe's career was not interrupted by her marriage to Edouard's brother Eugène Manet, in 1874. Edma's children, as well as those of the third sister, Yves (Mme Paule Gobillard), were to become some of Morisot's most memorable subjects.

This watercolor was painted in the surroundings of Cambrai, where Berthe visited Yves in the autumn of 1875. It is one of a series of watercolors that includes a very free depiction, probably of Yves and two of her daughters, *By the Seashore* (private collection; see Mount Holyoke and Washington 1987, pl. 24). Another watercolor, now in the Art Institute of Chicago, shows Edma and her little girl on the terrace at Meudon. With her own marriage and eventual maternal duties, Berthe worked increasingly in watercolor, and her work in this medium tends to be freer and livelier than any of her earlier works on paper.

Certain critics, notably Roger Marx (1907, p. 496), remarked that Morisot's watercolors, along with those produced by Jongkind, were the most successful impressionist watercolors. Marx made special note of the touching grace of Morisot's work and, above all, of her mastery of the watercolor technique. Although her paintings and pastels documented her changing concerns and subject matter, Morisot expressed herself with utter naturalness and freedom in this medium. In the present work she characterized her subjects in a deft pencil sketch and finished the drawing with rapid assurance in watercolor. The girl in the Thaw drawing, Yves's daughter, is the future Mme Paul Valéry. Paul Valéry remarked of Morisot's work, "La singularité de son œuvre fut de vivre sa peinture et de peindre sa vie. L'ensemble du son œuvre fait songer à ce que serait le journal d'une femme dont les moyen [*sic*] d'expression serait la couleur et le dessin."

Provenance:
Mme Paule Gobillard; Valéry family; Galerie Hopkins-Thomas, Paris, 1993.

Bibliography:
Bataille and Wildenstein 1961, no. 634, fig. 614; Rey 1982, p. 48, repr. in color.

Exhibitions:
Paris 1896, no. 292; Paris 1922; Paris 1929a, no. 117; Paris 1941, no. 295; Paris 1945, no. 18; Paris 1961, no. 634; Thaw III, no. 87, repr.

CDD

Berthe Morisot

Pierre-Auguste Renoir

Limoges 1841–1919 Cagnes

86

View of a Park

Watercolor, touches of white gouache, on wove paper. 12 1/16 × 19 7/8 inches (307 × 494 mm). Watermark: none visible through lining.

This brilliant watercolor was formerly in the collection of the French dealer, publisher, and writer Ambroise Vollard (1867–1939). Renoir's ability to suggest form simply by modulating his brushstrokes and colors is exemplified by the figures summarily sketched in at the left near the water as well as by the lush foliage. The two trees in the center foreground not only function as a screen through which we are drawn to the water and distant shore but also serve to emphasize the vertical movement within the composition. Without these two trees—which conceptually owe much to Cézanne—the landscape would lose a great deal of its dynamic sense of space, movement, and structure.

In this watercolor, the sensuousness and physicality that are so often remarked upon in connection with Renoir's aesthetic are apparent. The autumnal greens, yellows, and russets of Renoir's palette as well as the handling of foliage and careful pictorial organization also appear in a watercolor landscape in the Seattle Art Museum. Indeed, both this sheet and the Seattle watercolor look as though they may have been executed at the same site, although from different points of view. François Daulte has dated the Seattle watercolor and a similar one in the Annenberg Collection, *Landscape with Trees*, to about 1886, the period to which the Thaw sheet should also be dated (Philadelphia 1989, p. 39).

Provenance:
Ambroise Vollard, Paris; Robert de Galea, Paris; M. Knoedler & Co., Inc., New York; John T. Dorrance, Jr., Philadelphia; sale, New York, Sotheby's, 18–19 October 1989, lot 101, repr. in color.

Bibliography:
Vollard 1918, II, p. 145, repr.

Exhibition:
Thaw III, no. 88, repr.

SW

Paul Gauguin

Paris 1848–1903 Atuana, Hivaoa, Marquesas Islands

87
Queen of Beauty

Watercolor with pen and black ink over black chalk. Verso: study of a head and feet in black chalk. 6 $^{15}/_{16}$ × 9 $^{1}/_{4}$ inches (176 × 235 mm). Signed at lower left, *PG*; inscribed, lower center, *TE ARII VAHINE.*

When Gauguin returned to Tahiti in January 1896 from his visit to France, he found that Tehamana, the Tahitian woman with whom he had so happily lived, had married during his absence. Obliged to find another *vahine*, he soon took up with Pahura, a young girl who was only thirteen and a half. Gauguin had convinced himself that only in Tahiti would he be able to create something really new. In Tahiti, which he saw as a new paradise, he would take inspiration from the experience of recapturing man's childhood from a primitive race of people. Shortly after his return he painted *Te Arii Vahine*, now in the Pushkin Museum, Moscow. Much has been written about the painting and its antecedents, notably its link with Manet's *Olympia*, which Gauguin had seen on his last visit to Paris. The most arresting commentary on the subject, however, is that provided by Gauguin himself in the illustrated letter of April 1896 that he sent to his friend Daniel de Monfreid in Paris:

> I have just finished a canvas . . . that I believe to be much better than anything I've done previously: a naked queen, reclining on a green rug, a female servant gathering fruit, two old men, near the big tree, discussing the tree of science; a shore in the background: this light trembling sketch only gives you a vague idea. I think that I have never made anything of such deep sonorous colors. The trees are in blossom, the dog is on guard, the two doves at the right are cooing (Washington and elsewhere 1988–89, p. 398).

Insight into Gauguin's symbolist ideas about color is provided by an interview published in *L'Echo de Paris* in 1895:

> I borrow some subject or other from life or from nature, and, using it as a pretext, I arrange lines and colors so as to obtain symphonies, harmonies that do not represent a thing that is real, in the vulgar sense of the word, and do not directly express any idea, but are supposed to make you think the way music is supposed to make you think unaided by ideas or images, simply through the mysterious affinities that exist between our brains and such arrangements of colors and lines (Guérin 1978, p. 109).

In the Thaw sheet, Gauguin's choice of color is very different from and noticeably brighter than that of the oil. The effect is provocative and poetically charged. The sonorous color, which so pleased Gauguin when he described the canvas to his friend, is very different in the watercolor: The ground on which Pahura reclines, for example is blue, not the jewel-like "green rug" that Gauguin described.

Most recent writers believe that the watercolor was executed after the painting. While this appears to be the case, the watercolor differs from the oil not only with respect to the color but also in the placement of certain compositional elements, notably the old men and the doves.

The chalk sketches on the verso of the sheet, a study of a woman's head and a much slighter sketch of some feet, are not related to the watercolor of the recto. They are connected to another painting executed at the end of 1896 or even January 1897, *Te Tamari No Atua*, now in the Bayrische Staatsgemälde Sammlungen, Munich (Paris 1990a, no. 221, repr. in color). While the feet are exactly those of the woman lying on the bed, the study of a woman's head is similar to that of an angel in the background. The angel is reinterpreted from another work of about the same time, *Bébé* (now in the Hermitage, St. Petersburg; repr. Paris 1990a, p. 398, under no. 221).

In 1898 Gauguin reworked the composition as a woodcut, printing at least thirty impressions on Japanese paper, mostly monogrammed by the artist in ink or pencil at the lower right corner. One of these impressions is in The Metropolitan Museum of Art, New York; the original woodblock is in the National Gallery, Prague.

Provenance:
Ambroise Vollard, Paris; Baron Von Bodenhausen; Mr. and Mrs. Ward Cheney, New York; private collection; Acquavella Galleries, New York.

Bibliography:
Goldwater 1957, as *Woman with Mangoes*, repr. in color; Rewald 1958, no. 100, repr.; Leymarie 1962, pl. 23 in color; Wildenstein 1964, under no. 542, p. 224; Selz 1968, repr. in color p. 179; Pickvance 1970, p. 40, pl. 98; Goldwater 1972, repr. in color; Washington and elsewhere 1988–89, no. 215a, repr.; Leymarie 1989, p. 75, repr. in color.

Exhibitions:
Paris 1906, no. 82; Berlin 1928, no. 124; New York 1956, no. 69; Chicago and New York 1959, no. 112, repr.; New Haven 1960, no. 190, repr.; Paris and New York 1993–94, no. 125, repr. in color; Thaw III, no. 89, repr. (recto [in color] and verso).

CDD

Georges Seurat

Paris 1859–1891 Paris

88

Nurse with a Child's Carriage

Conté crayon on Ingres paper. Verso:
woman standing, arms extended.
12³⁄₁₆ × 9⁷⁄₈ inches (310 × 250 mm).
Watermark: illegible fragment.
Inscribed by Maximilien Luce in blue
chalk at left, *G. Seurat*; his own initial *L* below, in blue chalk; and inventory number *317*, in red chalk.

By the early 1880s Seurat had turned away from Ecole
des Beaux-Arts assignments and moved toward natu-
ralism, taking most if not all of his subjects from
everyday life. This practice was not new to him since he
had begun these studies while in the Ecole des Beaux-
Arts, where it was considered standard practice for students to draw directly from nature. *Nurse with a
Child's Carriage*, an independent drawing dating
around 1883–84, slightly before the period of the
Grande Jatte (1884–86), is just such a study.

In his simplification of the back view of the nurse's
figure, Seurat eliminated all detail except the fall of the
long ribbons of her bonnet and the white panel of her
apron, which both serve to point up the verticality of
the slender curvilinear silhouette. At the same time
there is a calculated repetition of shapes in the manner
in which the edge of the skirt flares out to echo the
upper corner of the carriage, which Robert Herbert
interprets as that of an invalid. The nurse and her distinctive costume lent themselves to the artist's interest
in the manipulation of shapes in terms of black and
white, and he made several other independent drawings
on this theme. Two show the nurse standing holding a
child (De Hauke 1961, nos. 486, 488, repr.; no. 486 is in
the Heinz Berggruen Collection, Paris, while no. 488 is
in the Woodner family collection, see New York 1990a,
no. 135, repr.), and one shows her seated with a child
(Musée du Louvre, RF 29.302; De Hauke 1961, no. 487,
repr.). The drawing on the verso of the Thaw sheet, a
young woman shown in profile with her arms in a
position indicating that she, too, is pushing a pram, is
much freer in conception than the geometric configuration of the nurse. This study was discovered only after
the sheet was removed from its frame at the time it
entered the Thaw Collection.

The first owner of this drawing was Seurat's friend
and champion Félix Fénéon, the symbolist author and
critic who collaborated with César de Hauke in the early stages of the preparation of the monumental catalogue raisonné that was begun in the 1930s and which,
when it finally appeared in 1961, was dedicated to
Fénéon's memory. After Seurat's death, his family
appointed Fénéon, Paul Signac, and Maximilien Luce to
compile the inventory of the artist's work.

Provenance:
Félix Fénéon, Paris; Edmond Cousturier, Paris (by 1908, until
at least 1926); François Cousturier, Paris (by 1937); Lucie
Cousturier; A. & R. Ball, New York; Mr. and Mrs. Samuel
Sair, Winnipeg (until 1959); sale, New York, Parke-Bernet, 9
December 1959, lot 24, repr.; A. & R. Ball, New York.

Bibliography:
De Hauke 1961, no. 485, repr.; Herbert 1962, no. 99, repr.,
verso, fig. 170.

Exhibitions:
Paris 1908–9, no. 121; Paris 1926, no. 127 (not shown); Paris
1936a, no. 87; London 1937, no. 48; Thaw I, no. 104, repr.;
New York 1977, no. 7; London 1978, no. 12; Bielefeld and
Baden-Baden 1983–84, no. 34; Paris and New York 1991–92,
no. 43, repr.; Thaw III, no. 91, repr. (recto and verso).

CDD

Vincent van Gogh

Groot-Zundert 1853–
1890 Auvers-sur-Oise

89

Two Cottages at Saintes-Maries-de-la-Mer

Reed pen and brown ink, over pencil.
12⅜ × 18¾ inches (315 x 474 mm).
Watermark: PL BAS.

Van Gogh moved from Paris to Arles in February 1888. On 9 April 1888, he wrote to his brother, Theo, in Paris: "I must do a *tremendous* lot of drawing" (*Van Gogh* 1958, II, p. 541, Letter 474). Later in the month, he described the drawings he had sent on to Paris: "These drawings were made with a reed sharpened the way you would a goose quill; I intend to make a series of them, and hope to do better ones than the first two. It is a method that I had already tried in Holland some time ago, but I hadn't such good reeds there as here" (*Van Gogh* 1958, II, p. 549, Letter 478, ca. 21 April 1888). As Ronald Pickvance has pointed out, part of the reason Van Gogh decided to make this series of pen-and-ink drawings was his discovery (or rediscovery) of the reed pen coupled with the abundance of reeds growing around the canal network of Arles, the quality of which Van Gogh felt was better than those he had used while working in Etten in June 1881 (Otterlo 1990, p. 218).

It was in Arles that Van Gogh decided to make the four-hour journey to the small fishing village of Saintes-Maries-de-la-Mer. Upon his arrival, he wrote to his brother: "I do not think there are 100 houses in the village, or town. . . . And the houses—like those on our heaths and peat bogs of Drenthe; you will see some specimens of them in the drawings. . . . I am staying till tomorrow afternoon, I still have some drawings to do" (*Van Gogh* 1958, II, pp. 588–89, Letter 499, 2 June 1888).

Van Gogh remained in Saintes-Maries for five days, during which time he produced nine drawings. Among these were seven half-page drawings on Ingres paper with the watermark AL PL BAS; five, including the Thaw sheet, are of the distinctive thatched cottages of the area. Van Gogh began each with a quick pencil sketch, followed by the long and broad strokes of the reed pen; he used a quill pen for more delicate details.

The Thaw sheet is one of three drawings of thatched cottages that the artist kept upon his return to Arles; the remaining works were sent to his brother in Paris. While his plan was to use these sketches as the basis for oil paintings, this more delicate drawing apparently was never employed for that purpose.

Provenance:
Mrs. J. van Gogh-Bonger, Amsterdam; Miss E. Bonger, Amsterdam; Willem Mengelberg, Amsterdam; Mr. and Mrs. Louis Ritter, Scarsdale, New York; private collection; Acquavella Galleries, New York.

Bibliography:
De la Faille 1928, IV, no. 1440, pl. CLV; De la Faille 1970, no. 1440, repr.; Roskill 1971, pp. 152 and 169, cited as F 1440; Millard 1974, p. 159, as F 1440; Hulsker 1980, p. 331, no. 1451, repr.

Exhibitions:
Amsterdam 1905, no. 380; New York 1955, no. 100; Los Angeles 1957, no. 33; New York 1959a, no. 15, repr.; New York 1966, p. 20, no. 9; New York 1984a, no. 5, repr.; New York 1984b, no. 35, repr.; Thaw II, no. 53, repr.; Otterlo 1990, no. 181, repr.; Thaw III, no. 92, repr.

EJP

Vincent van Gogh

Groot-Zundert 1853–
1890 Auvers-sur-Oise

90

Saint-Rémy, Workers in a Field

Pencil, with some stumping. 9¼ × 12¹/₁₆ inches (235 × 306 mm). Verso: man digging and other figure studies in pencil, black chalk, and traces of blue pencil. Watermark: none.

In a letter to his mother and sister, Wil, Van Gogh wrote: "I continued painting even when my illness was at its height, among other things, a memory of Brabant, hovels with moss-covered roofs and beech trees. . . . Also a turnip field with women gathering green stuff in the snow . . ." (*Van Gogh* 1958, III, Letter 629a). Following one of his most serious breakdowns while at the asylum of Saint-Paul-de-Mausole in Saint-Rémy, the artist wrote another letter to his brother, Theo, in which he related that "While I was ill I nevertheless did some little canvases from memory which you will see later, memories of the North . . ." (*Van Gogh* 1958, III, Letter 629 [29 April 1890]). Van Gogh had admitted himself to the asylum in May 1889, remaining there for one year before going on to Auvers-sur-Oise and his tragic end.

While the few letters written during his recovery speak only of paintings from memory, a large group of drawings, including the Thaw double-sided sheet, have been attributed to this period. De la Faille described the recto of this sheet as follows: "Une maisonnette à toit de chaume couvert de neige . . . un homme et une femme . . . piqué ça et là de quelques légumes . . ." (De la Faille 1928, no. 1620). This is interesting in light of Van Gogh's letter to his mother and sister that mentions a painting of "a turnip field with women gathering green stuff in snow. . . ." According to Hulsker, "the snow-covered field of turnips was an old motif with Vincent" (Hulsker 1980, p. 442), one that he believes refers to Van Gogh's Nuenen period of 1885, specifically to a letter that states: "I am slogging away these days at a drawing of a woman I saw last winter pulling up carrots in the snow" (*Van Gogh* 1958, III, Letter 418). Hulsker sees the Thaw drawing as among those the artist worked on during his illness in an attempt to maintain control over his mind. In the letter to his mother and sister cited above, Van Gogh also requested that they send him any of his old drawings they might have at home—"they may serve to refresh my memory, and so be the subjects of new work. . . ."

The return to peasants and the depiction of the northern thatch-roofed cottages refer to Van Gogh's own earlier works as well as to his copies after works by other artists, including Rembrandt and Millet. The rounded outline of the cottage and trees, along with the bold parallel marks that delineate the clothing of these figures working in the field, is typical of the decorative style he used in these "memories of the North" drawings. Van Gogh's need to return to previous times points to the great sadness he felt in his confinement and perhaps his hopelessness toward the future.

Provenance:
Paul Ferdinand Gachet, Auvers; Paul Gachet, Auvers; Wildenstein and Co., New York; T. Edward Hanley, Bradford, Pennsylvania.

Bibliography:
De la Faille 1928, III, no. 1620; De la Faille 1970, p. 550, fig. 1620 ("Saint-Rémy Jan.–Apr. 1890"); Hulsker 1980, pp. 440, 442, 444, nos. 1911, 1934, repr.; Thaw III, p. 253, repr.

Exhibitions:
Paris 1937b, no. 81; Buffalo 1960, no. 30; New York 1961, no. 119; New York and Philadelphia 1967, p. 68; Columbus 1968, no. 138, repr.; Thaw I, no. 115, repr.

EJP

Henri-Marie-Raymond de Toulouse-Lautrec

Albi 1864–1901 Château de Malromé

91
Mlle Lender

Black crayon with touches of blue on the eyelids. 12⁵⁄₁₆ × 7¾ inches (312 × 200 mm). Signed with monogram at lower right, *HTL*; faint, mostly illegible numbers and inscription in pencil on verso, *35-48* / [illegible] / *rose* / [illegible] *n. york?* / *203* [illegible] *blanc et or.*

As one of Toulouse-Lautrec's favorite models, the well-known actress Marcelle Lender (Anne-Marie Bastien, 1861–1926) was portrayed in paintings and prints no fewer than twenty-six times during the years 1893–96. She must have made a strong impression on him when, in February 1895, she opened at the Variétés in the role of Galswinthe, daughter of the king of Spain, in the Hervé operetta *Chilpéric*. No doubt her flamboyant performance of the bolero caught the artist's eye, for he was inspired to depict her dance in the painting that for many years was in the collection of Mr. and Mrs. John Hay Whitney, New York (Dortu 1971, III, P.627, repr.). His other painting of Mlle Lender is a cartoon for the Whitney picture; the lithograph also depicts her dance (Dortu 1971, III, P.626, A.231, repr.). The Thaw drawing, the Louvre sheet with its double representation (RF 29.583 bis, discussed but not reproduced in Albi and Paris 1964, no. 108), and at least three other drawings (Dortu 1971, VI, D.3.327, D.3.767, D.3.810, repr.) also portray Lender in her *Chilpéric* costume, which consisted of a low-cut black gown worn with a diamond dog-collar necklace and an amazing headdress of two enormous pink poppies secured with a band of black tulle.

The artist must have been equally struck by the comedienne's extremely mobile face, with its almost desperately bright smile and glittering eyes, as by her general air of theatricality, since in many of the drawings he chose to depict just her head and shoulders. In the Thaw drawing, she is rendered in black crayon enlivened with touches of blue to indicate her heavily made-up eyes. Lautrec's rapid execution of the drawing, with its lively variation from soft to strong accents, matches the animation of his subject.

At one time the drawing belonged to Dr. T. Edward Hanley, the noted collector of modern literary manuscripts, who in 1964 presented it to his wife, Tullah, through whom the Thaws acquired it. (For other drawings of Mlle Lender, see Dortu 1971, VI, D.3.766, D.3.813, D.3.815, D.3.896, D.3.897, D.3.898, D.4.241, and D.4.242, repr.)

Provenance:
S. Sévadjian, Paris; his sale, Paris, Hôtel Drouot(?), 22 March 1920, no. 28, repr.; M. Kroller; T. Edward Hanley, Bradford, Pennsylvania; Mrs. Tullah Hanley; her sister Elizabeth Molnar.

Bibliography:
Joyant 1926–27, II, 1927, p. 208; Dortu 1971, VI, D.3.765, repr.; Thaw III, p. 270, repr.

Exhibitions:
Buffalo 1946, no. 34, repr.; Philadelphia 1957, unnumbered checklist; New York 1961, no. 115; New York 1964a, no. 73; Thaw I, no. 105, repr.; Humlebæk 1994–95, no. 68, not repr.

CDD

191

Edouard Vuillard

Cuiseaux, Saône-et-Loire
1868–1940 La Baule

92
Les Chapeaux

Watercolor over pencil on wove paper. 8 3/16 × 11 5/8 inches (207 × 295 mm). Watermark: none visible through lining. Stamped at lower right, *EV*.

Along with Pierre Bonnard and Maurice Denis, Vuillard was one of the leaders of the French Nabis, a group that took its inspiration from the work of Paul Gauguin. Although today Vuillard is primarily known for his depictions of women in domestic interiors, he also received a number of important decorative commissions in which he explored the theme of the public garden. As early as 1892, in six panels commissioned by Paul Desmarais, Vuillard juxtaposed interior and exterior scenes. The following year Alexandre Natanson, editor of *La Revue blanche*, commissioned Vuillard to paint nine decorative panels, known as the *Jardins publics*, for the dining room of his townhouse at 60 avenue du Bois. The artist signed the panels in 1894 (of the nine, one has disappeared; five are in the Musée d'Orsay, Paris; and the remaining three are in the Musées Royaux des Beaux-Arts, Brussels; the Cleveland Museum of Art; and the Museum of Fine Arts, Houston). For this commission Vuillard chose the theme of the public park.

The subject of the Thaw watercolor suggests that it may have been executed around 1893, when Vuillard was working on the Natanson commission. The artist captured a moment of conversation among three women whom he silhouetted against the dashes of quickly noted dense green foliage that suggest an outdoor setting. While Vuillard's watercolor gives prominence to the head and shoulders of the women, thereby emphasizing their hats—particularly the one touched with red watercolor worn by the figure in the right foreground—the intimate grouping is similar to that found in two panels of the *Jardins publics. La Conversation* and *Les Premiers pas* both depict seated women conversing against a decorative background of dappled foliage. Vuillard used attire as a foil to the shimmering effects of light, having commented in his journal that to capture the transparency of shadows and light one must contrast them with the opacity of costumes, parasols, hats, and tree trunks (Vuillard, Journal I, vol. 2, p. 50, 10 September 1894, as quoted in Paris and elsewhere 1993–94, p. 86).

Provenance:
Estate of the artist (Lugt S. 909a); Alfred Ayrton, Switzerland; J.P.L. Fine Arts, London.

Bibliography:
Apollo 1985, p. 9, repr. in color for advertisement for J.P.L. Fine Arts; Thaw III, p. 270, repr.

Exhibitions:
London 1985b, p. 13, no. 10, repr. in color; Thaw II, no. 54, repr.; Katonah 1989, no. 35, repr. in color p. 6.

SW

Henri Matisse

Cateau Cambrésis 1869–
1954 Nice

93
Still Life with a Chocolatière

Brush and black ink. 9 × 11¾ inches
(228 × 299 mm). Watermark: none.
Signed at lower right, *Henri.
Matisse.*

Although Matisse treated the subject in several paintings, this drawing is a study for the *Still Life with Chocolatière* of 1900 in the Hermitage, St. Petersburg (repr. Flam 1986). The painting, which is vertical, includes a more detailed interior view with the still life placed on a table set further back in space. However, certain details, including the placement of the three objects on the table and the light reflecting off the chocolatière, are the same in the drawing and painting. The composition of the Thaw sheet has its origins in a simple brush drawing, *Still Life with Chocolate Pot* of 1899 (private collection), in which the artist quickly delineated the shape and placement of the chocolatière, cup, saucer, and what is presumably a sugar bowl (repr. Schneider 1984 [1992], p. 34).

The bold, energetic brushwork in the present drawing is comparable to that of several other pen-and-brush portraits and nudes that Matisse executed about the same time. The dramatic play between the ink—at times very dense—and the white paper suggests the influence of Van Gogh's drawings, two of which Matisse acquired around 1899. However, as Elderfield has pointed out, it is Cézanne's work that provided the basis for this kind of drawing, and it was Cézanne who taught Matisse that drawing could be purely "a relationship of contrasts or simply the relationship between two tones, black and white" (London and New York 1984–85, p. 31). Matisse's grasp of this is nowhere more evident than on the righthand side of the drawing, where the flat, inky black background is interrupted by the white top of the sugar bowl. This vests the object with a three-dimensional quality, which is negated with the bold stroke of black ink representing the handle of the chocolatière.

Provenance:
Philip J. Savage, Detroit; sale, New York, Parke-Bernet, 16 March 1960, lot 20, repr. p. 12; Edward Bragaline, New York.

Bibliography:
Izerghina 1978, under no. 7, repr.; Flam 1986, no. 52, repr. p. 71; Thaw III, p. 270, repr.

Exhibitions:
Paris 1975, no. 4, repr.; London and New York 1984–85, no. 4, repr. p. 139; Thaw II, no. 55, repr.

SW

Henri Matisse

Cateau Cambrésis 1869–
1954 Nice

94
*Portrait of a Girl
(Cocoly Agelasto)*

Graphite. 13¾ × 10 inches (350 × 254 mm). Watermark: none. Signed at lower right, in graphite, *Henri Matisse.*

Beginning in 1913, when Matisse was back in Paris, he began to develop a strong interest in cubism, meeting with such artists as Picasso and Juan Gris. Matisse confronted the movement in a highly personal way and used its technique, in part, to achieve a new flexibility in his painting. A reference to its impact on his work appears in his description of a 1915 painting, *Variation on a Still Life by de Heem,* as using "methods of modern construction" (London and New York 1984–85, p. 64).

Some of Matisse's most powerful and moving works from this period are his portraits of family and friends. He wrote in "Notes of a Painter," in 1908, that studying the figure "best permits me to express my almost religious awe toward life . . . I penetrate amid the lines of the face those that suggest the deep gravity which persists in every human being" (London and New York 1984–85, p. 70). Certainly the provocative gaze of the young girl must have intrigued the artist, who heightened her mysterious appearance by smudging heavy graphite over her eyes. The soft falling waves of her hair are contrasted with the strong vertical lines of her costume. A number of drawings made about the same time, including Matisse's portrait of Juan Gris's wife, Josette, have analogous physical characteristics, such as a stiff, tubular neck below an oval head cut off at the top. John Elderfield has described these works as being alike as "portraits of figures confined in their own masks" but "unlike each other in the kinds of emotion they convey." Matisse must have considered this drawing to be among his best portraits, since he included it in his book *Portraits,* published in the last year of his life. There the sitter is identified as Cocoly Agelasto, and the drawing is dated 1915.

Provenance:
Jean Matisse, Paris; Harold Diamond & Co., New York.

Bibliography:
Matisse and Sauret 1954, p. 30, repr.; Schneider 1984, repr. p. 318 (reprint: Paris, 1992, p. 318); Flam 1986, no. 401, repr. p. 401; Thaw III, p. 270, repr.

Exhibitions:
London and New York 1984–85, no. 35, repr.; Thaw II, no. 56, repr.

SW

Paul Klee

Bern 1879–1940 Murallo-Locarno

95
Red, Green Gradation

Point of brush and watercolor; borders of the drawing extended 6 mm onto the mount, in pen and black ink. 9¼ × 12¹⁄₁₆ inches (235 × 305 mm). Watermark: none visible through lining. Signed at upper right, *Klee*; dated and numbered on mount at lower left in pen and black ink, *1921 / 102* and inscribed in graphite, *Stufung rot / grün. (roter Zinnober).*

From January 1921 through April 1931, Klee taught at the Bauhaus, where he came into contact with Wassily Kandinsky and Lyonel Feininger. Teaching required him to develop a theoretical system, and his two essays *Ways of Nature Study* (1923) and *Exact Experiments in the Realm of Art* (1928), published during his Bauhaus period, are concerned with questions of teaching method. The close interrelationship between his theoretical ideas and artistic output at this time can be studied in the watercolors he produced beginning in 1921 that he called "Stufungen." The *Color Gradations*, to which this sheet belongs, were the result of experiments in color movement, in which the artist explored the color theories of artists, including Goethe, Philipp Otto Runge, Delacroix, and Kandinsky. Klee began with abstract elements of form in these watercolors and measured the gradation of color by glazing or applying transparent layers of watercolor over a ground, keeping exact records in his catalogue of the color he used as a starting point for each gradation (Geelhaar 1973, p. 35). In this work, Klee used the complementary colors (what he called "echte Farbpaare") red and green, specifying the red as vermilion. The same complementary colors were used in the succeeding work in the series, a vertically oriented watercolor, now in the Yale University Art Gallery, New Haven, *Rot / Grüne Stufung, 1921/103* (repr. Köln 1979, no. 44).

Provenance:
Dr. William R. Valentiner, Detroit; Heinz Berggruen, Paris; Helen Serger (Galerie La Boetie), New York; Acquavella Galleries, New York.

Bibliography:
Thaw III, p. 273, repr.

Exhibitions:
Tokyo 1981, p. 67, no. 9, repr.; Thaw II, no. 59, repr.

SW

1921/102   *Steigung rot/grün i. (unter einander)*

Pablo Picasso

Malaga 1881–1973 Mougins

96

Pipe and Wineglass

Pasted papers and pencil, mounted on heavy gray board. 7 × 9½ inches (179 × 240 mm). Watermark: none visible through lining. Signed at lower right, *Picasso,* in pencil.

Picasso and Georges Braque (1882–1963) have been credited with the creation of cubism, a movement begun around 1907, which challenged and changed the traditional representation of an object in space. Cubism attempted to describe an object's volume and density on a two-dimensional surface without creating an illusionary three-dimensional picture space. Various sides and aspects of the subject could be shown simultaneously, representing as much what the mind knows as what the eye sees. The further development of collage and the papier collé technique, initiated by Braque in 1912, removed the object even further from the traditional representation of space and volume.

In this work, which dates from early 1914, cut and pasted papers of varying browns and white form a still life of two familar motifs in Picasso's oeuvre, the pipe and wineglass. Here, a combination of heavily drawn pencil outlines and cut shapes re-create the objects on a table. The roundness of the pipe, indicated by the shading at the edges, is negated by the flatness of the cut paper pasted down. The wineglass is also created by a combination of cut and pasted paper and drawn lines, but here the cut shape is only part of the goblet; drawing defines the form. Further, the goblet has been gutted, demonstrating the volume of its shape as well as its contents. Picasso created a comparable effect of ambiguous space in a sculpture of 1914, *Glass of Absinthe*, in which he cut an opening in the already three-dimensional glass. The table surface on which the objects both stand and lie flat is suggested by three drawn lines and a strip of brown paper heavily drawn with a molding design. These lines describing the tabletop further flatten out the surrounding space, eliminating the depth necessary to carry the pipe and wineglass.

Provenance:
Galerie Kahnweiler, Paris; probably sale, Paris, Hôtel Drouot, 17–18 November 1921, lot 165; Galerie Georges Petit, Paris(?); Marcel C. Coard, Paris; Martin Janis, Buffalo, New York; Sidney Janis Gallery, New York; Heinz Berggruen, Paris.

Bibliography:
Zervos 1942–78, II, [1942], no. 445, repr.; Daix and Rosselet 1979, no. 665, repr.; Thaw III, p. 271, repr.

Exhibitions:
Probably Paris 1932, no. 90; probably Zurich 1932, no. 80; Thaw II, no. 62, repr.; New York 1989–90, p. 310, repr. in color.

EJP

Pablo Picasso

Malaga 1881–1973 Mougins

97
Portrait of Lydia Lopokova

Pencil. 14 × 10 inches (357 × 254 mm). Watermark: illegible, cut off.

In early May 1919, Picasso went to London to design the sets and costumes for the new Ballets Russes production, *The Three-Cornered Hat*, with music by Manuel de Falla and choreography by Léonide Massine. This was not Picasso's first collaboration with Serge Diaghilev's company; in 1916, he had worked on Cocteau's avant-garde ballet, *Parade*. During this period the artist met Olga Koklova, a dancer with the Ballets Russes, who subsequently became his lover and then wife in 1918.

During the three months spent in London in 1919, Picasso not only created numerous sketches for sets and costumes, he also made a series of line drawings in pencil, portraying the dancers and musicians connected with the company. With Koklova, he attended rehearsals and performances, making quick recordings of "groups of dancers performing, at rest, or in classical poses" (Cooper 1968, p. 52). He also created a number of portrait drawings, which are often referred to as Ingresque in their more academic style but remain distinctly Picasso in feeling. Among these portraits is this fine drawing of Lydia Lopokova, one of the principal dancers with the Ballets Russes. Lopokova, who would marry John Maynard Keynes, the British economist and a member of the Bloomsbury group, is shown comfortably seated in an upholstered chair, legs and arms crossed, looking to her left. The figure is depicted with an economy of line. The rendering of her long, columnar neck and full figure anticipates Picasso's neoclassical phase of the early 1920s. A further classical reference appears in the architectural decoration behind the sitter, perhaps the molding of a fireplace. A nearly identical drawing of Lydia is in the Lady Keynes collection, Firle, while a third drawing of Lydia is in the Fitzwilliam Museum, Cambridge (fig. 1). Picasso certainly created these three pencil drawings of the dancer in a single sitting.

Fig. 1 Pablo Picasso. *Lydia Lopokova.* Fitzwilliam Museum, Cambridge.

Provenance:
Estate of the artist; Adrian Ward-Jackson, London.

Bibliography:
Zervos 1942–78, III, [1949], p. 106, no. 299, repr.; Picasso 1995, no. 19–218, repr.

Exhibitions:
Thaw III, no. 95, repr.; New York and Paris 1996–97, p. 310, repr.

EJP

Pablo Picasso

Malaga 1881–1973 Mougins

98

Portrait of Marie-Thérèse Walter

Pen and black ink and gray wash.
20¾6 × 13⅜ inches (510 x 339 mm).
Watermark: ARCHES A LA MAIN.
Inscribed at upper left, in black ink,
28 juillet / XXXVI.

Picasso first met Marie-Thérèse Walter in 1927, when she was just seventeen years old. He introduced himself to her with the words "Mademoiselle, you have an interesting face. I would like to make your portrait. I am Picasso" (New York 1980, p. 253). Six months later, she became the artist's lover. Recognizable in his drawings, sculptures, and paintings, Marie-Thérèse would be a recurring presence in his artistic output for the next ten years, until she was replaced by the young photographer Dora Maar.

In October 1935, Marie-Thérèse gave birth to their daughter, María de la Concepcíon, called Maïa; the following year their relationship began to deteriorate. The unhappiness of Marie-Thérèse is highly visible in this large portrait drawing. A hurt, yet resigned, young woman regards the viewer and the artist with knowing eyes and a penetrating stare. Her self-contained stillness greatly contrasts with the agitation of the artist revealed in the almost violent pen strokes that define the features of his mistress. The stark juxtaposition of black ink and white paper, with the dark surrounding shadow of the gray wash, seems appropriate to the mood of this portrait.

Provenance:
Estate of the artist; Marina Picasso; Jan Krugier, New York.

Exhibitions:
Munich 1981, no. 185, repr.; Venice 1981, no. 234, repr.; Mexico City 1982, no. 73; Thaw II, no. 63, repr.; Los Angeles and New York 1994 (exhibited in New York only), exh. pamphlet, no. 34, repr.; Thaw III, no. 96, repr.; New York and Paris 1996–97, p. 367, repr.

EJP

28 juillet
XXXVI.

Jackson Pollock

Cody, Wyoming 1912–
1956 East Hampton, New York

99
Untitled, 1943

Pen and black ink, gray and black wash, gouache, and red chalk. 18⅞ × 24¾ inches (479 × 613 mm). Watermarks: letters *MBM* followed by *MADE IN FRANCE* (at lower center); *INGRES D'ARCHES* (at lower right); illegible letters (along left edge). Signed and inscribed at lower center in brown ink, *Jackson Pollock / for P.G.* [Peggy Guggenheim]; numbered on verso in red pencil, *3*.

Art of This Century, Peggy Guggenheim's New York gallery, opened in October 1942 at 30 West 57th Street. This important exhibition site was designed both to show Guggenheim's own collection of avant-garde art as well as to present changing exhibitions of the work of artists she admired. These included émigré European artists, such as Hans Hofmann, and emerging American artists like Pollock and Robert Motherwell. Pollock's work was brought to Guggenheim's attention by the Chilean painter Matta. In July 1943, Guggenheim commissioned a mural for her apartment from Pollock and offered him a year's contract, which provided a monthly stipend and included a sales agreement. In November of that year, she held Pollock's first one-man show, composed of eight titled and six untitled paintings along with gouaches and drawings, including the present sheet, at her gallery.

Pollock drew from a number of different sources: Jungian psychoanalysis, Native American cultures, and surrealism as well as the work of the Mexican muralists Orozco and Siqueiros, to which he was introduced in the early 1930s. This drawing contains biomorphic images similar to those in *Red* (O'Connor and Thaw 1978, no. 970) and *Blue (Moby Dick*; O'Connor and Thaw 1978, no. 971), both executed about 1943. In each of these works there is an emphasis on the combination of ink, wash, and watercolor applied with fine pen lines and broader strokes, which alternately suggest detail and assert freedom and spontaneity. It is the organic nature of Pollock's imagery accentuated by the pen (seen here in the intentional splattering of ink at the lower right and the dig in the paper at the center) that underscores the act of creation. The fantastic human-, animal-, and plantlike forms; hieroglyphs and petroglyphs; and a marvelously ambiguous weather vane in this sheet reveal that the imagery Pollock worked out and developed was extraordinarily personal and original. As Francis O'Connor has observed, the image of a woman and a bull appears at the center of the drawing. Perhaps it was intended as a variation on the theme of Europa and the Bull or was inspired by Picasso (O'Connor 1995, pp. 6–7).

Provenance:
Peggy Guggenheim, Venice; possibly Miss Carol Biba, Bryn Mawr, Pennsylvania (according to *Supplement*); Bob P. Haboldt & Co., New York.

Bibliography:
O'Connor and Thaw 1978, IV, p. 50, no. 972; Haboldt 1989, p. 24, repr.; O'Connor 1995, no. 17, repr. in color.

Exhibitions:
New York 1943; Chicago and San Francisco 1945; Newport Beach 1986, no. 104, repr.; New York 1988, no. 1, repr. in color; New York 1992a, no. 1, repr.; Thaw III, no. 100, repr.; New York 1995, pp. 6–7, fig. 24.

SW

Jackson Pollock

Cody, Wyoming 1912–
1956 East Hampton, New York

100

Sketchbook

38 drawings on 40 sheets of cream-colored Japanese mulberry paper, most of which are folded to form double-sided pages, with several missing or torn (probably by the artist), bound between heavier paper covers with twine and stamped in red ink on the spine, MADE IN CHINA, and with Chinese characters surrounded by an oval. Chiefly executed in felt pen, blue-ink pen, brush and gray-black ink, and pencil; approximately one-third is in brush and gray-black ink, and pencil; approximately one-third is in brush and gray-black ink. Binding: 5⅝ × 12⅞ inches (143 × 327 mm). Leaves approximately 5⅝ × 11¹³⁄₁₆ inches (143 × 301 mm). Watermark: none.

In about 1951 Pollock entered a period in which he turned away from nonfigurative art and color to reintroduce the figure using only black paint. It was during this period that the Thaw sketchbook was used. Although it is not known precisely when or by whom the pad was acquired, it became Pollock's early in 1950 for use by the telephone, for memoranda, and for drawing. His wife, Lee Krasner, also used it occasionally for notes, and there are messages left by others as well. Among the items recorded are telephone numbers, three dreams Pollock jotted down and illustrated (probably in conjunction with a telephone conversation held with his psychoanalyst), and a list made in May 1950 of vanguard artists involved in a protest against a proposed competition of contemporary art to have been held by The Metropolitan Museum of Art the following December (see Lieberman 1982, pp. 5–10). But as William Lieberman has written, it is the last fourteen drawn pages, which he dates no earlier than 1952 and no later than 1953, that are the most interesting from an artistic viewpoint. Executed in brush and gray-black ink, these pages form a continuous whole, an outpouring of shapes and images that are marvelous in their intimacy and form.

In January 1951, Pollock, writing to a friend, referred to drawings he had made on Japanese paper with which he was pleased. Referring not to the sketchbook but rather to a few large drawings on Japanese paper, Pollock may have been intrigued by what he had created in the small sketchbook and wished to further explore this kind of spontaneous imagery in a larger format. If Lieberman is correct, Pollock returned to his sketchbook to produce the last fourteen drawings after completing the large drawings on Japanese paper. Perhaps the sketchbook afforded him the privacy to search for what he found in the gentle, almost lyrical configurations. As Lieberman has observed, Pollock never again used this particular technique of applying first a wash and then drawing in brush and ink.

Pollock used several other sketchbooks during the course of his life. There are three known from the 1930s, at least one from the forties, and only one—the Thaw sketchbook—from the fifties. "I don't work from drawings," Pollock stated in a taped interview in 1950. "I don't make sketches and drawings and color sketches into a final painting" (O'Connor and Thaw 1978, p. 79). "The source of my painting is the unconscious," he said elsewhere. "I approach painting the same way I approach drawing. That is direct—no preliminary studies. The drawings I do are relative to my painting but not for it" (O'Connor and Thaw 1978, p. 40). It is per-

haps best then to view the images in the Thaw sketchbook as a complete series that sheds light on the thoughts and working habits of an artist ranked among the greatest of the twentieth century.

Provenance:
Lee Krasner Pollock, New York.

Bibliography:
O'Connor and Thaw 1978, III, pp. 338–63, nos. 879–915, repr.; Glueck 1982, p. 19; Lieberman 1982; Thaw III, p. 251, repr.

Exhibitions:
Thaw II, no. 66, repr.; Thaw III, not in catalogue.

SW

fol. 25

fol. 27

209

fol. 30

fol. 37

210

Versos

1 Rhenish school (?)

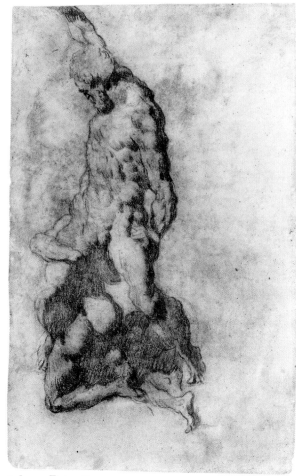

8 Jacopo Tintoretto

20 Claude Gellée, called Claude Lorrain

21 Claude Gellée, called Claude Lorrain

24 Jean Antoine Watteau

33 Antonio Canal, called Canaletto

81 Paul Cézanne

34 Francesco Guardi

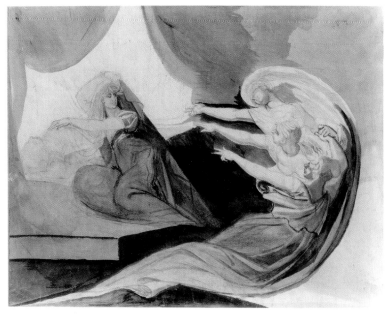

41 Henry Fuseli

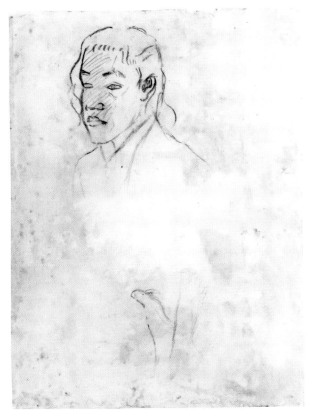

87 Paul Gauguin

88 Georges Seurat

90 Vincent van Gogh

Sources Cited in Abbreviated Form

Aaron 1985
Olivier Aaron, *Dessins insolites du XVIIIe français*, Paris, 1985.

Adhémar and Cachin 1973
Jean Adhémar and Françoise Cachin, *Degas, gravures et monotypes*, Paris, 1973.

Aimé-Azam 1956
D. Aimé-Azam, *Mazeppa-Géricault et son temps*, Paris, 1956.

Alfrey 1985
Nicholas Alfrey, "London, Nineteenth-Century Drawings," exhibition review, *Burlington Magazine* 118, no. 989, August 1985, pp. 554–57.

Ananoff 1961–70
Alexandre Ananoff, *L'Œuvre dessiné de Jean-Honoré Fragonard (1732–1806)*, 4 vols., Paris, 1961–70.

Andersen 1970
Wayne V. Andersen, *Cézanne's Portrait Drawings*, Cambridge, Massachusetts, 1970.

Apollo 1985
Apollo, March 1985, p. 9.

Arisi 1986
Ferdinando Arisi, *Giovanni Paolo Panini e i fasti della Roma del '700*, Rome, 1986.

Armstrong 1902
Sir Walter Armstrong, *Turner*, London and New York, 1902.

Arslan 1944
W. Arslan, "Per la definizione dell'arte di Francesco, Giannantonio e Nicolò Guardi," *Emporium* 100, 1944, pp. 1–28.

Art Journal 1964–65
Art Journal, Winter 1964–65, p. 187.

Arts 1960
"Rembrandt Drawings from American Collections," unsigned exhibition review, *Arts* 34, 1960, p. 29.

A.S.M. 1922
Odilon Redon, *A Soi-Même. Journal (1867–1915)*, Paris, 1922.

Athenaeum 1873
"The Private Collections of England, no. IV, Tynemouth-Gateshead," *The Athenaeum*, September 27, 1873, p. 408.

Athenaeum 1879
"The Private Collections of England, no. XLVI, Farnley Hall, Otley," *The Athenaeum*, October 18, 1879.

Bacou 1956
Roseline Bacou, *Odilon Redon*, Geneva, 1956.

Bacou 1975
Roseline Bacou, *Millet Dessins*, Paris, 1975.

Badt 1956
Kurt Badt, *Die Kunst Cézannes*, Munich, 1956.

Badt 1985
Kurt Badt, *The Art of Cézanne*, Sheila Ann Ogilvie, trans., New York, 1985.

Baljöhr 1990
Ruth Baljöhr, *Die Skulptur Michelangelos in der Druckgraphik*, master's thesis, Cologne University, 1990.

Bartsch
Adam Bartsch, *Le Peintre-graveur*, 21 vols., Vienna, 1803–21.

Bataille and Wildenstein 1961
Marie-Louise Bataille and Georges Wildenstein, *Berthe Morisot, catalogue des peintures, pastels et aquarelles*, Paris, 1961.

Bazin 1987–94
Germain Bazin, *Théodore Géricault, étude critique, documents et catalogue raisonné*, 6 vols., Paris, 1987–94.

Bean [1966]
Jacob Bean, *Italian Drawings in the Art Museum*, Princeton University, [1966].

Bean 1982
Jacob Bean, with the assistance of Lawrence Turčić, *15th and 16th Century Italian Drawings in The Metropolitan Museum of Art*, New York, 1982.

Becker 1938
Hanna I. Becker, *Die Handzeichnungen Albrecht Altdorfers*, Munich, 1938.

Benesch 1935
Otto Benesch, *Rembrandt: Werk und Forschung*, Vienna, 1935.

Benesch 1947
Otto Benesch, *Venetian Drawings of the Eighteenth Century in America*, New York, 1947.

Benesch 1947a
Otto Benesch, *Rembrandt. Selected Drawings*, London, 1947.

Benesch 1954–57
Otto Benesch, *The Drawings of Rembrandt*, 6 vols., London, 1954–57.

Benesch and Auer 1957
Otto Benesch and Erwin M. Auer, *Die Historia Friderici et Maximiliani*, Berlin, 1957.

Benesch 1960
Otto Benesch, *Rembrandt as a Draughtsman*, London, 1960.

Benesch 1973
Otto Benesch, *The Drawings of Rembrandt*, 6 vols., London, 1973.

Berger 1950
Klaus Berger, *French Master Drawings of the Nineteenth Century*, New York, 1950.

Berger 1952
Klaus Berger, *Géricault und sein Werk*, Vienna, 1952.

Berger 1964
Klaus Berger, *Odilon Redon: Fantasy and Colour*, Michael Bullock, trans., London, 1964.

Berger 1966
Klaus Berger, *Odilon Redon: Fantasy and Colour*, New York, 1966.

Berger 1968
Klaus Berger, *Géricault*, Paris, 1968.

Berger and Johnson 1969
K. Berger and D. Chalmers Johnson, "Art as Confrontation: The Black Man in the Work of Géricault," *The Massachusetts Review*, Spring 1969.

Bernhard 1976
Marianne Bernhard, ed., *Rembrandt Handzeichnungen*, II, Munich, 1976.

Berthold 1958
Gertrude Berthold, *Cézanne und die alten Meister*, Stuttgart, 1958.

Białostocki 1964
Jan Białostocki, "The Descent from the Cross in Works by Peter Paul Rubens and His Studio," *Art Bulletin* 46, no. 4, December 1964, pp. 511–24.

Białostocki 1972
Jan Białostocki, *Spätmittelalter und beginnende Neuzeit, Malerei*, Berlin, 1972.

Boerner 1976
C. G. Boerner, *Zwanzig ausgewählte Blätter der graphischen Kunst 1826–1976*, 1976, anniversary album with color plates from the catalogue *Ausgewählte Graphik und Zeichnungen aus sechs Jahrhunderten*.

Bonicatti 1971
M. Bonicatti, "Il Problema dei Rapporti fra Domenico e Giovanbattista Tiepolo," *Atti del congresso internazionale di Studi sul Tiepolo*, Milan, 1971.

Boon 1978
K. G. Boon, *Netherlandish Drawings of the Fifteenth and Sixteenth Centuries. Catalogue of the Dutch and Flemish Drawings in the Rijksmuseum*, 2 vols., The Hague, 1978.

Bordeaux 1983
Jean-Luc Bordeaux, "An Important Discovery: David's First Compositional Idea for Brutus," *Art International* 26, January–March 1983, pp. 46–48.

Borghini 1584
Raffaello Borghini, *Il riposo*, Florence, 1584, reprint ed. M. Rosci, Milan, 1967.

Börsch-Supan and Jähnig 1973
Helmut Börsch-Supan and Karl Wilhelm Jähnig, *Caspar David Friedrich: Gemälde, Druckgraphik und bildmässige Zeichnungen*, Munich, 1973.

Brame and Reff 1984
Philippe Brame and Theodore Reff, *Degas et son œuvre, A Supplement*, New York, 1984.

Bredius-Gerson
A. Bredius, *Rembrandt: The Complete Edition of the Paintings*, rev. by H. Gerson, 2 vols., London, 1969.

Briquet
C. M. Briquet, *Les Filigranes: Dictionnaire historique des marques du papier*, 4 vols., Geneva, 1907.

Bromberg 1974
Ruth Bromberg, *Canaletto's Etchings. A catalogue and study illustrating and describing the known states, including those hitherto unknown*, London and New York, 1974.

Browse 1949
Lillian Browse, *Degas Dancers*, London, 1949.

Burchard and d'Hulst 1963
Ludwig Burchard and Roger-A. d'Hulst, *Rubens Drawings*, Brussels, 1963.

Butlin 1981
Martin Butlin, *The Paintings and Drawings of William Blake*, 2 vols., New Haven and London, 1981.

Byam Shaw 1936
James Byam Shaw, "Francesco Guardi: A Street in Venice," *Old Master Drawings* 11, December 1936, p. 47.

Byam Shaw 1951
James Byam Shaw, *The Drawings of Francesco Guardi*, London, 1951.

Byam Shaw 1962
James Byam Shaw, *The Drawings of Domenico Tiepolo*, London, 1962.

Byam Shaw 1976
James Byam Shaw, *Maestri Veneti del Quattrocento, Biblioteca dei Disegni*, III, Florence, 1976.

Caldesi 1864
L. Caldesi, *The Farnley Hall Collection of Turner Drawings in the Possession of F. H. Fawkes Esq.*, 1864.

Calmann [1952]
H. M. Calmann, London, [1952].

Campbell 1975
Colin Campbell, "Raphael door Rembrandts pen herschapen," *De Kroniek van het Rembrandthuis* 27, 1975, p. 28.

Carré 1939
Jean-Marie Carré, *La Vie adventureuse de J.-A. Rimbaud*, nouvelle édition, revue et augmentée, Paris, 1939.

Chappuis 1973
Adrien Chappuis, *The Drawings of Paul Cézanne, A Catalogue Raisonné*, 2 vols., Greenwich, Connecticut, 1973.

Coffin 1969
David Coffin, *The Villa d'Este at Tivoli*, Princeton, 1969.

Cohn and Siegfried 1980
Marjorie B. Cohn and Susan L. Siegfried, *Works by J.-A.-D. Ingres in the Collection of the Fogg Art Museum*, Cambridge, 1980.

Collobi 1967
Licia Ragghianti Collobi, "Disegni di Francesco Guardi nella Fondazione Horne a Firenze," *Problemi Guardeschi*, Venice, 1967.

Congrès 1952
XVIIme Congrès Internationale d'Histoire de l'Art, Amsterdam, 1952, p. 39.

Constable 1962
W. G. Constable, *Canaletto. Giovanni Antonio Canal 1697–1768*, Oxford, 1962.

Constable 1965
John Constable's Correspondence, III, *The Correspondence with C. R. Leslie, R.A.*, edited, with an introduction and notes, by R. B. Beckett, Suffolk, 1965.

Constable-Links 1976
W. G. Constable, *Canaletto. Giovanni Antonio Canal 1697 1768*, 2d ed., rev. by J. G. Links, Oxford, 1976.

Cook and Wedderburn 1903–12
E. T. Cook and Alexander Wedderburn, *The Works of John Ruskin*, 39 vols., London and New York, 1903–12.

Cooper 1952
Douglas Cooper, *Pastels by Degas*, Basel, 1952.

Cooper 1968
Douglas Cooper, *Picasso Theatre*, New York, 1968.

Cranach 1980
Cranach: A Family of Master Painters, Helen Sebba, trans., New York, 1980.

Cranach 1994
Lucas Cranach: Ein Maler-Unternehmer aus Franken, Claus Grimm, Johannes Erichsen, and Evamaria Brockhoff, eds., Regensburg, 1994.

Crispolti 1958
Enrico Crispolti, "Otto nuove pagine del Taccuino 'Di Madrid' di Goya ed Alcuni problemi ad esso relativi," *Commentari* 9, no. 3, July–September 1958, pp. 181–205.

Cuzin 1983
Jean-Pierre Cuzin, "De Fragonard à Vincent," *Bulletin de la Société de l'Histoire de l'Art français 1981*, 1983, pp. 103–24.

Cuzin 1988
Jean-Pierre Cuzin, *Jean-Honoré Fragonard: Life and Work*, New York, 1988.

Daix and Rosselet 1979
Pierre Daix and Joan Rosselet, *Picasso: The Cubist Years, 1907–1916: A Catalogue Raisonné of the Paintings and Related Works*, trans. by Dorothy S. Blair, London, 1979 (French edition, *Le Cubisme de Picasso. Catalogue raisonné de l'œuvre, 1907–1916*, Neuchâtel, 1979).

Daulte 1968
François Daulte, *French Watercolors of the 20th Century*, New York, 1968.

Daulte 1987
François Daulte, "Quatre grands du printemps des arts," *L'Oeil* 382, May 1987, p. 66.

David 1880
Jules David, *Le Peintre Louis David 1748–1825*, Paris, 1880.

David 1973
Documents complémentaires au catalogue de l'œuvre de Louis David, Daniel and Guy Wildenstein, eds., Paris, 1973.

Dealer's Record 1981
A Dealer's Record, Agnew's 1967–81, London, 1981.

Degenhart and Schmitt 1968
Bernhard Degenhart and Annegrit Schmitt, *Corpus der italienischen Zeichnungen 1300–1450*, II, Berlin, 1968.

Dobei 1991
Katharina Dobei, *Studien zu Tintoretto und die florentinische Skulptur der Michelangelo-Nachfolge*, Bern, 1991.

Dobroklonsky 1930–31
M. V. Dobroklonsky, "Einige Rubenszeichnungen in der Eremitage," *Zeitschrift für bildende Kunst* 44, 1930–31, p. 32.

Dodgson 1931
Campbell Dodgson, "Jörg Breu the Younger," *Old Master Drawings* 6, June 1931, p. 15.

Dodgson 1934–35
Campbell Dodgson, "Ein Miniaturwerk Jörg Breus d.J.," *Münchner Jahrbuch der bildenden Kunst* 11, 1934–35, no. 2, p. 203.

Dortu 1971
M. G. Dortu, *Toulouse-Lautrec et son œuvre*, 6 vols., New York, 1971.

Drawing 1987
"Museum Acquisitions," *Drawing* 8, no. 6, March-April 1987, p. 135.

Egerton 1979
Judy Egerton, *English Watercolour Painting*, Oxford, 1979.

Eitner 1972
Lorenz Eitner, *Géricault's Raft of the Medusa*, London, 1972.

Eitner 1983
Lorenz Eitner, *Géricault, His Life and Work*, London, 1983.

Eitner 1993
Lorenz Eitner, Betsy G. Fryberger, and Carol M. Osborne, with contributions by Dwight Miller et al., *Stanford University Museum of Art, The Drawing Collection*, Seattle, 1993.

Elderfield 1971
J. Elderfield, "Drawing in Cézanne," *Artforum* 9, June 1971, pp. 51–57.

Engwall 1933
Gustaf V. Engwall, "Antoine Watteau (1684–1721): A Woman Reclining on a Chaise-Longue," *Old Master Drawings* 8, June 1933, p. 7.

Erdmann 1929
Karl Erdmann, "Zwei neue Historien-Bilder von Francesco Guardi," *Pantheon*, 1929, pp. 506–10.

Evers 1943
Hans G. Evers, *Rubens und sein Werk*, Brussels, 1943.

De la Faille 1928
Jacob Baart de la Faille, *L'Œuvre de Vincent van Gogh*, 4 vols., Paris, 1928.

De la Faille 1970
Jacob Baart de la Faille, *The Works of Vincent van Gogh*, Amsterdam, 1970.

Federmann 1927
Arnold Federmann, *Johann Heinrich Füssli: Dichter und Maler 1741–1825*, Zurich and Leipzig, 1927.

Finberg [1912]
A. J. Finberg, *Turner's Water-Colours at Farnley Hall*, London, [1912].

Finberg 1961
A. J. Finberg, *The Life of J. M. W. Turner*, 2d ed., Oxford, 1961.

Flam 1986
Jack Flam, *Matisse, The Man and his Art, 1869–1918*, Ithaca and London, 1986.

Focillon 1963
Henri Focillon, *Giovanni Battista Piranesi*, Maurizio Calvesi and Augusta Monferini, eds., Bologna, 1963.

Freise and Wichmann 1925
Kurt Freise and Heinrich Wichmann, *Rembrandts Handzeichnungen III: Staatliches Kupferstichkabinett und Sammlung Friedrich August II zu Dresden*, Parchim a. M., 1925.

Friedländer and Rosenberg 1978
Max J. Friedländer and Jakob Rosenberg, *The Paintings of Lucas Cranach*, Ithaca, New York, 1978.

Gassier 1972
Pierre Gassier, "Une source inédite de dessins de Goya en France au XIXe siècle," *Gazette des Beaux-Arts* 80, July-August 1972, pp. 109–20.

Gassier 1973
Pierre Gassier, *The Drawings of Goya*, London, 1973.

Gassier 1973a
Pierre Gassier, *Francisco Goya Drawings: The Complete Albums*, New York and Washington, D.C., 1973.

Gassier and Wilson 1970
Pierre Gassier and Juliet Wilson, *Vie et œuvre de Goya*, Fribourg, 1970.

Gassier and Wilson 1971
Pierre Gassier and Juliet Wilson, *Goya: His Life and Work*, London, 1971.

Gealt 1986
Adelheid Gealt, *Domenico Tiepolo: The Punchinello Drawings*, New York, 1986.

Geelhaar 1973
Christian Geelhaar, *Paul Klee and the Bauhaus*, Bath, 1973.

Geissler 1979
Heinrich Geissler, *Zeichnung in Deutschland: Deutsche Zeichner 1540–1640*, I, Stuttgart, 1979.

Gerszi 1990
Teréz Gerszi, "Neue Aspekte der Kunst Frederik van Valckenborchs," *Jahrbuch der Berliner Museen* 32, 1990, pp. 173–89.

Gibbons 1977
Felton Gibbons, *Catalogue of Italian Drawings in the Art Museum, Princeton University*, Princeton, 1977.

Gilchrist 1863 [1880]
Alexander Gilchrist, *The Life of William Blake*, London and Cambridge, 1863 [1880].

Glueck 1982
Grace Glueck, "Pollock Telephone Pad Moves to Coffee Table," *The New York Times*, December 2, 1982.

Goldner 1993
George R. Goldner, "Andrea Mantegna," exhibition review, *Master Drawings* 31, no. 2, 1993, pp. 172–76.

Goldwater 1957
Robert Goldwater, *Gauguin*, New York, 1957.

Goldwater 1972
Robert Goldwater, *Paul Gauguin*, New York, 1972.

Goncourt 1876
Edmond de Goncourt, *Catalogue raisonné de l'œuvre peint, dessiné et gravé de P.-P. Prud'hon*, Paris, 1876.

Grancourt 1948
Bergeret de Grancourt, *Voyage d'Italie, 1773–1774*, Jacques Wilhelm, ed., Paris, 1948.

Grasselli 1987
Margaret Morgan Grasselli, "New Observations on Some Watteau Drawings," in *Antoine Watteau (1684–1721): le peintre, son temps et sa légende*, François Moureau and Margaret Morgan Grasselli, eds., Paris and Geneva, 1987.

Grasselli 1993
Margaret Morgan Grasselli, "Eighteen Drawings by Antoine Watteau: A Chronological Study," *Master Drawings* 31, no. 2, 1993, pp. 103–27.

Grigson 1937
Geoffrey Grigson, "Samuel Palmer at Shoreham," *Signature*, no. 7, November 1937, pp. 11, 13, and 14.

Grigson 1947
Geoffrey Grigson, *Samuel Palmer: The Visionary Years*, London, 1947.

Grigson 1960
Geoffrey Grigson, *Samuel Palmer's Valley of Vision*, London, 1960.

Gronau 1957
Drawings of Landscapes and Trees by Fra Bartolommeo, Sold at Auction on Wednesday the 20th November . . . at Sotheby & Co., introduction by C[armen] G[ronau], London, 1957.

De Groot 1906
Cornelis Hofstede de Groot, *Die Handzeichnungen Rembrandts*, Haarlem, 1906.

Guérin 1978
Daniel Guérin, ed., Eleanor Lerieux, trans., *Gauguin, The Writings of a Savage*, New York, 1978.

Guiffrey 1924
Jean Guiffrey, *L'Œuvre de Pierre Paul Prud'hon*, Paris, 1924.

Guiraud 1913
Lucien Guiraud, *Dessins de l'école française du XVIIIe siècle provenant de la collection H. [Heseltine]*, Paris, 1913.

Haboldt 1989
Bob P. Haboldt & Co., *Old Master Paintings and Drawings: The First Five Years*, New York and Paris, 1989.

Haboldt 1990
Bob P. Haboldt & Co., *Netherlandish and Italianate Old Master Drawings*, New York and Paris, 1990.

Haboldt 1995
Bob P. Haboldt & Co., *Fifty Paintings by Old Masters*, New York and Paris, 1995.

Hadeln 1929
Detlev Baron von Hadeln, *The Drawings of G. B. Tiepolo*, 2 vols., Paris, 1929.

Halévy 1949
Edgar Degas, Album de dessins, Daniel Halévy, ed., Paris, 1949.

Hannes 1984
H. Hannes, "Der Croyteppich. Entstehung, Geschichte und Sinngehalt," *Baltische Studien*, n.s., 70, 1984.

Hass 1993
Angela Hass, "Michelangelo's Samson and the Philistine [sic]: Conception, Meaning and Subsequent Influence," *Apollo* 139, December 1993, pp. 383–86.

De Hauke 1961
César de Hauke, *Seurat et son œuvre*, Paris, 1961.

Heinemann 1962
Fritz Heinemann, *Giovanni Bellini e i Belliniani*, 2 vols., Venice, 1962.

Held 1959
Julius S. Held, *Rubens. Selected Drawings*, London, 1959.

Held 1974
Julius S. Held, "Some Rubens Drawings—Unknown or Neglected," *Master Drawings* 12, no. 3, 1974, pp. 252–53.

Held 1981
Jutta Held, "Goyas Bilddialektik," in *Goya Zeichnungen und Druckgraphik*, Frankfurt am Main, 1981.

Held 1981a
Julius S. Held, "*European Drawings, 1375–1825*," exhibition review, *Master Drawings* 19, no. 2, 1981, pp. 172–77.

Held 1985
Jutta Held, "Goyas Bildwelt zwischen bürgerlicher Aufklärung und Volkskultur," *Idea, Jahrbuch der Hamburger Kunsthalle* 4, 1985, pp. 107–31.

Held 1986
Julius S. Held, *Rubens. Selected Drawings*, 2d ed., New York, 1986.

Held 1993
Julius S. Held, "Felice Stampfle, with the assistance of Ruth S. Kraemer and Jane Shoaf Turner, *Netherlandish Drawings of the Fifteenth and Sixteenth Centuries and Flemish Drawings of the Seventeenth and Eighteenth Centuries in The Pierpont Morgan Library*," review, *Master Drawings* 31, no. 2, 1993, pp. 285–99.

Hell 1930
Hans Hell, "Die späten Handzeichnungenn Rembrandts II," *Repertorium für Kunstwissenschaft* 51, 1930, p. 127.

Hendy 1974
Philip Hendy, *European and American Painting in the Isabella Stewart Gardner Museum*, Boston, 1974.

Henkel 1942
M. D. Henkel, *Tekeningen van Rembrandt en zijn school. Catalogus van de Nederlandse tekeningen in het Rijksmuseum te Amsterdam*, The Hague, 1942.

Henriot 1926–28
Gabriel Henriot, *Collection David Weill*, 3 vols., Paris, 1926–28.

Herbert 1962
Robert L. Herbert, *Seurat's Drawings*, New York, 1962.

[Heseltine 1900]
Drawings by A. Watteau in the Collection of J. P. H. [Heseltine], [London, 1900].

Hind 1922
Arthur Hind, *Giovanni Battista Piranesi, A Critical Study*, London, 1922.

Hinz 1966
Sigrid Hinz, *Caspar David Friedrich als Zeichner. Ein Beitrag zur stilistischen Entwicklung und ihrer Bedeutung für die Datierung der Gemälde*, Ph.D. diss., University of Greifswald, 1966.

Hollstein
F. W. H. Hollstein, *Dutch and Flemish Etchings, Engravings and Woodcuts ca. 1450–1700*, vol. 1–, Amsterdam, 1949–.

Hollstein (German)
F. W. H. Hollstein, *German Engravings, Etchings and Woodcuts ca. 1400–1700*, vol. 1–, Amsterdam, 1954–.

Hugelshofer 1927
Walter Hugelshofer, "Albrecht Altdorfer," *Old Master Drawings* 4, March 1927, p. 57.

Hulsker 1980
Jan Hulsker, *The Complete Van Gogh*, New York, 1980.

Ingamells 1985–92
John Ingamells, *The Wallace Collection Catalogue of Pictures*, 4 vols., London, 1985–92.

Isermeyer 1940
Christian Adolf Isermeyer, *Philipp Otto Runge (Die Kunstbücher des Volkes 32)*, Berlin, 1940.

Isola 1976
Maria Catelli Isola, *Disegni di Stefano della Bella dalle collezioni del Gabinetto Nazionale delle Stampe*, Rome, 1976.

Izerghina 1978
Antonina Izerghina, *Henri Matisse: Paintings and Sculpture in Soviet Museums*, Leningrad, 1978.

Jaffé 1989
Michael Jaffé, *Rubens, Catalogo Completo*, Rome, 1989.

Jaffé 1991
Michael Jaffé, "New York and Fort Worth: Drawings by Van Dyck," exhibition review, *Burlington Magazine* 133, no. 1058, May 1991, p. 341.

Jewell 1944
Edward Alden Jewell, *Paul Cézanne*, New York, 1944.

Johnson 1981–89
Lee Johnson, *The Paintings of Eugène Delacroix: A Critical Catalogue*, 6 vols., Oxford, 1981–89.

Joyant 1926–27
M. Joyant, *Henri de Toulouse-Lautrec*, 2 vols., Paris, 1926–27.

Keynes 1957
Geoffrey Keynes, *William Blake's Illustrations to the Bible*, Clairvaux, 1957.

Klossowski 1923
Erich Klossowski, *Honoré Daumier*, Munich, 1923.

Knox 1975
George Knox, *Catalogue of the Tiepolo Drawings in the Victoria and Albert Museum*, 2d ed., London, 1975.

Knox 1983
George Knox, "Domenico Tiepolo's Punchinello Drawings, Satire or Labor of Love?" in *Satire in the Eighteenth Century*, J. D. Browning, ed., New York, 1983.

Krafft and Schümann 1969
Eva Maria Krafft and Carl-Wolfgang Schümann, *Katalog der Meister des 19. Jahrhunderts in der Hamburger Kunsthalle*, Hamburg, 1969.

Lafond
Paul Lafond, *Goya*, Paris, [n.d.].

Lasareff 1925
Victor Lasareff, "Two Unknown Paintings by Guardi," *Burlington Magazine* 46, no. 263, February 1925, pp. 58–63.

Laughton 1991
Bruce Laughton, *The Drawings of Daumier and Millet*, New Haven and London, 1991.

Lem 1962
F. H. Lem, "Le Thème du nègre dans l'œuvre de Géricault," *L'Arte* 37, 1962.

Lemoisne 1946
Paul André Lemoisne, *Degas et son œuvre*, 4 vols., Paris, 1946.

Leslie 1937
C. R. Leslie, *Memoirs of the Life of John Constable, R.A.*, London, 1937.

Lettres 1960
Lettres de Gauguin, Gide, Huysmans, Jammes, Mallarmé, Verhaeren . . . à O. R., Paris, 1960.

Lévêque 1987
Jean-Jacques Lévêque, *L'art et la Révolution Française 1789–1804*, Neuchâtel, 1987.

Leymarie 1962
Jean Leymarie, *Paul Gauguin, Watercolors, Pastels*, New York, 1962.

Leymarie 1989
Jean Leymarie, *Gauguin: Watercolors, Pastels, Drawings*, New York, 1989.

Lieberman 1982
Jackson Pollock, The Last Sketchbook, introduction by William S. Lieberman, New York, 1982.

Lightbown 1986
Ronald W. Lightbown, *Mantegna*, Oxford, Berkeley, and Los Angeles, 1986.

Lister 1985
Raymond Lister, *The Paintings of Samuel Palmer*, Cambridge, 1985.

Lister 1988
Raymond Lister, *Catalogue Raisonné of the Works of Samuel Palmer*, Cambridge, 1988.

Logan 1977
Anne-Marie Logan, "Rubens Exhibitions 1977," review, *Master Drawings* 15, no. 4, 1977, pp. 403–17.

Logan 1987
Anne-Marie Logan, "Julius S. Held, *Rubens. Selected Drawings*," review, *Master Drawings* 25, no. 1, 1987, p. 73.

Lugt
Frits Lugt, *Les Marques de collections de dessins et d'estampes . . .* , Amsterdam, 1921.

Lugt S.
Frits Lugt, *Les Marques de collections de dessins et d'estampes . . . Supplément*, The Hague, 1956.

Magimel 1851
A. Magimel, *Œuvres de J. A. Ingres, gravées au trait sur acier par A. Réveil. 1800–1851*, Paris, 1851.

Maison 1956
K. E. Maison, "Further Daumier Studies, II: Preparatory Drawings for Paintings," *Burlington Magazine* 98, June 1956, pp. 199–203.

Maison 1968
K. E. Maison, *Honoré Daumier. Catalogue raisonné . . .* , 2 vols., London, 1968.

Maquoy-Hendrickx 1956
Marie Maquoy-Hendrickx, *L'Iconographie d'Antoine van Dyck*, Brussels, 1956.

Maquoy-Hendrickx 1991
Marie Maquoy-Hendrickx, *L'Iconographie d'Antoine van Dyck, Seconde édition revue et augmentée*, Brussels, 1991.

Mariacher 1969
Giovanni Mariacher, "Restauri di affreschi di Gian Domenico Tiepolo," *Bollettino dei Musei Civici veneziani*, 1969.

Mariette 1775
Catalogue raisonné des differens objets de curiosités dans les sciences et arts, qui composoient le Cabinet de feu Mr. Mariette, Paris, 1775.

Mariuz 1971
Adriano Mariuz, *Giandomenico Tiepolo*, Venice, 1971.

Marx 1907
Roger Marx, "Berthe Morisot," *Gazette des Beaux-Arts*, December 1907, pp. 491–508.

Master Drawings 1978
Master Drawings from the collection of the National Gallery of Art and Promised Gifts, 1978.

Matisse and Sauret 1954
Henri Matisse and André Sauret, *Portraits*, Monte Carlo, 1954.

Meadmore 1963
W. S. Meadmore, *Lucien Pissarro: A Biography*, New York, 1963.

Meusel 1808
Johan Georg Meusel, ed., *Teutsches Künstlerlexikon*, 2d ed., Lemgo, 1808.

Michel 1987
Marianne Roland Michel, *Le Dessin français au XVIIIe siècle*, Fribourg, 1987.

Millard 1974
Charles W. Millard, "A Chronology for Van Gogh's Drawings of 1888," *Master Drawings* 12, no. 2, 1974, pp. 156–65.

Mireur 1911
H. Mireur, *Dictionnaire des vents d'art faites en France et en l'étranger pendant les XVIIIe et XIXe siècles*, III, Paris, 1911.

Mongan 1949
Agnes Mongan, *One Hundred Master Drawings*, Cambridge, 1949.

Montaiglon and Guiffrey 1887–1908
A. de Montaiglon and J. Guiffrey, *Correspondance des directeurs de l'Académie de France à Rome*, 17 vols., Paris, 1887–1908.

Morassi 1941
Antonio Morassi, "Giambattista e Domenico Tiepolo alla Villa Valmarana," *Le Arti* 3, fasc. 4, April-May 1941, pp. 251–62.

Morassi 1941a
Antonio Morassi, "Domenico Tiepolo," *Emporium* 93, 1941, pp. 265–82.

Morassi 1958
Antonio Morassi, *Dessins vénitiens du dix-huitième siècle de la collection du Duc de Talleyrand*, Milan, 1958.

Morassi 1973
Antonio Morassi, *Antonio e Francesco Guardi*, Venice, 1973.

Morassi 1975
Antonio Morassi, *Guardi. Tutti i disegni di Antonio, Francesco e Giacomo Guardi*, Venice, 1975.

Morassi 1984
Antonio Morassi, *Guardi*, 3 vols., Milan, 1984.

Moreau-Nélaton 1916
Etienne Moreau-Nélaton, *Delacroix, raconté par lui-même*, 2 vols., Paris, 1916.

Moreau-Nélaton 1921
Etienne Moreau-Nélaton, *Millet, raconté par lui-même*, 3 vols., Paris, 1921.

Morgan Library 1993
In August Company: The Collections of The Pierpont Morgan Library, New York, 1993.

Morgan Library, *Fellows Reports*
The Pierpont Morgan Library, *Report to the Fellows of The Pierpont Morgan Library*, reports edited by Frederick B. Adams, Jr., through 1968, by Charles Ryskamp 1969 through 1986, entries by members of the staff and Department of Drawings and Prints, New York, 1950–89.

Moskowitz and Sérullaz 1962
Ira Moskowitz and Maurice Sérullaz, *Drawings of the Masters: French Impressionists*, New York, 1962.

Mras 1962
George P. Mras, "Crouching Royal Tiger by Delacroix," *Record of the Art Museum, Princeton University* 21, no. 1, 1962, pp. 16–24.

MRC
Mellerio Redon Chronology (MRC), from Odilon Redon's documentation of his art, contained in the Mellerio Redon Papers, in the collection of the Ryerson and Burnham Libraries at the Art Institute of Chicago (forthcoming).

Münz 1961
Ludwig Münz, *Bruegel, The Drawings, Complete Edition*, London, 1961.

Murphy 1968
Richard W. Murphy, *The World of Cézanne*, New York, 1968.

Naef 1977–80
Hans Naef, *Die Bildniszeichnungen von J.-A.-D. Ingres,* 5 vols., Bern, 1977–80.

Naef and Lerch 1964
Hans Naef and Ch.-H. Lerch, "Ingres et M. Devillers," *Bulletin du Musée Ingres* 15, September 1964, pp. 5–16.

Noad 1950
Algy S. Noad, "Les Anglais Rococo: The Georgian French," *Art News* 49, May 1950, pp. 30–35.

Noël 1991
Bernard Noël, *Géricault,* Paris, 1991.

Nugent 1925–30
M. Nugent, *Alla mostra della pittura italiana del sei e settecento,* 2 vols., San Casciano, 1925–30.

O'Connor 1995
Francis Valentine O'Connor, ed., *Jackson Pollock: A Catalogue Raisonné of Paintings, Drawings, and Other Works. Supplement Number One,* New York, 1995.

O'Connor and Thaw 1978
Francis V. O'Connor and Eugene V. Thaw, *Jackson Pollock,* 4 vols., New Haven, 1978.

L'Oeil 1967
"Quelques Tableaux et dessins vénitiens du XVIIIe siècle," *L'Oeil* 147, March 1967, pp. 2–21.

L'Oeil 1977
"Marché de l'art: les maîtres du dessin français au XVIIIe siècle," *L'Oeil* 261, April 1977, pp. 42–45.

Oettinger 1959
Karl Oettinger, *Altdorfer Studien,* Erlanger Beiträge zur Sprach- und Kunstwissenschaft, Nürnberg, 1959.

Pallucchini 1943
Rodolfo Pallucchini, *I disegni del Guardi al Museo Correr di Venezia,* Venice, 1943.

Parker 1928
Karl T. Parker, "Some Drawings by Rubens and His School in the Collection of Mrs. G. W. Wrangham," *Old Master Drawings* 3, June 1928, pp. 1–2.

Parker 1936
Karl T. Parker, "Peter Paul Rubens (1577–1640), Study of a Standing Man," *Old Master Drawings* 11, December 1936, pp. 50–51.

Parker and Byam Shaw 1962
Karl Theodor Parker and James Byam Shaw, *Canaletto e Guardi,* Venice, 1962.

Parker and Mathey 1957
K. T. Parker and J. Mathey, *Antoine Watteau,* Paris, 1957.

Parnassus 1931
"List of Important Redons in the United States," *Parnassus* 3, no. 4, April 1931, p. 37.

Pérouse de Montclos 1968
Jean-Marie Pérouse de Montclos, ed., *Architecture, essai sur l'art,* Paris, 1968.

Pérouse de Montclos 1994
Jean-Marie Pérouse de Montclos, *Etienne-Louis Boullée,* Paris, 1994.

Petrucci 1953
Carlo Alberto Petrucci, *Catalogo generale delle stampe tratte dai rami incisi posseduti dalla Calcografia Nazionale,* Rome, 1953.

Phimister 1992
Evelyn J. Phimister, "English Landscape Drawings and Watercolors," *Antiques* 141, no. 6, June 1992, pp. 956–76.

Picasso 1995
The Picasso Project, *Picasso's Paintings, Watercolors, Drawings and Sculpture: A Comprehensive Illustrated Catalogue 1885–1973. From Cubism to Neoclassicism 1917–1919,* San Francisco, 1995.

Piccard 1961
Gerhard Piccard, *Die Kronenwasserzeichen,* VI, Stuttgart, 1961.

Piccard 1980
Gerhard Piccard, *Wasserzeichen Werkzeug und Waffen,* Stuttgart, 1980.

Pickvance 1963
Ronald Pickvance, "Degas's Dancers: 1872–6," *Burlington Magazine* 105, no. 723, June 1963, pp. 256–66.

Pickvance 1970
Ronald Pickvance, *The Drawings of Gauguin,* New York, 1970.

Pigeon 1881
A[madée]. P[igeon]., *Le Courrier républicaine,* 15 May 1881, p. 3.

Pigeon 1881a
Amadée Pigeon, "Les Dessins de M. Odilon Redon," *La Gironde* [Bordeaux], 1 June 1881.

Pignatti
Terisio Pignatti, *I disegni veneziani del Settecento,* Milan, [n.d.].

Pignatti 1967
Terisio Pignatti, *Disegni dei Guardi,* Florence, 1967.

Pogge 1930
G. Pogge, "Neues über Caspar David Friedrich," *Stralsunder Tageblatt,* November 1, 1930.

Pope-Hennessy 1970
John Pope-Hennessy, assisted by Anthony F. Radcliffe, *The Frick Collection. An illustrated catalogue, III, Sculpture. Italian,* New York, 1970.

Portalis 1889
Roger de Portalis, *Fragonard, sa vie et son œuvre,* Paris, 1889.

Posner 1973
Donald Posner, *Watteau: A Lady at Her Toilet,* London, 1973.

Powell 1951
Nicolas Powell, *The Drawings of Henry Fuseli,* London, 1951.

Powell 1987
Cecilia Powell, *Turner in the South. Rome, Naples, Florence,* New Haven and London, 1987.

Prat 1988
Louis Antoine Prat, *Théodore Chassériau 1819–1856,* Cahiers du dessin français, no. 5, Paris, 1988.

Prat 1990
Véronique Prat, "Sur Parc Avenue, un collection de dessins 'qualité musée' (collection d'Eugene Thaw)," *Le Figaro-Magazine* 14241, June 9, 1990, p. XVI.

Prokofiev 1963
N. C. Prokofiev, *Géricault,* Moscow, 1963.

Provost 1989
Louis Provost, *Honoré Daumier: A Thematic Guide to the Oeuvre,* New York, 1989.

Radius 1968
E. Radius, *L'Opera Completa di Ingres,* Milan, 1968.

Réau 1956
Louis Réau, *Fragonard, sa vie et son œuvre,* Brussels, 1956.

Reff 1960
Theodore Reff, "A New Exhibition of Cézanne," *Burlington Magazine* 102, no. 684, March 1960, pp. 114–18.

Reff 1976
Theodore Reff, *The Notebooks of Edgar Degas, A Catalogue of the Thirty-Eight Notebooks in the Bibliothèque Nationale and other Collections,* 2 vols., Oxford, 1976.

Reff 1985
Theodore Reff, *The Notebooks of Edgar Degas,* rev. ed., 2 vols., New York, 1985.

Van Regteren Altena 1952
J. Q. van Regteren Altena, "Retouches aan ons Rembrandt-beeld," *Oud Holland* 67, 1952, pp. 60–63.

Van Regteren Altena 1983
I. Q. van Regteren Altena, *Jacques de Gheyn. Three Generations,* 3 vols., The Hague, Boston, and London, 1983.

Rewald 1950
John Rewald, *Camille Pissarro, Lettres à son fils Lucien,* Paris, 1950.

Rewald 1951
John Rewald, *Carnets de dessins,* 2 vols., Paris, 1951.

Rewald 1958
John Rewald, *Gauguin Drawings,* New York, 1958.

Rewald 1982
John Rewald, *Paul Cézanne Sketchbook, 1875–1885,* New York, 1982.

Rewald 1983
John Rewald, *Paul Cézanne: The Watercolors. A Catalogue Raisonné,* Boston, 1983.

Rey 1982
Jean-Dominique Rey, *Berthe Morisot,* Paris, 1982.

Reynolds 1984
Graham Reynolds, *The Later Paintings and Drawings of John Constable,* 2 vols., New Haven and London, 1984.

Reznicek 1961
F. K. J. Reznicek, *Die Zeichnungen von Hendrick Goltzius,* II, Utrecht, 1961.

Richter 1906
Helene Richter, *William Blake,* Strassburg, 1906.

Rimbaud 1955
Rimbaud: Pages choisies, Paris, 1955.

Robertson 1952
The Blake Collection of W. Graham Robertson Described by the Author, edited, with an introduction, by Kerrison Preston, London, 1952.

Robertson 1968
G. Robertson, *Giovanni Bellini,* Oxford, 1968.

Robison 1986
Andrew Robison, *Piranesi, Early Architectural Fantasies: A Catalogue Raisonné of the Etchings,* Washington, D.C., 1986.

Roethlisberger 1961
Marcel Roethlisberger, *Claude Lorrain: The Paintings,* 2 vols., New Haven, 1961.

Roethlisberger 1962
Marcel Roethlisberger, *Claude Lorrain: L'Album Wildenstein,* Paris, 1962.

Roethlisberger 1962a
Marcel Roethlisberger, "Claude Lorrain: ses plus beaux dessins retrouvés," *Connaissance des Arts,* no. 130, December 1962, pp. 138–47.

Roethlisberger 1965
Marcel Roethlisberger, *The Drawings of Claude Lorrain,* Alhambra, California, 1965.

Roethlisberger 1968
Marcel Roethlisberger, *Claude Lorrain: The Drawings,* 2 vols., Berkeley and Los Angeles, 1968.

Roethlisberger 1971
Marcel Roethlisberger, *The Claude Lorrain Album in the Norton Simon Inc. Museum of Art,* Los Angeles, 1971.

Roger-Marx 1950
Claude Roger-Marx, *Redon: Fusains,* Paris, 1950.

Roger-Marx 1956
Claude Roger-Marx, "Odilon Redon, peintre et mystique," *L'Oeil* 17, May 1956, pp. 21–27.

Rosenberg 1959
Jakob Rosenberg, "Otto Benesch, *The Drawings of Rembrandt,*" review, *Art Bulletin* 41, 1959, p. 114.

Rosenberg 1960
Jakob Rosenberg, *Die Zeichnungen Lucas Cranachs d. Ä,* Berlin, 1960.

Roskill 1971
Mark W. Roskill, "Van Gogh's exchanges of work with Emile Bernard in 1888," *Oud Holland* 86, nos. 2-3, 1971, pp. 142–79.

Rossi 1975
Paola Rossi, *I Disegni di Jacopo Tintoretto, Corpus Graphicum* 1, Florence, 1975.

Rotermund 1963
Hans-Martin Rotermund, *Rembrandts Handzeichnungen und Radierungen zur Bibel,* Stuttgart, 1963.

Rouart 1945
Denis Rouart, *Degas, à la recherche de sa technique,* Paris, 1945.

Royalton-Kisch 1988
Martin Royalton-Kisch, *Adriaen van de Venne's Album in the Department of Prints and Drawings in the British Museum,* London, 1988.

Royalton-Kisch 1992
Martin Royalton-Kisch, *Drawings by Rembrandt and His Circle in the British Museum,* London, 1992.

Ruchau 1946
François Ruchau, *Rimbaud: Documents iconographiques,* Geneva, 1946.

Russell and Wilton 1976
John Russell and Andrew Wilton, *Turner in Switzerland,* Zurich, 1976.

Russoli and Minervino 1970
Franco Russoli and Fiorello Minervino, *Degas,* Milan, 1970.

Sack 1910
Ernst Sack, *Giambattista und Domenico Tiepolo,* Hamburg, 1910.

Sayre 1958
Eleanor A. Sayre, "An Old Man Writing: A Study of Goya's Albums," *Bulletin, Museum of Fine Arts, Boston* 56, no. 305, Autumn 1958, pp. 116–36.

Schade 1974
Werner Schade, *Die Malerfamilie Cranach*, Dresden, 1974.

Schiff 1973
Gert Schiff, *Johann Heinrich Füssli, 1741–1825*, 2 vols., Zurich and Munich, 1973.

Schilling 1973
Edmund Schilling, *Städelsches Kunstinstitut, Frankfurt am Main. Katalog der deutschen Zeichnungen. Alte Meister*, 3 vols., Munich, 1973.

Schneider 1984 [1992]
Pierre Schneider, *Matisse*, New York, 1984 [reprint Paris, 1992].

Schönbrunner and Meder 1896–1908
Joseph Schönbrunner and Joseph Meder, *Handzeichnungen alter Meister aus der Albertina und anderen Sammlungen*, 12 vols., Vienna, 1896–1908.

Schwartz and Bok 1989
Gary Schwartz and Marten Jan Bok, *Pieter Saenredam: The Painter and His Time*, New York, 1989.

Scott 1975
Jonathan Scott, *Piranesi*, New York, 1975.

Sellars 1974
James Sellars, *Samuel Palmer*, London, 1974.

Selz 1968
Jean Selz, *XIXth Century Drawings and Watercolors*, New York, 1968.

Selz 1971
Jean Selz, *Odilon Redon*, Lugano, 1971.

Sensier 1872
Alfred Sensier, *Souvenirs sur Théodore Rousseau*, Paris, 1872.

Sérullaz 1975
Maurice Sérullaz, "Delacroix et la Nature," *Eugène Delacroix aux Pyrénées*, Lourdes, 1975.

Shinoda 1957
Yujiro Shinoda, *Degas, Der Einzug des Japanischen in die französische Malerei*, Cologne, 1957.

Shoolman and Slatkin 1947
Regina Shoolman and Charles E. Slatkin, *Six Centuries of French Master Drawings in America*, New York, 1947.

Singer 1921
Hans Wolfgang Singer, *Zeichnungen aus der Sammlung Friedrich August II . . .* , 1921.

Sloan 1985
Kim Sloan, "A new chronology for Alexander Cozens, Part I: 1717–59," *Burlington Magazine* 127, no. 983, February 1985, pp. 70–75.

Sloan 1985a
Kim Sloan, "A new chronology for Alexander Cozens, Part II: 1759–86," *Burlington Magazine* 127, no. 987, June 1985, pp. 355–63.

Sloan 1986
Kim Sloan, *Alexander and John Robert Cozens*, London, 1986.

Söding 1987
Ulrich Söding, "Julius S. Held: *Rubens—Selected Drawings*, 2d ed.," review, *Zeitschrift für Kunstgeschichte* 50, no. 4, 1987, pp. 564–71.

Spicer 1985–86
Joaneath Spicer, "Unrecognized Studies for Van Dyck's *Iconography* in the Hermitage," *Master Drawings* 23–24, no. 4, 1985–86, pp. 537–44.

Spicer 1994
Joaneath A. Spicer, "Anthony van Dyck's Iconography: An Overview of Its Preparation," in *Van Dyck 350*, Susan J. Barnes and Arthur K. Wheelock, Jr., eds., Washington, D.C., 1994, pp. 326–64 (proceedings of the symposium "Van Dyck 350," sponsored by the Center for Advanced Study in the Visual Arts and the Department of Art History, University of Maryland at College Park, February 8–9, 1991).

Stampfle 1978
Felice Stampfle, *Giovanni Battista Piranesi: Drawings in The Pierpont Morgan Library*, New York, 1978.

Stampfle 1991
Netherlandish Drawings of the Fifteenth and Sixteenth Centuries and Flemish Drawings of the Seventeenth and Eighteenth Centuries in The Pierpont Morgan Library, catalogue by Felice Stampfle, with the assistance of Ruth S. Kraemer and Jane Shoaf Turner, New York, 1991.

Strauss 1974
Walter L. Strauss, *The Complete Drawings of Albrecht Dürer*, 6 vols., New York, 1974.

Strauss 1984
Walter L. Strauss, *The Illustrated Bartsch*, XIII, Commentary, New York, 1984.

Sumowski 1961
Werner Sumowski, *Bemerkungen zu Otto Beneschs Corpus der Rembrandtzeichnungen II*, Bad Pyrmont, 1961.

Sumowski 1970
Werner Sumowski, *Caspar David Friedrich: Studien*, Wiesbaden, 1970.

Sumowski 1979–92
Werner Sumowski, *Drawings of the Rembrandt School*, 10 vols., New York, 1979–92.

Sumowski 1983
Werner Sumowski, *Gemälde der Rembrandt-Schüler*, I, Landau and Pfalz, 1983.

Sutton 1974
Denys Sutton, "The Paradoxes of Cézanne," *Apollo* 100, August 1974, p. 99.

Sutton 1986
Denys Sutton, *Edgar Degas: Life and Work*, New York, 1986.

Sutton 1987
Denys Sutton, "Jean-Honoré Fragonard: The World as Illusion," *Apollo* 125, February 1987, pp. 102–13.

Terrasse 1981
Antoine Terrasse, *Edgar Degas*, Frankfurt am Main, 1981.

Testori 1963
G. Testori, "Un disegno di Géricault per la 'Traite des nègres'," *Paragone*, January 1963, pp. 57–59.

Thieme-Becker
Ulrich Thieme and Felix Becker, *Allgemeines Lexikon der bildenden*

Künstler von der Antike bis zur Gegenwart, 37 vols., Leipzig, 1907–50.

Thoenes 1983
Christof Thoenes, "Vignolas 'Regola delli Cinque Ordini,'" *Römisches Jahrbuch für Kunstgeschichte* 20, 1983, pp. 345–76.

Thomas 1952–55
Hylton Thomas, "Piranesi and Pompeii," *Kunstmuseets Årsskrift*, 1952–55.

Thompson 1979
Richard Thompson, "Degas in Edinburgh," exhibition review, *Burlington Magazine* 121, no. 919, October 1979, pp. 674–77.

Thöne 1936
Friedrich Thöne, *Tobias Stimmer Handzeichnungen*, Freiburg, 1936.

Thornbury 1862
Walter Thornbury, *The Life of J. M. W. Turner, R.A.*, 2 vols., London, 1862.

Tietze and Tietze-Conrat 1944
Hans Tietze and E. Tietze-Conrat, *The Drawings of the Venetian Painters in the 15th and 16th Centuries*, New York, 1944.

Tolnay 1975
Charles de Tolnay, *Corpus dei Disegni di Michelangelo*, I, Novara, 1975.

Traeger 1975
Jörg Traeger, *Philipp Otto Runge und sein Werk*, Munich, 1975.

Turner Studies 1983
"Comings and Goings: Private Collections," *Turner Studies* 2, no. 2, Winter 1983, p. 64.

Valentiner 1925–34
Wilhelm R. Valentiner, *Die Handzeichnungen Rembrandts*, 2 vols., New York, 1925–34.

Valéry 1938
Paul Valéry, *Degas, danse, dessin*, Paris, 1938.

Van Gogh 1958
The Complete Letters of Vincent van Gogh, 3 vols., Greenwich, Connecticut, 1958.

Varshavskaya 1975
M. Varshavskaya, *Rubens' Paintings in the Hermitage Museum*, Leningrad, 1975.

Vasari
Giorgio Vasari, *Le Vite dei più eccellenti Pittori Scultori e Architetori nelle redazioni del 1550 e 1568 . . . a cura di Rosanna Bettarini . . . Paola Barocchi*, Florence since 1966.

Venturi 1936
Lionello Venturi, *Cézanne, son art, son œuvre*, Paris, 1936.

Veronesi 1951
Giulia Veronesi, "Parigi: Capolavori delle raccolte parigine," *Emporium* 113, 1951, pp. 139–41.

Vetrocq 1983
Marcia Ellen Vetrocq, *The Divertimento per li Regazzi of Domenico Tiepolo* (1979), Ann Arbor, Michigan, University Microfilm, 1177, 1983.

Vialla 1988
Jean Vialla, *Odilon Redon*, Courbevoie, 1988.

Viatte 1974
Françoise Viatte, *Inventaire général des dessins italiens. II. Dessins de Stefano della Bella*, Paris, 1974.

Virginia 1972
Virginia Museum Bulletin 32, no. 9, May 1972.

Vollard 1918
Ambroise Vollard, *Tableaux, pastels et dessins de Pierre-Auguste Renoir*, 2 vols., Paris, 1918.

Vollard 1924
Ambroise Vollard, *Paul Cézanne, His Life and Work*, London, 1924.

Waagen 1857
Gustav Friedrich Waagen, *Galleries and Cabinets of Art in Great Britain . . .* , London, 1857 (reprint 1970).

Waetzoldt 1951
Stephan Waetzoldt, *Philipp Otto Runges "Vier Zeiten,"* diss., Hamburg, 1951.

Wehle 1938
Harry Wehle, *Fifty Drawings by Francisco Goya*, New York, 1938.

Weil 1957
Brigitte Weil, *Über das Verhältnis von Malerei und Dichtung bei Johann Heinrich Füssli*, Ph.D. diss., Johannes Gutenberg-Universität, Mainz, 1957.

Wichmann 1970
Siegfried Wichmann, *Wilhelm von Kobell, Monographie und kritisches Verzeichnis der Werke*, Munich, 1970.

Wilde 1930
Johannes Wilde, "Ein zeitgenössisches bildnis des kaisers Sigismund," *Jahrbuch der Kunsthistorischen Sammlungen in Wien* 4, 1930, pp. 213–22.

Wildenstein 1964
Georges Wildenstein, *Gauguin*, Paris, 1964.

Wildenstein 1992–94
Alec Wildenstein, *Odilon Redon: Catalogue raisonné de l'œuvre peint et dessiné*, 2 vols., Paris, 1992–94.

Wilson 1983
Michael Wilson, "Degas at Artemis," *Burlington Magazine* 125, no. 968, November 1983, p. 713.

Wilton 1977
Andrew Wilton, *British Watercolours, 1750–1850*, New York, 1977.

Wilton 1979
Andrew Wilton, *The Life and Work of J. M. W. Turner*, London and New York, 1979.

Wilton 1982
Andrew Wilton, *J. M. W. Turner: France, Italy, Germany, Switzerland*, New York, 1982.

Winner 1961
Matthias Winner, "Zeichnungen des Älteren Jan Brueghel," *Jahrbuch der Berliner Museen* 3, 1961, pp. 190–241.

Winner 1985
Matthias Winner, "Vedute in Flemish Landscape Drawings of the 16th Century," *Netherlandish Mannerism*, Nationalmusei Skriftserie N.S. 4, 1985 (proceeding of a symposium at Nationalmuseum Stockholm, 21–22 September 1984).

Winter 1974
David Winter, "Girtin's Sketching Club," *The Huntington Library Quarterly* 37, 1974, p. 135.

Winzinger 1952
Franz Winzinger, *Albrecht Altdorfer. Zeichnungen. Gesamtausgabe*, Munich, 1952.

Winzinger 1960
Franz Winzinger, "Neue Zeichnungen Albrecht und Erhard Altdorfers," *Wiener Jahrbuch für Kunstgeschichte* 18, 1960, pp. 7–27.

Winzinger 1963
Franz Winzinger, *Albrecht Altdorfer. Graphik,* Munich, 1963.

Zervos 1942–78
Christian Zervos, *Pablo Picasso,* vol. 1–, Paris, 1942–78.

Zieseniss 1955
Charles O. Zieseniss, *Les Aquarelles de Barye,* Paris, 1955.

EXHIBITIONS

Albi and Paris 1964
Palais de la Berbie, Albi, and Petit Palais, Paris, *Centenaire de
Toulouse-Lautrec, 1964.*

Amsterdam 1905
Stedelijk Museum, Amsterdam, *Vincent van Gogh,* 1905.

Amsterdam 1936
Stedelijk Museum, Amsterdam, *Catalogus van de tentoonstelling
twee eeuwen engelsche kunst,* 1936.

Amsterdam and elsewhere 1991–92
Rijksprentenkabinet, Rijksmuseum, Amsterdam, Graphische Samm-
lung Albertina, Vienna, The Pierpont Morgan Library, New York, and
Fogg Art Museum, Harvard University, Cambridge, *Seventeenth-
Century Dutch Drawings: A Selection from the Maida and George
Abrams Collection,* catalogue by William W. Robinson, 1991–92.

Ann Arbor 1962
University of Michigan Museum of Art, Ann Arbor, *A Generation of
Draughtsmen,* 1962.

Antwerp 1956
Rubens House, Antwerp, *Tekeningen van P. P. Rubens,* catalogue by
Ludwig Burchard and Roger-A. d'Hulst, 1956.

Antwerp 1977
Royal Museum of Fine Arts, Antwerp, *P. P. Rubens. Paintings—Oil
Sketches—Drawings,* 1977.

Atlanta 1983
High Museum of Art, Atlanta, *The Rococo Age,* catalogue by Eric M.
Zafran, 1983.

Augsburg 1980
Zeughaus and Rathaus, Augsburg, *Welt im Umbruch: Augsburg
zwischen Renaissance und Barock,* 1980.

Baltimore 1980
Walters Art Gallery, Baltimore, *African Image—Representation of
Blacks Throughout History,* 1980.

Baltimore and elsewhere 1984–85
Baltimore Museum of Art, Museum of Fine Arts, Boston, and Minneapolis Institute of Arts, *Regency to Empire: French Printmaking
1715–1814,* catalogue by Victor I. Carlson, John W. Ittmann, et al.,
1984–85.

Basel 1943
Kunstmuseum, Basel, *Ausstellung von Werken des 19. Jahrhunderts
aus Basler Privatbesitz,* 1943.

Berlin 1928
Galerie Thannhauser, Berlin, *Paul Gauguin,* 1928.

Berlin 1975
Kupferstichkabinett, Berlin, *Pieter Bruegel d. Ä. als Zeichner.
Herkunft und Nachfolge,* 1975.

Berlin and Regensburg 1988
Kupferstichkabinett, Berlin, and Museen der Stadt Regensburg,
Albrecht Altdorfer. Zeichnungen, Deckfarbenmalerei, Druckgraphik,
catalogue by Hans Mielke, 1988.

Berlin and elsewhere 1991–92
Kupferstichkabinett, Berlin, Rijksmuseum, Amsterdam, and National
Gallery, London, *Rembrandt: The Master and His Workshop. Draw-
ings & Etchings,* catalogue by Holm Bevers, Peter Schatborn, and
Barbara Welzel, 1991–92.

Bern 1958
Kunsthalle, Bern, *Odilon Redon,* 1958.

Bielefeld and Baden-Baden 1983–84
Kunsthalle, Bielefeld, and Staatliche Kunsthalle, Baden-Baden, *Georges Seurat Zeichnungen,* 1983–84.

Boston 1945
Museum of Fine Arts, Boston, *A Thousand Years of Landscapes East and West,* 1945.

Boston 1974
Museum of Fine Arts, Boston, *Degas—The Reluctant Impressionist,* 1974.

Boston and elsewhere 1984–85
Museum of Fine Arts, Boston, Philadelphia Museum of Art, and Arts Council of Great Britain, Hayward Gallery, London, *Edgar Degas: The Painter as Printmaker,* catalogue by Sue Welsh Reed and Barbara Stern Shapiro, with contributions by Clifford S. Ackley, Roy L. Perkinson, Douglas Druick, and Peter Zegers, 1984–85.

Brussels 1994
Musée Communal d'Ixelles, Brussels, *Gainsborough to Ruskin, British Landscape Drawings & Watercolors from the Morgan Library,* catalogue by Cara D. Denison, Evelyn J. Phimister, and Stephanie Wiles, 1994.

Buffalo 1935
Albright Art Gallery, Buffalo, *Master Drawings Selected from Museums and Private Collections of America,* 1935.

Buffalo 1946
Albright Art Gallery, Buffalo, New York, *The T. Edward Hanley Collection,* 1946.

Buffalo 1960
Albright Art Gallery, Buffalo, *The T. Edward Hanley Collection,* 1960.

Cambridge 1929
Fogg Art Museum, Harvard University, Cambridge, *French Painting of the 19th and 20th Centuries,* 1929.

Cambridge 1948
Fogg Art Museum, Harvard University, Cambridge, *Seventy Master Drawings,* 1948.

Cambridge 1962
Fogg Art Museum, Harvard University, Cambridge, *Forty Master Drawings from the Collection of John Nicholas Brown,* 1962.

Cambridge 1968
Fogg Art Museum, Harvard University, Cambridge, *Degas Monotypes,* catalogue by Eugenia Parry Janis, 1968.

Cambridge 1969
Fogg Art Museum, Harvard University, Cambridge, *Grenville L. Winthrop: Retrospective for a Collector,* 1969.

Chicago 1941
Art Institute of Chicago, *The Art of Goya,* 1941.

Chicago 1969
Art Institute of Chicago, *Rembrandt after Three Hundred Years,* catalogue by Egbert Haverkamp-Begemann and Anne-Marie Logan, 1969.

Chicago and New York 1952
Art Institute of Chicago and the Metropolitan Museum of Art, New York, *Cézanne: Paintings, Watercolors and Drawings,* catalogue by Theodore Rousseau and Patrick T. Malone, 1952.

Chicago and New York 1959
Art Institute of Chicago and the Metropolitan Museum of Art, New York, *Gauguin: Paintings, Drawings, Prints, Sculpture,* 1959.

Chicago and San Francisco 1945
The Arts Club of Chicago and San Francisco Museum of Art, *Jackson Pollock,* 1945.

Chicago and elsewhere 1969–70
Art Institute of Chicago, Minneapolis Institute of Arts, and Detroit Institute of Arts, *Rembrandt after 300 Years,* 1969–70.

Chicago and elsewhere 1994–95
Art Institute of Chicago, Van Gogh Museum, Amsterdam, and Royal Academy of Arts, London, *Odilon Redon: Prince of Dreams, 1840–1916,* catalogue by Douglas W. Druick et al., 1994–95.

Cleveland 1947
Cleveland Museum of Art, *Works by Edgar Degas,* 1947.

Columbus 1939–40
Columbus Gallery of Fine Arts, Columbus, Ohio, *Watercolors by Paul Cézanne,* 1939–40.

Columbus 1968
Columbus Gallery of Fine Arts, Columbus, Ohio, *Works from the Hanley Collection,* 1968.

Detroit and Chicago 1981–82
Detroit Institute of Arts and Art Institute of Chicago, *The Golden Age of Naples: Art and Civilization under the Bourbons, 1734–1805,* 2 vols., 1981–82.

Detroit and Philadelphia 1968
Detroit Institute of Arts and Philadelphia Museum of Art, *Romantic Art in Britain, Paintings and Drawings, 1760–1860,* catalogue by Frederick Cummings and Allen Staley, 1968.

Dresden 1963
Gemäldegalerie Alte Meister, Dresden, *Altdeutsche Zeichnungen,* 1963.

Düsseldorf 1976
C. G. Boerner, Düsseldorf, *Ausgewählte Graphik und Zeichnungen aus sechs Jahrhunderten,* 1976.

Edinburgh 1979
National Gallery of Scotland, Edinburgh, *Degas 1879,* catalogue by Ronald Pickvance, 1979.

Florence 1922
Palazzo Pitti, Florence, *Mostra della pittura italiana del seicento e settecento,* 1922.

Florence 1931
Palazza Vecchio, Florence, *Mostra del giardino italiano,* 1931.

Florence 1965
Palazzo Strozzi, Florence, *70 pitture e sculture del '600 e '700 fiorentino,* catalogue by Mina Gregori, 1965.

Frankfurt 1987–88
Städtische Galerie im Städelschen Kunstinstitut, Frankfurt am Main, *Eugène Delacroix: Themen und Variationen, Arbeiten auf Papier,* catalogue by Margret Stuffmann et al., 1987–88.

Frankfurt and New York 1992–93
Städelsches Kunstinstitut, Frankfurt am Main, and the Metropolitan Museum of Art, New York, *Daumier Drawings,* catalogue by Colta Ives, Margret Stuffmann, and Martin Sonnabend, 1992–93.

The Hague 1956
Gemeentemuseum, The Hague, *Paul Cézanne,* 1956.

Hamburg 1935
Kunstverein Hamburg, *Frühjahrsaustellung des Hamburger Künstlerverein im Kunstverein*, 1935.

Humlebæk 1994–95
Louisiana Museum of Modern Art, Humlebæk, Denmark, *Toulouse-Lautrec and Paris*, 1994–95.

Kamakura and elsewhere 1987–88
Museum of Modern Art, Kamakura, Japan, National Museum of Modern Art, Tokyo, and Fukuoka Art Museum, Fukuoka, *Géricault*, 1987–88.

Katonah 1989
The Katonah Gallery, Katonah, New York, *The Intimate Eye of Edouard Vuillard*, 1989.

Köln 1979
Kunsthalle Köln, *Paul Klee, Das Werk der Jahre 1919–1933, Gemälde, Handzeichnungen, Druckgraphik*, 1979.

Leeds 1826
Northern Society for the Encouragement of the Arts, Leeds, *Exhibition of Ancient and Modern Masters*, 1826.

Leeds 1839
Music Hall, Leeds, *Leeds Public Exhibition in Aid of the Mechanics' Institute*, 1839.

Lille 1988–89
Musée des Beaux-Arts, Lille, *Boilly, 1761–1845: un grand peintre français de la Révolution à la Restauration*, catalogue by Anne Scottez-De Wambrechies and Sylvain Laveissière, 1988–89.

London 1878 and 1900
The Fine Art Society, London, [exhibitions of John Ruskin's drawings of J. M. W. Turner], 1878 and 1900.

London 1898
International Society of Sculptors, Painters and Gravers, London, *Exhibition of International Art, Knightsbridge*, 1898.

London 1899
Guildhall Art Gallery, London, *Catalogue of the Loan Collection of Pictures and Drawings of J.M.W. Turner*, 1899.

London 1902
Lawrie & Co., London, *The Farnley Hall Collection of Pictures and Drawings by J. M. W. Turner, R.A.*, 1902.

London 1908
New Gallery, London, *Eighth Exhibition of the International Society of Sculptors, Painters and Gravers*, 1908.

London 1926
Victoria and Albert Museum, London, *Drawings, Etchings and Woodcuts by Samuel Palmer and Other Disciples of William Blake*, 1926.

London 1929
Thos. Agnew & Sons, Ltd., London, *Annual Exhibition of Watercolour Drawings*, 1929.

London 1929a
Royal Academy, Burlington House, London, *Exhibition of Dutch Art*, 1929.

London 1937
Wildenstein and Co., London, *Seurat and His Contemporaries*, 1937.

London 1951
Thos. Agnew & Sons, Ltd., London, *Centenary Loan Exhibition of Turner Watercolours*, 1951.

London 1952
Marlborough Fine Art Ltd., London, *Théodore Géricault*, 1952.

London 1953
Royal Academy of Arts, London, *Drawings by Old Masters*, 1953.

London 1957
Arts Council of Great Britain, London, *Samuel Palmer and His Circle: The Shoreham Period*, 1957.

London 1959
Matthiesen Gallery, London, *Odilon Redon*, 1959.

London 1967
Thos. Agnew & Sons, Ltd., London, *Loan Exhibition of Paintings and Watercolours by J.M.W. Turner, R.A.*, 1967.

London 1968
Royal Academy of Arts, London, *The Eighteenth Century*, 1968.

London 1969
Sotheby's, London, *Important Old Master Drawings*, 26 June 1969.

London [1972]
Baskett & Day, London, *Exhibition of Drawings*, [1972].

London 1974
Tate Gallery, London, and Royal Academy of Arts, London, *Turner 1775–1851*, catalogue by Andrew Wilton, 1974.

London 1974a
Baskett & Day, London, *Exhibition of Thirty Old Master Drawings*, 1974.

London 1975
Thos. Agnew & Sons, Ltd., London, *106th Annual Exhibition of Watercolours and Drawings*, 1975.

London 1976
Tate Gallery, London, *Constable*, catalogue by Leslie Parris, Jan Fleming-Williams, and Conal Shields, 1976.

London 1977
Hazlitt, Gooden & Fox, London, *French Drawings of the Nineteenth Century*, 1977.

London 1978
Artemis Group (David Carritt Limited), London, *Seurat: Paintings and Drawings*, 1978.

London 1983
Artemis Group (David Carritt Limited), *Edgar Degas, 1834–1917*, catalogue by Ronald Pickvance, 1983.

London 1985
Hazlitt, Gooden & Fox, London, *Nineteenth-Century French Drawings*, 1985.

London 1985a
Arts Council of Great Britain, Hayward Gallery, London, *Degas Monotypes*, catalogue by Anthony Griffiths, 1985.

London 1985b
J.P.L. Fine Arts, London, *Edouard Vuillard*, 1985.

London 1990
Sotheby's, London, *18th and 19th Century British Drawings and Watercolours*, 15 March 1990.

London 1992
Katrin Bellinger, London, *Drawings Related to Sculpture 1520–1620*, 1992.

London 1993
Tate Gallery, London, *Turner: The Final Years, Watercolours 1840–1851*, catalogue by Robert Upstone, 1993.

London 1994
Hazlitt, Gooden & Fox, London, *Nineteenth Century French Drawings,* 1994.

London 1995
Tate Gallery, London, *Through Switzerland with Turner, Ruskin's First Selection from the Turner Bequest,* catalogue by Ian Warrell, 1995.

London and New York 1984–85
Arts Council of Great Britain, Hayward Gallery, London, and Museum of Modern Art, New York, *The Drawings of Henri Matisse,* catalogue by John Elderfield and Magdalena Dabrowski, 1984–85.

London and New York 1992
Royal Academy of Arts, London, and the Metropolitan Museum of Art, New York, *Andrea Mantegna,* catalogue by Suzanne Boorsch et al., 1992.

London and elsewhere 1946
Tate Gallery, London, Museum and Art Gallery, Leicester, and Graves Art Gallery, Sheffield, *Paul Cézanne, An Exhibition of Watercolors,* 1946.

Los Angeles 1957
Municipal Art Gallery, Los Angeles, *Vincent van Gogh, A Loan Exhibition of Paintings and Drawings,* 1957.

Los Angeles 1958
Los Angeles County Museum of Art, *Honoré Daumier,* 1958.

Los Angeles 1965
Los Angeles County Museum of Art, *Special Exhibition for College Art Associates,* 1965.

Los Angeles and New York 1994
Los Angeles County Museum of Art and the Metropolitan Museum of Art, New York, *Picasso and the Weeping Women: The Years of Marie-Thérèse and Dora Maar,* 1994.

Los Angeles and elsewhere 1971–72
Los Angeles County Museum of Art, Detroit Institute of Arts, and Philadelphia Museum of Art, *Géricault,* catalogue by Lorenz Eitner, 1971–72.

Louisville and Fort Worth 1983–84
J. B. Speed Art Museum, Louisville, and Kimbell Art Museum, Fort Worth, *In Pursuit of Perfection, The Art of J.-A.-D. Ingres,* catalogue by Patricia Condon, with Marjorie B. Cohn and Agnes Mongan, 1983–84.

Manchester 1961
Manchester Art Gallery, *German Art 1400–1800 from Collections in Great Britain,* 1961.

Mexico City 1982
Museo Rufino Tamayo, Mexico City, *Los Picassos de Picasso en México,* catalogue by William S. Lieberman, 1982.

Midland and Columbus 1967–68
Museum of the Southwest, Midland, Texas, and Columbus Gallery of Fine Arts, Columbus, Ohio, *The Hanley Collection,* 1967–68.

Midland and Denver 1967
Museum of the Southwest, Midland, Texas, and Denver Art Museum, *Selections from the Collection of Dr. and Mrs. T. Edward Hanley,* 1967.

Montreal 1950
Montreal Museum of Fine Arts, *The Eighteenth Century Art of France and England,* 1950.

Montreal 1993–94
Canadian Centre for Architecture, Montreal, *Exploring Rome: Piranesi and His Contemporaries,* catalogue by Cara D. Denison, Myra Nan Rosenfeld, and Stephanie Wiles, 1993–94.

Moscow 1995–96
Pushkin State Museum of Fine Arts, Moscow, *Five Centuries of European Drawings: The Former Collection of Franz Koenigs,* 1995–96.

Mount Holyoke and Washington 1987
Mount Holyoke College Art Museum and the National Gallery of Art, Washington, D.C., *Berthe Morisot, Impressionist,* 1987.

Munich 1956
Haus der Kunst, Munich, *Paul Cézanne,* 1956.

Munich 1956a
Haus der Kunst, Munich, *Französische Malerei des 19. Jahrhunderts, von David bis Cézanne,* 1956.

Munich 1981
Haus der Kunst, Munich, *Pablo Picasso. Eine Ausstellung zum hundertsten Geburtstag. Werke aus der Sammlung Marina Picasso,* 1981.

Neufchâtel 1956
Musée des Beaux-Arts, Neufchâtel, *Cézanne,* 1956.

Newcastle-upon-Tyne and London 1973
Arts Council of Great Britain, Laing Art Gallery, Newcastle-upon-Tyne, and Hayward Gallery, London, *Watercolor and Pencil Drawings by Cézanne,* 1973.

Newport Beach 1986
Newport Harbor Art Museum, Newport Beach, California, *The Interpretive Link: Abstract Surrealism into Abstract Expressionism,* 1986.

New Haven 1960
Yale University Art Gallery, New Haven, *Paintings, Drawings, and Sculpture Collected by Yale Alumni,* 1960.

New Haven 1979
Yale Center for British Art, New Haven, *The Fuseli Circle in Rome: Early Romantic Art of the 1770s,* 1979.

New Haven 1980
Yale Center for British Art, New Haven, *The Art of Alexander and John Robert Cozens,* catalogue by Andrew Wilton, 1980.

New Haven 1986
Yale Center for British Art, New Haven, *Thomas Girtin 1775–1802,* catalogue by Susan Morris, 1986.

New York 1928
C. M. de Hauke & Co., New York, *Exhibition of Odilon Redon,* 1928.

New York 1938
Wildenstein and Co., New York, *French Eighteenth-Century Pastels, Water-Colors and Drawings from the David-Weill Collection,* 1938.

New York 1942
Parke-Bernet, New York, *French and English Art Treasures of the 18th Century,* December 1942.

New York 1943
Art of This Century, New York, *First Exhibition, Jackson Pollock, Paintings and Drawings,* introduction by James Johnson Sweeney, 1943.

New York 1943a
Knoedler Galleries, New York, *Loan Exhibition of the Collection of Pictures of Erich Maria Remarque,* 1943.

New York 1944
Wildenstein and Co., New York, *French Pastels and Drawings from Clouet to Degas*, 1944.

New York 1947
Wildenstein and Co., New York, *Cézanne*, 1947.

New York 1949
Durlacher Brothers, New York, *The Work of Samuel Palmer*, 1949.

New York 1950
Wildenstein and Co., New York, *Rembrandt*, 1950.

New York 1952
Museum of Modern Art, New York, *Picasso, His Graphic Art: Redon, Drawings and Lithographs*, 1952.

New York 1955
Wildenstein and Co., New York, *Vincent van Gogh, A Loan Exhibition*, 1955.

New York 1956
Wildenstein and Co., New York, *Gauguin*, 1956.

New York 1959
The Metropolitan Museum of Art, New York, *French Drawings from American Collections: Clouet to Matisse*, 1959.

New York 1959a
Fine Arts Associates, New York, *Paintings from the Ritter Foundation*, 1959.

New York 1959b
Wildenstein and Co., New York, *Cézanne*, 1959.

New York 1960
Helene C. Seiferheld Gallery, Inc., New York, *Tiepolo Drawings* (mimeographed checklist), 1960.

New York 1961
Wildenstein and Co., New York, *Loan Exhibition of Paintings and Drawings from the Hanley Collection*, 1961.

New York 1963
Knoedler Galleries, New York, *Cézanne Watercolors*, 1963.

New York 1964
E. V. Thaw & Co., New York, *19th and 20th Century Master Drawings*, 1964.

New York 1964a
Wildenstein and Co., New York, *Toulouse-Lautrec*, 1964.

New York 1966
The Metropolitan Museum of Art, New York, *Summer Loan Exhibition: Paintings, Drawings and Sculpture from Private Collections*, 1966.

New York 1971
The Metropolitan Museum of Art, New York, *Drawings from New York Collections III: The Eighteenth Century in Italy*, catalogue by Jacob Bean and Felice Stampfle, 1971.

New York 1972
The Metropolitan Musem of Art, New York, *French Drawings and Prints of the Eighteenth Century*, 1972.

New York 1972a
William H. Schab Gallery, New York, 1972.

New York 1973
The Pierpont Morgan Library, New York, *Drawings from the Collection of Lore and Rudolf Heinemann*, 1973.

New York 1974
The Pierpont Morgan Library, New York, *Gifts in Honor of the Fiftieth Anniversary*, catalogue by Felice Stampfle, 1974.

New York 1977
The Metropolitan Museum of Art, New York, *Seurat: Drawings and Oil Sketches from New York Collections*, 1977.

New York 1980
Museum of Modern Art, New York, *Pablo Picasso*, 1980.

New York 1980a
The Frick Collection, New York, *Domenico Tiepolo's Pulchinello Drawings*, catalogue by Marcia E. Vetrocq, 1980.

New York 1981
The Pierpont Morgan Library, New York, *European Drawings, 1375–1825*, catalogue by Cara D. Denison and Helen B. Mules, with assistance of Jane V. Shoaf, 1981.

New York 1982
The Pierpont Morgan Library, New York, *New Treasures for the Morgan Library*, 1982.

New York 1984
The Pierpont Morgan Library, New York, *French Drawings, 1550–1825*, catalogue by Cara D. Denison, 1984.

New York 1984a
Acquavella Galleries, New York, *XIX & XX Century Master Drawings & Watercolors*, 1984.

New York 1984b
The Metropolitan Museum of Art, New York, *Van Gogh in Arles*, catalogue by Ronald Pickvance, 1984.

New York 1988
Jason McCoy Inc., New York, *Jackson Pollock: Images Coming Through*, 1988.

New York 1989
The Pierpont Morgan Library, New York, *Exploring Rome: Piranesi and His Contemporaries*, 1989 (no catalogue).

New York 1989–90
Museum of Modern Art, New York, *Picasso and Braque: Pioneering Cubism*, catalogue by William Rubin, 1989–90.

New York 1990
P. & D. Colnaghi, Ltd., New York, *Claude to Corot: The Development of Landscape Painting in France*, 1990.

New York 1990a
The Metropolitan Museum of Art, New York, *Woodner Collection, Master Drawings*, catalogue by Ann Dumas et al., 1990.

New York 1991
The Metropolitan Museum of Art, New York, *Eugène Delacroix, Paintings, Drawings, and Prints from North American Collections*, catalogue by Lee Johnson and members of the curatorial staff of the Department of Drawings, 1991.

New York 1991a
The Pierpont Morgan Library, New York, *Masterpieces of the Morgan Library*, 1991.

New York 1992
The Pierpont Morgan Library, New York, *Sketching at Home and Abroad: British Landscape Drawings, 1750–1850*, catalogue by Evelyn J. Phimister, Stephanie Wiles, and Cara D. Denison, 1992.

New York 1992a
Jason McCoy, New York, *Jackson Pollock, Pollock in the Mid-Forties: A Close-Up*, introduction by Elizabeth Frank, 1992.

New York 1992b
The Metropolitan Museum of Art, New York, *Masterworks from the Musée des Beaux-Arts, Lille*, catalogue by Marc Fumarolo et al., 1992.

New York 1992c
Marc de Montebello Fine Art, New York, *Odilon Redon. Drawings and Pastels*, 1992 (no catalogue).

New York 1994
Wildenstein and Co., New York, *The Wild Kingdom of Antoine-Louis Barye, 1795–1875*, catalogue by Joseph Baillio, 1994.

New York 1994a
The Metropolitan Museum of Art, New York, *Sixteenth Century Italian Drawings in New York Collections*, catalogue by William M. Griswold and Linda Wolk-Simon, 1994.

New York 1995
Jason McCoy Inc., New York, *Jackson Pollock: New Found Works*, essay by Francis V. O'Connor, 1995.

New York 1995a
The Pierpont Morgan Library, New York, *Fantasy and Reality. Drawings from the Sunny Crawford von Bülow Collection*, catalogue by Cara Dufour Denison with contributions by Stephanie Wiles and Ruth S. Kraemer, 1995.

New York and Cambridge 1960
The Pierpont Morgan Library, New York, and Fogg Art Museum, Harvard University, Cambridge, *Rembrandt Drawings from American Collections*, catalogue by Felice Stampfle and Egbert Haverkamp-Begemann, 1960.

New York and Fort Worth 1991
The Pierpont Morgan Library, New York, and Kimbell Art Museum, Fort Worth, *The Drawings of Anthony van Dyck*, catalogue by Christopher Brown, 1991.

New York and Houston 1977–78
Museum of Modern Art, New York, and Museum of Fine Arts, Houston, *Cézanne. The Late Work*, catalogue by John Rewald, 1977–78.

New York and Paris 1977–78
The Pierpont Morgan Library, New York, and Institut Néerlandais, Paris, *Rembrandt and His Century. Dutch Drawings of the Seventeenth Century from the Collection of Frits Lugt, Institut Néerlandais, Paris*, catalogue by Carlos van Hasselt, 1977–78.

New York and Paris 1996–97
Museum of Modern Art, New York, and Grand Palais, Paris, *Picasso and Portraiture: Representation and Transformation*, catalogue ed. William Rubin, 1996–97.

New York and Philadelphia 1967
Gallery of Modern Art, New York, and Philadelphia Museum of Art, *Selections from the Collection of Dr. and Mrs. T. Edward Hanley*, 1967.

New York and elsewhere 1985–86
The Pierpont Morgan Library, New York, San Diego Museum of Art, and Museum of Fine Arts, Houston, *Master Drawings by Géricault*, catalogue by Philippe Grunchec, 1985–86.

Notre Dame 1980
The Snite Museum of Art, University of Notre Dame, Notre Dame, Indiana, *Janos Scholz, Musician and Collector*, 1980.

Otterlo 1990
Rijksmuseum Kröller-Müller, Otterlo, *Vincent van Gogh: Drawings*, catalogue by Johannes van der Wolk, Ronald Pickvance, and E. B. F. Pey, 1990.

Paris 1874
Ecole des Beaux-Arts, Paris, *Exposition de l'œuvre de Prud'hon*, catalogue by Camille and Eudoxe Marcille, 1874.

Paris 1878
Galerie Durand-Ruel, Paris, *Exposition des peintres et dessins de Daumier*, 1878.

Paris 1878a
Paris, *Salon de 1878*, 1878.

Paris 1881
La Vie Moderne, Paris, *Fusains d'Odilon Redon*, 1881.

Paris 1887
Ecole des Beaux-Arts, Paris, *Catalogue descriptif des peintures, pastels, dessins, rehaussés . . . de J. F. Millet*, 1887.

Paris 1887a
Galerie Georges Petit, Paris, *Exposition de peinture et sculpture par trente-trois artistes français et étrangers*, 1887.

Paris 1889
Ecole des Beaux-Arts, Paris, *Barye*, 1889.

Paris 1896
Galerie Durand-Ruel, Paris, *Exposition Berthe Morisot*, 1896.

Paris 1901
Palais de l'Ecole des Beaux-Arts, Paris, *Exposition Daumier*, 1901.

Paris 1906
Salon D'Automne, Paris, *Retrospective Gauguin*, 1906.

Paris 1908–9
Galerie Bernheim-Jeune, Paris, *Exposition Georges Seurat*, 1908–9.

Paris 1913
Galerie La Boétie, Paris, *Deuxième Salon des artistes animaliers*, 1913.

Paris 1913a
Palais des Beaux-Arts de la Ville de Paris, *David et ses élèves*, 1913.

Paris 1921
Musée des Arts Décoratifs, Paris, *Exposition d'œuvres de Jean-Honoré Fragonard*, 1921.

Paris 1921a
Musée des Arts Décoratifs, Paris, [exhibition of Giovanni Domenico Tiepolo], 1921.

Paris 1922
Galerie Marcel Bernheim, Paris, *Exposition rétrospective Berthe Morisot*, 1922.

Paris 1924
Galerie Georges Petit, Paris, *Degas*, 1924.

Paris 1926
Galerie Bernheim-Jeune, Paris, *Les Dessins de Georges Seurat*, 1926.

Paris 1926a
Musée des Arts Décoratifs, Paris, *Odilon Redon, Exposition rétrospective de son œuvre*, 1926.

Paris 1929
Galerie Dru, Paris, *Barye*, 1929.

Paris 1929a
M. M. Bernheim-Jeune, Paris, *Berthe Morisot*, 1929.

Paris 1931
Exposition Coloniale Internationale de Paris, Paris, *Beaux-Arts*, 1931.

Paris 1931a
Jacques Seligmann, Paris, *Dessins de Fragonard*, 1931.

Paris 1932
Galerie Georges Petit, Paris, *Picasso*, catalogue by Charles Vranken, 1932.

Paris 1934
Musée de l'Orangerie, Paris, *Daumier: peintures, aquarelles, dessins*, 1934.

Paris 1936
Petit Palais, Paris, *Gros, ses amis, ses élèves*, 1936.

Paris 1936a
Galerie Paul Rosenberg, Paris, *Exposition Seurat (1859–1891)*, 1936.

Paris 1937
Galerie Bernheim-Jeune, Paris, *Exposition Géricault peintre et dessinateur*, 1937.

Paris 1937a
Bibliothèque Nationale, Paris, *Aquarelles de Turner, œuvres de Blake*, 1937.

Paris 1937b
Nouveaux Musées, Quai de Tokia, Paris, *Vincent van Gogh, Sa vie et son œuvre*, 1937.

Paris 1938
Musée du Louvre, Paris, *La Peinture anglaise, XVIIIe & XIXe siècles*, 1938.

Paris 1941
Musée de l'Orangerie, Paris, *Exposition Berthe Morisot*, 1941.

Paris 1942
Galerie Charpentier, Paris, *Un Siècle d'aquarelles*, 1942.

Paris 1945
Galerie des Quatre Chemins, Paris, *Exposition d'aquarelles de Berthe Morisot*, 1945.

Paris 1950
Galerie Bignou, Paris, *Géricault cet inconnu*, 1950.

Paris 1950a
Musée Carnevalet, Paris, *Chefs-d'œuvre des collections parisiennes*, 1950.

Paris 1952
Galerie Bernheim-Jeune, Paris, *Cent cinquante ans de dessins*, 1952.

Paris 1952a
Musée du Louvre, Paris, *J.-D. Ingres, 1780–1867*, catalogue by J. Alazard, 1952.

Paris 1952b
Galerie Cailleux, Paris, *Tiepolo et Guardi*, 1952.

Paris 1954
Galerie Bernheim-Jeune, Paris, *Gros, Géricault, Delacroix*, 1954.

Paris 1956
Galerie Alfred Daber, Paris, *Univers de Barye*, 1956.

Paris 1956–57
Orangerie des Tuileries, Paris, *Odilon Redon*, 1956–57.

Paris 1958
Musée Jacquemart-André, Paris, *Pierre-Paul Prud'hon, 1758–1823*, 1958.

Paris 1958a
Musée d'Art Moderne, Paris, *De l'Impressionnisme à nos jours*, 1958.

Paris 1958–59
Musée de l'Orangerie, Paris, *De Clouet à Matisse, dessins français des collections américaines*, 1958–59.

Paris 1961
Musée Jacquemart-André, Paris, *Exposition Berthe Morisot*, 1961.

Paris 1964
Galerie Claude Aubry, Paris, *Géricault dans les collections privées françaises*, 1964.

Paris 1967–68
Petit Palais, Paris, *Ingres*, 1967–68.

Paris 1970
Institut Néerlandais, Paris, *Saenredam 1597–1665 peintre des églises*, 1970.

Paris 1974
Institut Néerlandais, Paris, *Dessins flamands et hollandais du dix-septième siècle*, catalogue by Mária van Berge and Carlos van Hasselt, 1974.

Paris 1975
Musée National d'Art Moderne, Centre National d'Art et de Culture Georges Pompidou, Paris, *Henri Matisse. Dessins et sculpture*, 1975.

Paris 1978
Grand Palais, Paris, *Cézanne, les dernières années*, catalogue by John Rewald et al., 1978.

Paris 1987
Galerie Odermatt-Cazeau, Paris, *Exposition*, 1987.

Paris 1990
Grand Palais, Paris, *XVeme Biennale Internationale des Antiquaires*, 1990.

Paris 1990a
Grand Palais, Paris, *Gauguin*, 1990.

Paris 1991
Musée d'Orsay, Paris, *A. Rimbaud: portraits, dessins, manuscrits*, catalogue by H. Dufour and A. Guyaux, Les Dossiers du Musée d'Orsay, 1991.

Paris 1992
Bob P. Haboldt & Co., Paris, *Old Master Paintings: French, Northern, and Italian Schools*, 1992.

Paris 1994–95
Musée du Louvre, Paris, *Fra Bartolommeo et son atelier. Dessins et peintures des collections françaises*, catalogue by Chris Fischer, 1994–95.

Paris and New York 1987–88
Grand Palais, Paris, and the Metropolitan Museum of Art, New York, *Fragonard*, catalogue by Pierre Rosenberg, 1987–88.

Paris and New York 1991–92
Grand Palais, Paris, and the Metropolitan Museum of Art, New York, *Georges Seurat, 1859–1891*, catalogue by Robert L. Herbert et al., 1991–92.

Paris and New York 1993–94
Musée du Louvre, Paris, and The Pierpont Morgan Library, New York, *French Master Drawings from The Pierpont Morgan Library*, catalogue by Cara Dufour Denison, 1993–94.

Paris and Rouen 1924
Galerie Charpentier, Paris and Rouen, *Exposition du Centenaire*, 1924.

Paris and Versailles 1989–90
Musée du Louvre, Paris, and Musée National du Château, Versailles, *Jacques Louis David, 1748–1825*, catalogue by Antoine Schnapper and Arlette Sérullaz, 1989–90.

Paris and elsewhere 1979–80
Institut Néerlandais, Paris, Koninklijk Museum voor Schone Kunsten, Antwerp, The British Museum, London, and The Pierpont Morgan Library, New York, *Rubens and Rembrandt in Their Century: Flemish & Dutch Drawings of the 17th Century from The Pierpont Morgan Library*, catalogue by Felice Stampfle, 1979–80.

Paris and elsewhere 1988–89
Grand Palais, Paris, National Gallery of Canada, Ottawa, and the Metropolitan Museum of Art, New York, *Degas*, catalogue by Jean Sutherland Boggs, 1988–89.

Paris and elsewhere 1995–96
Grand Palais, Paris, Tate Gallery, London, and Philadelphia Museum of Art, *Cézanne*, catalogue by Françoise Cachin and Joseph J. Rishel with the assistance of Isabelle Cahn and Katherine Sachs, 1995–96.

Philadelphia 1936
Pennsylvania Museum of Art, Philadelphia, *Degas 1834–1917*, 1936.

Philadelphia 1957
Philadelphia Museum of Art, *The T. Edward Hanley Collection*, 1957.

Philadelphia 1989
Philadelphia Museum of Art, *Masterpieces of Impressionism & Post-Impressionism*, catalogue by Colin B. Bailey, 1989.

Pittsburgh 1939
Carnegie Institute, Pittsburgh, *Exhibition of Prints and Drawings from the Collection of J. H. Lockhart, Jun.*, 1939.

Princeton and elsewhere 1982–83
The Art Museum, Princeton University, the National Gallery of Art, Washington, D.C., and Museum of Art, Carnegie Institute, Pittsburgh, *Drawings from the Holy Roman Empire 1540–1680: A Selection from North American Collections*, catalogue by Thomas DaCosta Kaufmann, 1982–83.

Providence 1931
Rhode Island School of Design, Providence, *French Painting*, 1931.

Recklinghausen 1962
Städtische Kunsthalle, Recklinghausen, *Idee und Vollendung*, 1962.

Richmond 1972
Virginia Museum of Fine Arts, Richmond, *Francisco Goya: Portraits in Paintings, Prints and Drawings*, 1972.

Rome 1968
Villa Medici, Rome, *Ingres in Italia*, 1968.

Rome 1990–91
Villa Medici, Rome, *J. H. Fragonard e H. Robert a Roma*, catalogue by Jean-Pierre Cuzin, Pierre Rosenberg, and Catherine Boulot, 1990–91.

Rotterdam 1958
The Boijmans Van Beuningen Museum, Rotterdam, *Van Clouet tot Matisse*, 1958.

Rotterdam 1974
The Boijmans Van Beuningen Museum, Rotterdam, *Duitse Tekeningen, 1400–1700*, catalogue compiled by A. W. F. M. Meij, 1974.

Rotterdam 1991
The Boijmans Van Beuningen Museum, Rotterdam, *Perspectives: Saenredam and the Architectural Painters of the 17th Century*, catalogue by Jeroen Giltaij and Guido Jansen, 1991.

Rotterdam and Amsterdam 1956
The Boijmans Van Beuningen Museum, Rotterdam, and Rijksmuseum, Amsterdam, *Rembrandt: Tekeningen*, 1956.

Rotterdam and Paris 1974
The Boijmans Van Beuningen Museum, Rotterdam, and Institut Néerlandais, Paris, *Dessins flamands et hollandais du dix-septième siècle*, catalogue by Maria van Berge and Carlos van Hasselt, 1974.

Rotterdam and Washington 1985
The Boijmans Van Beuningen Museum, Rotterdam, and the National Gallery of Art, Washington, D.C., *Jacques de Gheyn II, Drawings*, catalogue by A. W. F. M. Meij and Jurrie Pot, 1985.

Rotterdam and elsewhere 1958–59
The Boijmans Van Beuningen Museum, Rotterdam, Musée de l'Orangerie, Paris, and the Metropolitan Museum of Art, New York, *French Drawings from American Collections: Clouet to Matisse*, 1958–59.

Rotterdam and elsewhere 1990–92
The Boijmans Van Beuningen Museum, Rotterdam, Museum of Fine Arts, Boston, Kimbell Art Museum, Fort Worth, and The Pierpont Morgan Library, New York, *Fra Bartolommeo: Master Draughtsman of the High Renaissance*, catalogue by Chris Fischer, 1990–92.

St. Petersburg 1912
Hermitage, St. Petersburg, *Centennial de l'art français*, 1912.

San Francisco 1973
The Fine Arts Museums of San Francisco, California Palace of the Legion of Honor, *Three Centuries of French Art, Selections from The Norton Simon Inc. Museum of Art and The Norton Simon Foundation*, 1973.

San José 1981
San José Museum of Art, *Mary Cassatt and Edgar Degas*, catalogue by Nancy Mowll Mathews, 1981.

Springfield 1937
Museum of Fine Arts, Springfield, Massachusetts, *Francesco Guardi, 1712–1793*, 1937.

Stuttgart 1979 80
Staatsgalerie, Graphische Sammlung, Stuttgart, *Zeichnung in Deutschland: Deutsche Zeichner 1540–1640*, catalogue ed. Heinrich Geissler, 1979–80.

Thaw I
The Pierpont Morgan Library, New York, Cleveland Museum of Art, Art Institute of Chicago, and the National Gallery of Canada, Ottawa, *Drawings from the Collection of Mr. and Mrs. Eugene V. Thaw*, catalogue by Felice Stampfle and Cara D. Denison, 1975–76.

Thaw II
The Pierpont Morgan Library, New York, and Virginia Museum of Fine Arts, Richmond, *Drawings from the Collection of Mr. and Mrs. Eugene Victor Thaw, Part II*, catalogue by Cara D. Denison, William W. Robinson, Julia Herd, and Stephanie Wiles, 1985.

Thaw III
The Pierpont Morgan Library, New York, *The Thaw Collection: Master Drawings and New Acquisitions*, catalogue by Cara D. Denison, Peter Dreyer, Evelyn J. Phimister, and Stephanie Wiles, 1994.

Tokyo 1981
Fuji Television Gallery, Tokyo, *Paul Klee,* 1981.

Tokyo and elsewhere 1974
National Museum of Western Art, Tokyo, Municipal Museum, Kyoto, and Cultural Center, Fukuoka, *Cézanne,* catalogue by Chuji Ikegami et al., 1974.

Toronto and elsewhere 1980–81
Art Gallery of Ontario, Toronto, Yale Center for British Art, New Haven, and British Museum, London, *Turner and the Sublime,* catalogue by Andrew Wilton, 1980–81.

Trentino 1993
Castel Caldés, Valle di Sole, Trentino, *Francesco Guardi: Disegni del Museo Correr di Venezia,* catalogue by Roberto Festi et al., 1993.

Tübingen 1978
Kunsthalle Tübingen, *Paul Cézanne: Zeichnungen,* catalogue by Götz Adriani, 1978.

Tübingen and Berlin 1984
Kunsthalle Tübingen and Nationalgalerie, Berlin, *Edgas Degas. Pastelle, Ölskizzen, Zeichnungen,* catalogue by Götz Adriani, 1984.

Utrecht 1961
Centraal Museum, Utrecht, *Catalogue Raisonné of the Works by Pieter Jansz. Saenredam,* catalogue by P. T. A. Swillens and J. Q. van Regteren Altena, 1961.

Venice 1962
Fondazione Cini, Venice, *Canaletto e Guardi,* 1962.

Venice 1962a
Venice, *Biennale XXXI,* 1962.

Venice 1965
Palazzo Grassi, Venice, *Mostra dei Guardi,* catalogue by Pietro Zampetti, 1965.

Venice 1981
Centro di Cultura di Palazzo Grassi, Venice, *Picasso: opere dal 1895 al 1971 dalla Collezione Marina Picasso,* 1981.

Vevey 1962
Musée Jenisch, Vevey, *De Cézanne à Picasso, Maîtres de l'aquarelle au XXe siècle,* 1962.

Vienna 1903
Secession XVI, Vienna, *Gebaüide der Secession,* 1903.

Washington and New York 1986
National Gallery of Art, Washington, D.C., and The Pierpont Morgan Library, New York, *The Age of Bruegel: Netherlandish Drawings in the Sixteenth Century,* catalogue by John Hand et al., 1986.

Washington and Paris 1982–83
National Gallery of Art, Washington, D.C., and Grand Palais, Paris, *Claude Lorrain 1600–1682,* catalogue by H. Diane Russell, 1982–83.

Washington and elsewhere 1971
Phillips Collection, Washington, D.C., Art Institute of Chicago, and Museum of Fine Arts, Boston, *Paul Cézanne,* catalogue by John Rewald, 1971.

Washington and elsewhere 1978–79
National Gallery of Art, Washington, D. C., Fogg Art Museum, Harvard University, Cambridge, and Frick Collection, New York, *Drawings by Fragonard in North American Collections,* catalogue by Eunice Williams, 1978–79.

Washington and elsewhere 1984–85
National Gallery of Art, Washington, D.C., Grand Palais, Paris, and Schloss Charlottenburg, Berlin, *Watteau, 1684–1721,* catalogue by Margaret Morgan Grasselli and Pierre Rosenberg, 1984–85.

Washington and elsewhere 1988–89
National Gallery of Art, Washington D.C., Art Institute of Chicago, and Grand Palais, Paris, *The Art of Paul Gauguin,* catalogue by Richard Brettell, Françoise Cachin, Claire Frèches-Thory, Charles F. Stuckey, 1988–89.

Wellesley and Cleveland 1993
Davis Museum and Cultural Center, Wellesley College, Wellesley, Massachusetts, and the Cleveland Museum of Art, *Flemish Drawings in the Age of Rubens. Selected Works from American Collections,* catalogue by Anne-Marie Logan, 1993.

York 1980
York City Art Gallery, *Turner in Yorkshire,* 1980.

Zurich 1932
Kunsthaus, Zurich, *Picasso,* catalogue by Charles Vranken and W. Wartman, 1932.

Zurich 1953
Kunstmuseum, Winterthur, Zurich, *Théodore Géricault,* 1953.

Zurich 1956
Kunsthaus, Zurich, *Paul Cézanne,* 1956.

Zurich and Paris 1993–94
Kunsthaus, Zurich, and Grand Palais, Paris, *Nabis 1888–1900,* 1993–94.

Index of Artists

Altdorfer, Albrecht, 5

Barye, Antoine Louis, 61

Beham, Hans Sebald, 6

Bella, Stefano della, 19

Blake, William, 43

Boilly, Louis Léopold, 31

Boullée, Etienne-Louis, 25

Breu, Jörg, the Younger, 7

Brueghel, Jan, 10

Canal, Antonio, *called* Canaletto, 33

Cézanne, Paul, 77, 78, 79, 80, 81

Chassériau, Théodore, 70

Constable, John, 55

Corot, Camille Jean-Baptiste, 62

Cozens, Alexander, 40

Cozens, John Robert, 42

Cranach, Lucas, the Elder, 4

Daumier, Honoré, 66, 67, 68

David, Jacques Louis, 28

Degas, Edgar, 71, 72, 73, 74, 75

Delacroix, Eugène, 63, 64, 65

Dyck, Anthony van, 13

Eeckhout, Gerbrand van den, 18

Fantin-Latour, Henri, 76

Fragonard, Jean Honoré, 26, 27

Friedrich, Caspar David, 48, 49

Fuseli, Henry, 41

Gauguin, Paul, 87

Gellée, Claude, *called* Claude Lorrain, 20, 21

Géricault, Théodore, 59, 60

Gheyn, Jacques de, II, 9

Girtin, Thomas, 51

Gogh, Vincent van, 89, 90

Goya y Lucientes, Francisco de, 44, 45, 46

Guardi, Francesco, 34, 35

Ingres, Jean Auguste Dominique, 57, 58

Klee, Paul, 95

Kobell, Wilhelm von, 47

Mantegna, Andrea, 2

Matisse, Henri, 93, 94

Millet, Jean-François, 69

Morisot, Berthe, 85

Palmer, Samuel, 56

Panini, Giovanni Paolo, 32

Picasso, Pablo, 96, 97, 98

Piranesi, Giovanni Battista, 36, 37a, 37b, 37c

Pollock, Jackson, 99, 100

Porta, Baccio della, *called* Fra Bartolommeo, 3

Prud'hon, Pierre Paul, 29, 30

Redon, Odilon, 82, 83, 84

Rembrandt Harmensz. van Rijn, 14, 15, 16, 17

Renoir, Pierre-Auguste, 86

Rhenish school (?), 1

Rubens, Peter Paul, 11

Runge, Philipp Otto, 50

Saenredam, Pieter, 12

Seurat, Georges, 88

Tiepolo, Giovanni Domenico, 38, 39

Tintoretto, Jacopo, 8

Toulouse-Lautrec, Henri de, 91

Turner, Joseph Mallord William, 52, 53, 54

Vuillard, Edouard, 92

Watteau, Jean-Antoine, 22, 23, 24

FRIENDS OF THE ROYAL ACADEMY

Mrs K.S. Hill
Mr R.J. Hoare
Mr Reginald Hoe
Mr Charles Howard
Mrs A. Howitt
Mr Norman J. Hyams
Mr David Hyman
Mrs Manya Igel
Mr C.J. Ingram
Mr S. Isern-Feliu
The Rt. Hon. The Countess of Iveagh
Mrs I. Jackson
Lady Jacobs
Mr and Mrs S.D. Kahan
Mr and Mrs J. Kessler
Mr D.H. Killick
Mr P.W. Kininmonth
Mrs L. Kosta
Mrs E. Landau
Mr and Mrs M.J. Langer
Mrs J.H. Lavender
Mr Andrew D. Law
Mr Morris Leigh
Mr J.R.A. Leighton
Mr Owen Luder
Mrs G.M.S. McIntosh
Mr Peter I. McMean
Mrs Susan Maddocks
Ms R. Marek
The Hon. Simon Marks
Mr and Mrs V.J. Marmion
Mr B.P. Marsh
Mr and Mrs J.B.H. Martin
Mr R.C. Martin
Mr and Mrs G. Mathieson
Mr J. Menasakanian
Mr J. Moores
Mrs A. Morgan
Mr A.H.J. Muir
Mr David H. Nelson
Mrs E.M. Oppenheim-Sandelson
Mr Brian R. Oury
Mrs J. Palmer
Mrs J. Pappworth
Mr J.H. Pattisson
Mrs M.C.S. Philip
Mrs Anne Phillips
Mr Ralph Picken
Mr G.B. Pincus
Mr W. Plapinger
Mrs J. Rich
Mr Clive and Mrs Sylvia Richards
Mr F.P. Robinson
Mr M. Robinson
Mr D. Rocklin
Mrs A. Rodman

Lady Rootes
Mr and Mrs O. Roux
The Hon. Sir Stephen Runciman CH
Sir Robert Sainsbury
Mr G. Salmanowitz
Mr Anthony Salz
Lady Samuel
Mrs Bernice Sandelson
Mrs Bernard L. Schwartz
Mr Mark Shelmerdine
Mrs Emma Shulman
Mr R.J. Simmons
Mr John H.M. Sims
Dr and Mrs M.L. Slotover
The Spencer Wills Trust
Mr and Mrs J.G. Studholme
Mr J.A. Tackaberry
Mr N. Tarling
Mr G.C.A. Thom
Mrs Andrew Trollope
Mr A.J. Vines
Mrs C.H. Walton
Mr D.R. Walton Masters
Mr Neil Warren
Miss J. Waterous
Mrs Roger Waters
Mrs J.M. Weingarten
Mrs C. Weldon
Mr Frank S. Wenstrom
Mr Julyan Wickham
Mrs I. Wolstenholme
Mr W.M. Wood
Mr R.M. Woodhouse
Mr and Mrs F.S. Worms

Cantor Fitzgerald
Christie's
Chubb Insurance Company
Cookson Group plc
Coopers & Lybrand
Courage Limited
C.S. First Boston Group
The Daily Telegraph plc
Datastream International
Department of National Heritage
The Diamond Trading Company
Dow Jones Telerate Ltd
Eaga Ltd
Robert Fleming & Co Limited
Gartmore Investment Management plc
Goldman Sachs International Limited
Grand Metropolitan plc
Guinness PLC
Hay Management Consultants Ltd
Hillier Parker May & Rowden
IBM
ICI
Industrial Bank of Japan, Limited
Jaguar Cars Ltd
John Laing plc
Lehman Brothers International
Lloyds Private Banking Limited
E.D.& F. Man Limited Charitable Trust
M & G Group P.L.C.
Marks & Spencer
Merrill Lynch Europe Ltd
Midland Bank
MoMart plc
Morgan Guaranty Trust, New York
Morgan Stanley International
Pearson plc
The Peninsular and Oriental Steam Navigation Co
Pentland Group plc
The Reader's Digest Association
Republic National Bank of New York
Reuters
Rothmans UK Holdings Limited
The Royal Bank of Scotland plc
The RTZ-CRA Group
Salomon Brothers
Santa Fe Exploration (U.K.) Limited
Sea Containers Ltd.
Silhouette Eyewear
SmithKline Beecham
Smith & Williamson
Société Générale, UK
Southern Water plc
Thames Water Plc
TI Group plc
Trafalgar House Construction Limited
Unilever UK Limited

CORPORATE ASSOCIATES

ABL Group
AT & T
Bass PLC
BHP Petroleum Ltd
BMP DDB Needham
The BOC Group
Booker plc
Bovis Construction Limited
Charterhouse plc
CJA (Management Recruitment Consultants) Limited
Clifford Chance
Coutts & Co
Credit Lyonnais Laing
The Dai-Ichi Kangyo Bank, Limited
Dalgleish & Co
De La Rue plc
Durrington Corporation Limited
Enterprise Oil plc
Fina plc
Foreign & Colonial Management Ltd
General Accident plc
The General Electric Company plc
Guardian Royal Exchange plc
H.J. Heinz Company Limited
John Lewis Partnership plc
Kleinwort Benson Charitable Trust
Lex Service PLC
Linklaters & Paines
Macfarlanes
Mars G.B. Limited
Nabarro Nathanson
NEC (UK) Ltd
Newton Investment Management Limited
Nortel Ltd
Ove Arup Partnership
The Rank Organisation Plc
Reliance National Insurance Company (UK) Ltd
Royal Insurance Holdings plc
Sainsbury's PLC
Save & Prosper Foundation
Schroders plc
Sears plc
Sedgwick Group plc
Slough Estates plc
Sotheby's
Sun Life Assurance Society plc
Tate & Lyle Plc
Tomkins PLC
Toyota Motor Corporation
United Biscuits (UK) Limited

SPONSORS OF PAST EXHIBITIONS

The Council of the Royal Academy thanks sponsors of past exhibitions for their support. Sponsors of major exhibitions during the last ten years have included the following:

ALITALIA
Italian Art in the 20th Century 1989

ALLIED TRUST BANK
Africa: The Art of a Continent 1995

AMERICAN EXPRESS FOUNDATION
Je suis le cahier: The Sketchbooks of Picasso 1986

ANGLO AMERICAN CORPORATION OF SOUTH AFRICA
Africa: The Art of a Continent 1995

THE BANQUE INDOSUEZ GROUP
Pissarro: The Impressionist and the City 1993

BANQUE INDOSUEZ AND W.I. CARR
Gauguin and The School of Pont-Aven: Prints and Paintings 1989

BBC RADIO ONE
The Pop Art Show 1991

BMW (GB) LIMITED
Georges Rouault: The Early Years, 1903-1920 1993
David Hockney: A Drawing Retrospective 1995

BOVIS CONSTRUCTION LTD
New Architecture 1986

BRITISH AIRWAYS
Africa: The Art of a Continent 1995

BRITISH ALCAN ALUMINIUM
Sir Alfred Gilbert 1986

BRITISH PETROLEUM PLC
British Art in the 20th Century 1987

BT
Hokusai 1991

CANARY WHARF DEVELOPMENT
New Architecture 1986

CANTOR FITZGERALD
From Manet to Gauguin: Masterpieces from Swiss Private Collections 1995

THE CAPITAL GROUP COMPANIES
Drawings from the J. Paul Getty Museum 1993

THE CHASE MANHATTAN BANK
Cézanne: the Early Years 1988

CHILSTONE GARDEN ORNAMENTS
The Palladian Revival: Lord Burlington and his House and Garden at Chiswick 1995

CHRISTIE'S
Frederic Leighton 1830-1896 1996

CLASSIC FM
Goya: Truth and Fantasy, The Small Paintings 1994
The Glory of Venice: Art in the Eighteenth Century 1994

CORPORATION OF LONDON
Bridging the City 1996

THE DAI-ICHI KANGYO BANK LIMITED
222nd Summer Exhibition 1990

THE DAILY TELEGRAPH
American Art in the 20th Century 1993

DE BEERS
Africa: The Art of a Continent 1995

DEUTSCHE MORGAN GRENFELL
Africa: The Art of a Continent 1995

DIGITAL EQUIPMENT CORPORATION
Monet in the '90s: The Series Paintings 1990

THE DRUE HEINZ TRUST
The Palladian Revival: Lord Burlington and his House and Garden at Chiswick 1995

THE DUPONT COMPANY
American Art in the 20th Century 1993

THE ECONOMIST
Inigo Jones Architect 1989

EDWARDIAN HOTELS
The Edwardians and After: Paintings and Sculpture from the Royal Academy's Collection, 1900-1950 1990

ELECTRICITY COUNCIL
New Architecture 1986

ELF
Alfred Sisley 1992

ESSO PETROLEUM COMPANY LTD
220th Summer Exhibition 1988

FIAT
Italian Art in the 20th Century 1989

FINANCIAL TIMES
Inigo Jones Architect 1989

FONDATION ELF
Alfred Sisley 1992

FORD MOTOR COMPANY LIMITED
The Fauve Landscape: Matisse, Derain, Braque and their Circle 1991

FRIENDS OF THE ROYAL ACADEMY
Sir Alfred Gilbert 1986

GAMLESTADEN
Royal Treasures of Sweden, 1550-1700 1989

JOSEPH GARTNER
New Architecture 1986

GENERALE DES EAUX IN THE UK
Bridging the City 1996

J. PAUL GETTY JR CHARITABLE TRUST
The Age of Chivalry 1987

GLAXO WELLCOME PLC
From Byzantium to El Greco 1987
Great Impressionist and other Master Paintings from the Emil G. Bührle Collection, Zurich 1991
The Unknown Modigliani 1994

THE GUARDIAN
The Unknown Modigliani 1994

GUINNESS PLC
Twentieth-Century Modern Masters: The Jacques and Natasha Gelman Collection 1990
223rd Summer Exhibition 1991
224th Summer Exhibition 1992
225th Summer Exhibition 1993
226th Summer Exhibition 1994
227th Summer Exhibition 1995
228th Summer Exhibition 1996

GUINNESS PEAT AVIATION
Alexander Calder 1992

HARPERS & QUEEN
Georges Rouault: The Early Years, 1903-1920 1993
Sandra Blow 1994
David Hockney: A Drawing Retrospective 1995
Roger de Grey 1996

THE HENRY MOORE FOUNDATION
Henry Moore 1988
Alexander Calder 1992
Africa: The Art of a Continent 1995

THE INDEPENDENT
The Art of Photography 1839-1989 1989
The Pop Art Show 1991

INDUSTRIAL BANK OF JAPAN, LIMITED
Hokusai 1991

INTERCRAFT DESIGNS LIMITED
Inigo Jones Architect 1989

JOANNOU & PARASKE-VAIDES (OVERSEAS) LTD
From Byzantium to El Greco 1987

THE KLEINWORT BENSON GROUP
Inigo Jones Architect 1989

LLOYDS BANK
The Age of Chivalry 1987

LOGICA
The Art of Photography, 1839-1989 1989

THE MAIL ON SUNDAY
Royal Academy Summer Season 1992
Royal Academy Summer Season 1993

MARKS & SPENCER
Royal Academy Schools Premiums 1994
Royal Academy Schools Final Year Show 1994

MARTINI & ROSSI LTD
The Great Age of British Watercolours, 1750-1880 1993

PAUL MELLON KBE
The Great Age of British Watercolours, 1750-1880 1993

MERCURY COMMUNICATIONS
The Pop Art Show 1991

MERRILL LYNCH
American Art in the 20th Century 1993

MIDLAND BANK PLC
The Art of Photography 1839-1989 1989
RA Outreach Programme 1992-1996
Lessons in Life 1994

MINORCO
Africa: The Art of a Continent 1995

MITSUBISHI ESTATE COMPANY UK LIMITED
Sir Christopher Wren and the Making of St Paul's 1991

MOBIL
From Byzantium to El Greco 1987

NATWEST GROUP
Reynolds 1986
Nicolas Poussin 1594-1665 1995

OLIVETTI
Andrea Mantegna 1992

OTIS ELEVATORS
New Architecture 1986

PARK TOWER REALTY CORPORATION
Sir Christopher Wren and the Making of St Paul's 1991

PEARSON PLC
Eduardo Paolozzi Underground 1986

PILKINGTON GLASS
New Architecture 1986

PREMIERCARE (NATIONAL WESTMINSTER
INSURANCE SERVICES)
Roger de Grey 1996

REDAB (UK) LTD
Wisdom and Compassion: The Sacred Art of Tibet 1992

REED INTERNATIONAL PLC
Toulouse-Lautrec: The Graphic Works 1988
Sir Christopher Wren and the Making of St Paul's 1991

REPUBLIC NATIONAL BANK OF NEW YORK
Sickert: Paintings 1992

ARTHUR M. SACKLER FOUNDATION
Jewels of the Ancients 1987

SALOMON BROTHERS
Henry Moore 1988

THE SARA LEE FOUNDATION
Odilon Redon: Dreams and Visions 1995

SEA CONTAINERS LTD.
The Glory of Venice: Art in the Eighteenth Century 1994

SILHOUETTE EYEWEAR
Egon Schiele and His Contemporaries: From the Leopold Collection, Vienna 1990
Wisdom and Compassion: The Sacred Art of Tibet 1992
Sandra Blow 1994
Africa: The Art of a Continent 1995

SOCIETE GENERALE, UK
Gustave Caillebotte: The Unknown Impressionist 1996

SOCIETE GENERALE DE BELGIQUE
Impressionism to Symbolism: The Belgian Avant-Garde 1880-1900 1994

SPERO COMMUNICATIONS
The Schools Final Year Show 1992

TEXACO
Selections from the Royal Academy's Private Collection 1991

THAMES WATER PLC
Habitable Bridge Competition 1996

THE ROYAL BANK OF SCOTLAND
The Schools Final Year Show 1996

THE TIMES
Old Master Paintings from the Thyssen-Bornemisza Collection 1988
Wisdom and Compassion: The Sacred Art of Tibet 1992
Drawings from the J. Paul Getty Museum 1993
Goya: Truth and Fantasy, The Small Paintings 1994
Africa: The Art of a Continent 1995

TRACTEBEL
Impressionism to Symbolism: The Belgian Avant-Garde 1880-1900 1994

UNILEVER
Frans Hals 1990

UNION MINIERE
Impressionism to Symbolism: The Belgian Avant-Garde 1880-1900 1994

VISTECH INTERNATIONAL LTD
Wisdom and Compassion: The Sacred Art of Tibet 1992

OTHER SPONSORS

Sponsors of events, publications and other items in the past two years:

Academy Group Limited
Agnew's
Air Hong Kong
Air Jamaica
Air UK
Alitalia
Allied Trust Bank
Arthur Andersen
John A. Anderson
Athenaeum Hotel and Apartments
Austrian Airlines
Mr and Mrs Martin Beisly
The Beit Trust
Berggruen & Zevi Limited
The Britto Foundation
The Brown Foundation
Bulgari Jewellery
James Butler RA
Cable & Wireless
The Calouste Gulbenkian Foundation (Lisbon)
Cathay Pacific
Chilstone Garden Ornaments
Christopher Wood Gallery
Citibank N.A.
Mr Terance Cole
Columbus Communications
Condé Nast Publications
Mrs Shimona Cowan
Deutsche Morgan Grenfell
Hamish Dewar
Jennifer Dickson RA
The Elephant Trust
Brenda Evans
Sebastian de Ferranti
Fina Plc
FORBES Magazine, New York
Forte Plc
The Four Seasons Hotels
Isabel Goldsmith
Ivor Gordon
Lady Gosling
Julian Hartnoll
Ken Howard RA
IBM UK Limited
Inter-Continental Hotels
Intercraft Designs Limited
Jaguar Cars Limited
John Lewis Partnership plc
A.T. Kearney Limited
KLM

Count and Countess Labia
The Leading Hotels of the World
The Leger Galleries, London
The A.G. Leventis Foundation
Mr and Mrs J.H.J. Lewis
The Maas Gallery
Mandarin Oriental Hotel Group
Martini & Rossi Ltd
Masterpiece
Mercury Communications Ltd
Merrill Lynch
NK
The Nigerian Friends of africa95
Novell U.K. Ltd
Richard Ormond
Patagonia
Penshurst Press Ltd
Mr and Mrs James Phelps
Stuart Pivar
Polaroid (UK) Ltd
Price Waterhouse
The Private Bank & Trust Company Limited
Ralph Lauren
The Regent Hotel
The Robina Group
The Rockefeller Foundation
N. Roditi & Co.
Royal Mail International
Mrs Basil Samuel
Sears Plc
Simon Dickinson Ltd
Peyton Skipwith
Swan Hellenic Ltd
Mr and Ms Daniel Unger
Kurt Unger
Vista Bay Club Seychelles
Vorwerk Carpets Limited
John Ward RA
Warner Bros.
W S Yeates plc
ZFL
Mrs George Zakhem

PUBLISHED BY

THE PIERPONT MORGAN LIBRARY

JULIANNE GRIFFIN, *Publisher*
PATRICIA EMERSON, *Editorial Coordinator*
KAREN BANKS, *Managing Editor*
NOAH CHASIN, *Publications Administrator*
DEBORAH WINARD, *Publications Associate*
LISA PETRUSKY, *Assistant*
SANDRINE HARRIS, *Rudin Intern*

PROJECT STAFF

DEPARTMENT OF DRAWINGS AND PRINTS
WILLIAM M. GRISWOLD, *Charles W. Engelhard Curator*
CARA DUFOUR DENISON, *Curator*
STEPHANIE WILES, *Associate Curator*
EVELYN J. PHIMISTER, *Frank Strasser Assistant Curator*
KATHLEEN STUART, *Assistant*

DAVID A. LOGGIE, *Chief Photographer*
MARILYN PALMERI, *Administrator, Photographic Services, Rights and Reproductions*
EUGENIA D. COUTAVAS, *Assistant, Photographic Services, Rights and Reproductions*
EDWARD SOWINSKI, *Assistant to the Photographer*

PATRICIA REYES, *Mellon Conservator*
REBA F. SNYDER, *Associate Conservator*
TOM FELLNER, *Art Preparator*
ALICE CANNON, *Conservation Intern*

D. W. WRIGHT, *Registrar*
BARBARA CLARK, *Assistant to the Registrar*

ELIZABETH O'KEEFE, *Head of Cataloguing*

Designed by CARL ZAHN *and typeset in Aldus by* CARL ZAHN *and* FRANCES PRESTI-FAZIO

Printed and bound in Italy by NEW INTERLITHO ITALIA, S.P.A., MILAN

247